STATISTICAL THEORY OF LIQUIDS

STATISTICAL THEORY OF LIQUIDS

By I. Z. FISHER

Translated by THEODORE M. SWITZ

With a supplement by STUART A. RICE *and* PETER GRAY

THE UNIVERSITY OF CHICAGO PRESS

CHICAGO AND LONDON

Part I of this book was originally published in 1961 by the State Press for Physical-Mathematical Literature, Moscow, as part of the series "Contemporary Problems in Physics." This series is under the general direction of the editors of the journal *Uspekhi Fizicheskikh Nauk* ("Advances in the Physical Sciences").

Library of Congress Catalog Card Number: 64-22249

The University of Chicago Press, Chicago & London
The University of Toronto Press, Toronto 5, Canada

Published 1964. Composed and printed by The University of Chicago Press, Chicago, Illinois, U.S.A.

PREFATORY NOTE

Interest in the theory of liquids has grown steadily over the last two decades, and, although no completely satisfactory solution of the several problems exists at present, important advances have been made. It is the purpose of Professor Fisher's monograph to survey the current understanding of the equilibrium properties of liquids. Much work of interest has appeared in the Russian literature wherein the influence of the pioneering studies by Bogolyubov has been much stronger than in the contemporary non-Russian work. This book provides a useful summary of studies previously available only in the Russian literature and relatively unknown in the United States and Western Europe. For that reason alone, it is a welcome addition to the extant works on the theory of liquids. However, Professor Fisher has also presented a simple synthesis of the available experimental data, their interpretation in terms of models, an analysis of the failures of various models and their relationships with general theory. This monograph, therefore, also has value as an introductory text for graduate students.

For these reasons, I believe this translation of Professor Fisher's monograph will prove useful to all investigators interested in the equilibrium properties of the liquid state.

To bring the monograph up to date, a supplement by Stuart A. Rice and Peter Gray dealing with recent developments has been added to the original text.

STUART A. RICE

Director, Institute for the Study of Metals
The University of Chicago

FOREWORD

Despite the obvious importance of the problems related to the molecular theory of the structure and physical properties of liquids, the rigorous methods of statistical physics have only recently begun to be applied to this field. This has only been found possible since the development of the method of reduced molecular distribution functions, or the method of correlation functions. Accordingly, the statistical theory of liquids, while still in its early stages, is doubtless already an effective branch of statistical physics.

The present volume represents an effort to make a systematic study of the statistical theory of the liquid state based on an examination of the correlation functions for groups of molecules. The book considers only the equilibrium properties of single-component liquids. The theory of solutions and kinetic problems are not discussed. The formalism of the method of correlation functions is given major attention—only to the extent, however, that it is important for physical applications. Many problems in the theory of correlation functions which are primarily of mathematical interest are not touched upon.

The author hopes that the book will be useful to all those who are studying, or interested in, the theory of liquids and dense gases.

It is a pleasant duty to acknowledge the help of editor K. P. Gurov both with the manuscript and with the book.

I. Z. F.

CONTENTS

PRESENT STATUS OF THE THEORY OF LIQUIDS

1. Peculiarities of the Liquid State and the Status of the Theory of Liquids 1
2. Thermal Motion of Molecules in Liquids 5
3. Simple and Complex Liquids 8

CHAPTER I THE CLASSICAL STATISTICAL INTEGRAL

1. Principles of Statistical Thermodynamics 12
2. Intermolecular Forces and the Law of Corresponding States 17
3. Quantum Corrections to the Statistical Integral and to the Law of Corresponding States 22
4. Calculation of the Configuration Integral for a Gas . . 23
5. The Free-Volume Theory 27
6. The Statistical Integral of a One-dimensional Model of a Liquid 31
7. The Thermodynamics of a One-dimensional System . . 35

CHAPTER II CORRELATION FUNCTIONS

1. The Determination of and General Properties of Correlation Functions 40
2. The Calculation of Average Values 44
3. The Stress Tensor and the Equation of State of Liquids . 46
4. Fluctuations in the Number of Particles in a Liquid . . 51
5. Entropy 54
6. Elastic Properties of Liquids 57

7. Kirkwood's Method and the Chemical Potential . . . 61
8. The Scattering of Light and X rays by Liquids . . . 64

CHAPTER III THE STRUCTURE OF SIMPLE LIQUIDS
1. The Radial Distribution Function of Real Liquids . . 69
2. The Radial Distribution Function of a One-dimensional Model of a Liquid 72
3. Comparison of the Structures of Liquids and Crystals . 77
4. A Structural-Diffusion Model of a Liquid 81
5. Fluctuations of the Coordination Numbers in Simple Liquids 84
6. Instantaneous and Average Order in Simple Liquids . . 90
7. The Relation of the Structure of Liquids to Their Physical Properties 93

CHAPTER IV EQUATIONS FOR CORRELATION FUNCTIONS
1. Derivation of the Basic Equations 97
2. Solution of the Equations for Correlation Functions in the Case of a Gas 101
3. Molecular System at an Ideal Wall 106
4. Equations for the Correlation Functions of a System of Electrically Charged Particles 109
5. A More Precise Solution of the Problem of Electrically Charged Particles 113
6. Calculations with Non-central Forces; Dipole Interaction 118
7. The Case of a Dipole Lattice 122
8. Equations for Correlation Functions in Phase Space . . 126

CHAPTER V THEORY OF LIQUIDS IN THE SUPERPOSITION APPROXIMATION
1. The Bogolyubov Equation for the Radial Distribution Function 131
2. Superposition Approximation in the Kirkwood Method . 134
3. General Examination of the Bogolyubov Equation . . 137
4. Accuracy of the Bogolyubov Equation for the Radial Distribution Function 140
5. The Problem of a System of Hard Spheres 144
6. Results of the Numerical Integration of the Bogolyubov Equation for a System of Interacting Particles 147
7. Refinement of the Superposition Approximation . . . 152

CHAPTER VI SURFACE PHENOMENA IN LIQUIDS

1. Correlation Functions of a Two-Phase System 156
2. Equations for the Correlation Functions of a Two-Phase System 159
3. General Examination of the Equations for the Correlation Functions of a Two-Phase System 163
4. The Structure of the Transition Layer between Liquid and Vapor 166
5. Expression of the Surface Tension of a Liquid in Terms of Correlation Functions 171
6. Approximate Theories of the Surface Tension 175

CHAPTER VII BOUNDARIES OF STABILITY OF LIQUIDS AND GASES

1. The Problem of the Stability of Phases and Phase Transformations 180
2. The Stability and Instability of the Solutions of the Bogolyubov Equation 183
3. Criteria for the Limit of Stability of a One-dimensional Phase 186
4. Limiting Points of Stability of the First Type 190
5. Limiting Points of Stability of the Second Type . . . 193
6. The Limit of Stability of a System with an Exponential Repulsion between Pairs of Particles 196
7. Approximate Theory of the Melting Curve 198
8. The Critical Point 202

CHAPTER VIII NUMERICAL METHODS IN THE THEORY OF LIQUIDS

1. The Use of Numerical Methods 206
2. The Monte Carlo Method in Statistical Physics . . . 208
3. Implementation of the Monte Carlo Method 212
4. Results of Calculations for a Model of a Real System . . 217
5. Results of Calculations for a System of Hard Spheres . . 222
6. Dynamical Calculations in a System of Hard Spheres . . 226

SUPPLEMENT OTHER ASPECTS OF THE EQUILIBRIUM PROPERTIES OF LIQUIDS

S1. Introduction 235
S1.1. Correspondence of Sections and Notation 236
S2. Summary of the Properties of Ensembles 236
S2.1. General Remarks 236
S2.2. Transition to a Classical Phase-Space Description . . 239
S3. The Theory of Imperfect Gases 241
S3.1. Preliminary Study 241
S3.2. A Different Expansion 246
S3.3. Kubo's Method of Cumulants 250
S3.3.1 General Formulation 250
S3.3.2. The Mayer Cluster Theory. 257
S3.4. Some Topological Arguments 261
S4. Distribution Functions 268
S4.1. Definitions 268
S4.1.1. Canonical Ensemble 268
S4.1.2. Correlation Functions 269
S4.1.3. Grand Canonical Ensemble 270
S4.1.4. Correlation Functions 271
S4.2. Thermodynamic Properties of a Fluid 272
S4.3. A Relationship between the Pair Distribution Function and the Free Energy 276
S5. Series Expansions for the Pair Correlation Function . 279
S5.1. 𝔘-Function Method 280
S5.2. The Cumulant Method 283
S6. Equations for the Pair Correlation Function . . . 286
S6.1. The Yvon-Born-Green Equation 287
S6.2. The Kirkwood Integral Equation 288
S6.3. The Equations of Cole and Fisher 290
S6.4. The Meaning of the Superposition Approximation . . 292
S6.5. The Hyper-netted Chain Equation 296
S6.6. The Percus-Yevick Equation 304
S6.7. The Method of Functional Differentiation 309
S7. Numerical Solutions of the Integral Equations . . . 314
S7.1. Low Density Solutions 314
S7.2. High Density Solutions 315

INDEX

PRESENT STATUS OF THE THEORY OF LIQUIDS

1. PECULIARITIES OF THE LIQUID STATE AND THE STATUS OF THE THEORY OF LIQUIDS

The development of a theory of the liquid state of matter is one of the most important problems of contemporary statistical physics. In view of the characteristics of the liquid state—the strong interaction of particles and their state of great disorder—which greatly complicate the theoretical analysis of the problem, understanding of the theory of liquids lags appreciably behind that of the theories of the gaseous and crystalline states of matter. Of great significance in the present high level of development of the statistical theories of gases and crystals is the fact that it is possible to rely on the obvious limiting cases of an ideal gas and of an ideal crystal. The first case corresponds to infinite dilution of the particles and a state of complete disorder; the second corresponds to a state of complete order of the particles at high density. For liquids, however, no simple and obvious model exists which might be taken as a "zeroth approximation" in constructing a theory, and serious difficulties arise as a result of this. However, an accurate and well-developed theory of the liquid state of matter is absolutely essential for the further development of many branches of physics and physical chemistry; also, it would be of great value in the solution of many important practical problems.

During the past fifteen years appreciable progress in the development of a theory of the liquid state of matter has occurred, and at the present time we may assume that the foundations of a statistical theory of liquids have been established. Despite these advances, the theory is still far from complete, and the difficulties that remain are important.

Our concepts regarding the structure of liquids have gone through considerable evolution with the passage of time. Following the successes of the theory of the continuity of transition between the gaseous and liquid states of matter developed by van der Waals, it was natural that the concept of the structural similarity of these states—as completely disordered states differing only in particle density—would be strengthened. The application of this viewpoint to the entire field of liquid states up to the solid-liquid coexistence curve gradually began to encounter greater and greater difficulty. A structureless model of a liquid, in view of its mistaken character (as was subsequently ascertained), could not serve as a starting point for further development of the theory. As a matter of fact, from the time of the classical studies of van der Waals up to the beginning of the 1930's, almost no development of the theory of the liquid state of matter occurred.

Decisive changes in our views of the nature of the liquid state occurred after the first X-ray structural studies of liquids, especially after the first successful interpretation of X-ray photographs in terms of the distribution of the particles of a liquid [1, 2]. It was ascertained that liquids are far from structureless. The distribution of particles within a small region about any fixed particle of a liquid was found to be partially ordered, a discovery somewhat reminiscent of crystalline order. Thus there arose a new concept, namely, short-range order in liquids, and the problem of the structure of liquids emerged.

Simultaneously with the first successes in X-ray structural analysis of liquids, attention was directed (principally by Frenkel [3] and Debye [4]) to the well-known similarity of liquids and solid crystalline bodies in certain other relationships. The approximate equality, in many cases, of the densities of a solid body and its melt led to the inference of approximately equal interatomic distances and of interatomic interactions of approximately equal intensity in both cases. From this follows the similarity of many thermodynamic properties of solid crystalline bodies and liquids near the melting point (which may be confirmed by experiment), and also the deduction regarding a certain similarity of the character of the thermal motion of particles in both states. Thus, for example, it has been confirmed experimentally that many monatomic substances near the melting point have a gram-atom heat capacity of $c_v \approx 6$ cal/deg both in the solid and liquid state.

The outstanding role played by Ya. I. Frenkel in confirming the new view of the nature of the liquid state should be especially noted.

It was he who first stated the idea regarding the similarity of liquids—far from the critical point—and crystals. He not only took an extremely active part in working out the new view on the nature of liquids, but also went much farther—from these concepts he succeeded in obtaining a large quantity of physical data relating primarily to the theory of transport processes in liquids and to the kinetics of crystallization. His numerous studies in this field have been collected in a widely known monograph [3]. The important role played by V. I. Danilov and his school in the experimental study and theoretical interpretation of the structure of many liquids should also be noted (see [5]).

The discovery of elements of similarity in the physical properties of liquids near the melting point and of crystals produced a large number of different models and theories of the structure of liquids, ascribing to the latter various degrees of "crystallinity" and "lattice-like" character. The majority of these models are now only of historical significance.

But even today the problem of the true structure of liquids cannot be considered as completely clarified. The significance of short-range order, which is indicated by X-ray studies of liquids, is treated differently by different authors, and differing content is assigned to the generally used phrase "quasi-crystalline structure of liquids." Often the "quasi-crystallinity" of liquids is used too literally, without sufficient foundation. Recently, however, there has been a departure from a too literal interpretation of the similarity of liquids and crystals. In this connection, the statement of J. Hildebrand [6] is significant; he gave an interesting analysis of the situation and came out decisively against "lattice-like" views of liquids. The quasi-crystalline theories of the structure of liquids have played an important role, in that, during the time that they were accepted, they drew the attention of investigators to the study of those properties of liquids which are essentially related to high density and to the strong interactions of the particles in them. But, at the same time, there is no doubt that the quasi-crystallinity of liquids, at least in a structural relationship, was overestimated by many authors. For any full characterization of the physical properties of liquids, not only are those features important in which they approximate solid bodies but, even more so, those features which result in a significant difference from the behavior of solid bodies.

The similarity of some properties of liquids and crystals near the melting point cannot be denied. However, within the range of the $p - T$ or $v - T$ states, the region where the liquid phase exists is fairly broad and it passes over continuously to the region where the gas phase exists. The task of a theory should be to describe and explain the properties of liquids throughout the ranges in which they exist, and not only in a narrow band near the melting-crystallization line. But no "quasi-crystallinity" exists far from this line. On the other hand, there is no difference in principle between the physical properties of liquids and highly compressed gases (for example, above the critical temperature), and the theory must describe both states simultaneously and in terms of general principles. It should be pointed out, by the way, that, from the modern viewpoint, the gas phase, in any of its states except the case of infinite rarefaction, is not without structure, and a continuous transition from gaseous to liquid order occurs.

In a certain sense it is possible to say that at the present time we have returned to the old views regarding the continuity of the gaseous and liquid states. But, if in the van der Waals theory the joining of the two phases was derived on the basis of the notion of their common disorderliness and the completely chaotic thermal motion of the particles, at the present time their joining is derived on the hypothesis of their common short-range order. The difference between a gas and a liquid is basically only one of density, in consequence of which the degree of short-range order is different in each case. Above the critical point, the transition from liquid to gaseous order is continuous.

From the point of view of the present rigorous theory, the problem of the structure of liquids is solved fairly simply. The structure of a liquid and all of its physical properties is exhaustively described by a set of distribution functions of the positions of groups of particles. Moreover, in the majority of cases it is sufficient to know a small number of distribution functions for very small groups, and the so-called radial distribution function is of principal importance. These functions, apparently, do not display any indications of the crystallinity of the short-range structure of liquids in the sense that effects of anisotropy and of repetition of structure in linear translations due to crystalline-type regularity do not occur. The theory does not require any supplementary hypotheses on the structure of liquids. The really important task of the theory of liquids is the study of these distribution functions.

The recent trend in the theory of liquids, based on the study of the molecular distribution functions of groups of particles—or, as we will call them, correlation functions—received its impetus primarily from the work of Kirkwood [7, 8], Bogolyubov [9], and Born and Green [10, 11]. Although serious mathematical difficulties stand in the path of development of this theory, it must be assumed that they will gradually be overcome. The theory rests on substantial theoretical foundations and has already attained very notable success.

2. THERMAL MOTION OF MOLECULES IN LIQUIDS

Liquids occupy an intermediate position between gases and crystals, not only in their structure and the intensity of intermolecular interaction but also in the thermal motion of their particles. In crystals, we describe the thermal motion of atoms, ions, or molecules as vibrations about well-defined equilibrium positions, and in rarefied gases, in the form of uncorrelated collisions of molecules at the end of each "free path." In the case of liquids, thermal motion is realized in the form of a certain combination of vibrational and translational motions of particles and is responsible for all the observed physical properties of liquids.

According to the concepts first introduced into physics by Ya. I. Frenkel and which have now been generally accepted, the thermal motion of atoms or molecules of a liquid far from the critical point consists of irregular vibrations with an average frequency of $1/\tau_0$, close to the vibrational frequencies of atoms in crystalline bodies and to the amplitude determined by the dimensions of the "free path" allowed the given particle by its neighbors. The center of vibrations is determined by the field of neighboring particles and is shifted together with the displacements of these particles. In this case, therefore, in contrast to a crystal, we have only temporary and unstable equilibrium positions. There exists an average time τ, where $\tau \gg \tau_0$, during which the center of vibrations of each particle is displaced in magnitude by interatomic distances. This is apparently a characteristic time which is related to self-diffusion or to the intermixing of the particles of the liquid.

If we designate the average interatomic distance in a liquid by r_1, then, for the self-diffusion coefficient D, we obtain

$$D \sim \frac{r_1^2}{6\tau}. \tag{1}$$

In view of the high density of particles in liquids and their strong interaction, one would expect that the displacements of particles at distances of the order r_1 during time τ would be accomplished not continuously, but as more or less sharply activated jumps overcoming the potential barrier which separates two possible regions of vibration of one particle. Then the characteristic time τ is, so to speak, the lifetime of an atom in a temporary equilibrium position between two activated jumps. This view, in connection with general statistical considerations, results in the expression

$$\tau \sim \tau_0 \exp\left(\frac{W}{kT}\right), \tag{2}$$

where W is the corresponding activation energy. Together with (1), this leads to the following expression for the temperature dependence of the self-diffusion coefficient,

$$D \sim \frac{r_1^2}{6\,\tau_0} \exp\left(-\frac{W}{kT}\right), \tag{3}$$

which is confirmed by experiment.

Thus, the thermal motion of atoms or molecules in liquids, according to a somewhat simplified but very graphic and qualitatively correct picture, should be conceived as comparatively rare jumps of particles from some temporary equilibrium positions to others and of thermal vibrations in the intervals between the jumps. In the case of non-spherical molecules the rotations and librations of the particles should be added. The duration of the stay of a molecule in a temporary equilibrium position, in accordance with expression (2), depends greatly on temperature, decreasing when the temperature increases.

The continuous and numerous transitions of particles from place to place that occur in a liquid give rise to marked self-diffusion of the particles, and also to the most characteristic property of liquids—their fluidity. If a constant external force is applied to the particles of a liquid, this results in the appearance of a preferred direction of the jumps of particles along the direction of action of the force and causes a flow of particles in the same direction. Moreover, if the magnitude of the applied force is sufficiently small, it does not influence the frequency of the jumps $1/\tau$. The statistical mechanism of this process results essentially in the fact that the current of liquid which arises is proportional to the applied force; this leads to the determination of the coefficient of viscosity of the liquid. Its reciprocal may be taken as a measure of the fluidity of the liquid.

The same thing takes place if, instead of a constant force, a variable external force is applied to the particles, but only if the characteristic time of change in this force is much greater than the lifetime of the particles τ. However, an entirely different result is obtained in the case of a variable force which changes so rapidly that its characteristic time of change is appreciably less than time τ. In the simplest case of a sudden force applied for a short time, the flow mechanism described above does not have time to operate; the reaction of the liquid to the external force applied proves to be an elastic deformation just as it would be in the case of a crystal. In this case, we may talk not only of deformations of the compression-expansion type but also of transverse elastic deformations due to the occurrence of tangential stresses. If, however, the external force applied acts for a very short time and is very great in intensity, this may lead to the disruption of the stability of the liquid in the form of fissures, fractures, etc., again, just as in the case of crystals. Such phenomena in liquids related to their elasticity and stability, which appear unusual at first glance, are actually observed experimentally and have been comparatively well studied [12].

In the case of a continuously acting but very short period external force applied to a liquid, mechanical reactions related to the same phenomena in crystals should be observed (and actually are observed). And only when there is a decrease in the frequency of change of the external force does the mechanism of atomic jumps between positions of temporary equilibrium result first in elastic-relaxational phenomena with a characteristic time of relaxation τ which corresponds to the lifetime of the atoms of the liquid, and then, at still lower frequencies, to the usual liquid flow. In this range of frequencies the fluidity of liquids completely masks their elasticity.

The numerical value of time τ in the case of various liquids may be altogether different depending on their nature. In the case of the usual low-viscosity liquids, time τ is unusually small and is approximately of the order of 10^{-11} seconds. It increases with increasing viscosity and reaches ranges that are entirely accessible to experimental study in the case of more viscous liquids and finally reaches times of the order of hours or even days in the case of glasses.

Thus, in consequence of the specific mechanism of thermal motion of the particles of a liquid, they, in the corresponding region of frequencies of change of the applied forces, possess elastic properties analogous to the properties of isotropic solid bodies. These properties may be characterized by the coefficients of compression and shear, and for ordinary liquids where the time τ is sufficiently small, these values, of course, have the character of the corresponding adiabatic moduli. For short-period deformation the process of thermal conduction does not have time to be accomplished, and the equalization of temperature differences, which have occurred during the course of the deformation due to the evolution or absorption of heat, does not take place.

Still another interesting physical phenomenon—the characteristic spectrum of light scattered by a liquid—is related to the specific mechanism of the thermal motion of particles in a liquid. The vibrational part of the thermal motion of the particles of a liquid may, as in crystals, be reduced to a collection of Debye waves permeating the system. Accordingly, the Mandelstam-Brillouin doublet may be observed in the spectrum of light scattered by a liquid, just as in the case of a crystal. If the incident light is monochromatic with frequency ω_0, the scattered light will contain two frequencies $\omega_0 \pm \Delta\omega$, while in order of magnitude the ratio $\Delta\omega/\omega_0$ will be equal to the ratio of the velocity of sound in the given medium to the velocity of light [13, 14]. In crystals practically all the thermal motion of particles may be reduced to their collective vibrations, and, accordingly, the spectrum of these vibrations extends right up to wavelengths comparable with the interatomic distances. In liquids, in contrast to this, the collective vibrations of the entire system in the form of Debye waves describe only the vibrational part of the thermal motion of the particles (and apparently not all of this) and do not take into consideration at all the very important translational movement of the particles. Accordingly, the spectrum of the collective Debye vibrations in liquids cuts off at longer wavelengths than in the case of crystals. The remaining disordered part of the thermal motion of particles, related primarily to the thermal translational motion, appears in the form of disturbances of the order of the liquid and, accordingly, in the scattered light spectrum there appears a supplementary non-displaced component which is absent in crystals and which is almost as intense as the lines of the Mandelstam-Brillouin doublet. In the thermodynamic theory of light scattering, this non-displaced component is treated as the result of the scattering of light by fluctuations of entropy [14]. It should be noted that, in a not very dense gas, only the non-displaced line in the spectrum is observed in accordance with our ideas about the purely translational character of the thermal motions of the particles of a gas.

3. SIMPLE AND COMPLEX LIQUIDS

The problems that arise in the theory of the liquid state regarding the description and explanation of the structure and physical properties of real liquids are extraordinarily complex, and, at the present time, they are still far from solution. The structure and physical properties of real liquids depend to a very great degree on the chemical individuality of the particles of which they are composed and on the character and intensity of the forces which act between these particles. In various types of liquids, structure and physical properties are different. Any complete theory must take this into consideration, and, therefore, the detailed content of the theory must in many respects be different for different types of liquids.

Here we encounter a situation analogous to that which exists in the theory of solid crystalline bodies, and this latter should be taken as an example in constructing a theory of liquids. "Crystals in general" as an object for study persisted in physics only during the early stages of the development of the theory of solid bodies. It soon became evident that it was essential to have a more precise classification of crystals, principally according to the types of bonding of the particles, and only within the boundaries of each of these narrow groups of substances is it possible, at the present time, to give a detailed description and molecular explanation of the physical properties of real crystalline bodies. Despite the presence of some regularities which are generally inherent in all crystalline bodies, the mechanical, electrical, magnetic, optical, and other properties, for example, in ionic crystals and metals, in molecular crystals, and in crystals with co-valent bonds between atoms are completely different. In each of these cases the very mechanism of the physical processes is often considerably different and, naturally, in each case these processes require individual theoretical examination.

The statistical and molecular theory of liquids has still not attained the level of development of the theory of solid crystalline bodies. Despite the accumulation of a great deal of empirical material on certain problems of the physics of liquids, its theoretical interpretation is often lacking, or does not go beyond the limits of phenomenological description. Many problems have still been very little studied experimentally. The theory of liquids is still in a very early stage of development and "liquids in general" occupy too large a place in it.

This applies to the basic problem of the theory—the problem of the molecular structure of liquids and of the character and nature of their short-range order. There is simply no doubt that the solution of this problem and an opinion on the degree of "quasi-crystallinity" of one liquid or another cannot be presented in general form, although up to the present this has been done by many authors. The shape and dimensions of molecules, and to an even greater degree the character and intensity of the intermolecular interaction, have a decisive influence on the relative distribution and relative motion of the particles of a liquid, and for various types of liquids they prove to be different. As yet these problems have been little studied experimentally and still less theoretically.

At present it is possible to isolate one class of liquids for which sufficient detailed X-ray data on their structure are available and for which the molecular theory of their structure and physical properties is to some degree already developed. These are liquids consisting of spherically symmetrical, non-dipolar particles with interactions which are non-directional and non-saturating van der Waals forces. We shall call these liquids *simple*. Strictly speaking, only the liquefied noble gases fall into this category. Some polyatomic liquids, carbon tetrachloride, for example, may be approximately classified thus. For simple liquids one would expect the least "quasi-crystallinity" of their structure in consequence of the non-directionality and non-saturating character of the intermolecular forces.

Liquid (molten) pure metals occupy a special place. They have been studied by X rays more than other liquids, and many experimental studies of their various physical properties also exist. The nature of the coupling forces in liquid metals is the same as that in crystalline metals and is caused by the collective interactions between ion cores and free electrons. In this respect, metallic liquids differ in principle from liquefied noble gases, and, as a result of this, there is also a significant difference in all their physical properties. Nevertheless, X-ray data show that the character of the short-range order in both these types of liquids is very similar. In structural relationships pure liquid metals are also simple liquids. This latter fact seems natural if we take into consideration the fact that the "metallic bond" caused by the free electrons, as well as the van der Waals bond, is non-directional and non-saturating and that metallic ions are spherically symmetrical and have an electron structure analogous to the electron structure of the atoms of noble gases. It should be noted that, in the crystalline phase, typical metals and elements of the zero group all attempt to crystallize into very densely packed structures.

Water is a typical non-simple liquid which has been comparatively well studied. The directional and saturating hydrogen bonds between molecules, which cause the larger part of the binding force in water, result in the fact that, on the average, water molecules preserve an approximately tetrahedral coordination which is close to that which exists in ice, and in this sense the "quasi-crystallinity" in the vicinity of any particle is comparatively strongly expressed. It appears simultaneously, however, that a strong stretching and deflection of the hydrogen bonds takes place; in addition, there is an appreciable fraction of ruptured hydrogen bonds and many "dislocated" molecules which fill the voids of the tetrahedral structure. Therefore, long-range order in the system is lacking, and there is no "quasi-crystallinity" in the sense of translational repetition of the true, instantaneous structure. (For more detailed information on the structure of water, see eq. [15].)

The situation with other non-simple liquids consisting of polyatomic molecules with complex interactions is still more complex. Problems of their structure and of a molecular explanation of their properties have as yet been little studied.

An effort to construct a strict theory of the liquid state of matter should naturally begin with the very simplest case. A comparatively well-developed statistical theory of simple liquids already exists. The present volume is devoted to its exposition.

REFERENCES

[1] F. Zernicke and J. Prins, *Z. Phys.*, **41** (1927), 184.
[2] P. Debye and H. Menke, *Ergeb. d. Tech. Röntg.*, **2** (1931).
[3] Ya. I. Frenkel, *Kineticheskaya teoriya zhidkostei*, Izd. AN SSSR (Kinetic Theory of Liquids), Acad. Sci. USSR., 1945.
[4] P. Debye, *Uspekhi Fiz. Nauk*, **21** (1939), 120.
[5] V. I. Danilov, *Stroenie i kristallizatsiya zhidkostei* (*sbornik*) (Structure and Crystallization of Liquids [symposium]), Kiev, 1956.
[6] J. Hildebrand, *Discussions Faraday Soc.*, **15** (1953), 9.
[7] J. Kirkwood and E. Monroe, *J. Chem. Phys.*, **9** (1941), 514.
[8] J. Kirkwood and E. Boggs, *J. Chem. Phys.*, **10** (1942), 394.
[9] N. N. Bogolyubov, *Problemy dinamicheskoi theorii v statisticheskoi fizike*, Gostekhizdat (Problems of Dynamic Theory in Statistical Physics), State Technical Press, 1946.
[10] M. Born and H. Green, *Proc. Roy. Soc., ser. A*, **188** (1946), 10; **189** (1947), 455.
[11] H. Green, *Molecular Theory of Liquids*, Amsterdam, 1952.
[12] M. Kornfeld, *Uprugost' i prochnost' zhidkostei*, Gostekhizdat (Elasticity and Firmness in Liquids), State Technical Press, 1951.
[13] M. V. Vol'kenshtein, *Molekulyarnaya Optika*, Gostekhizdat (Molecular Optics), State Technical Press, 1951.
[14] L. D. Landau and E. M. Lifshits, *Elektrodinamika sploshnykh sred*, Gostekhizdat (Electrodynamics of Complex Media), State Technical Press, 1957.
[15] O. Ya. Samoilov, *Struktura vodnykh rastvorov elektrolitov i gidratatsiya ionov*, AN SSSR (The Structure of Aqueous Solutions of Electrolytes and the Hydration of Ions), Acad. Sci. USSR, 1957.

CHAPTER 1

THE CLASSICAL STATISTICAL INTEGRAL

1. PRINCIPLES OF STATISTICAL THERMODYNAMICS

We shall now consider a system of a very large number N of identical particles (atoms or molecules), which are interacting with each other and which fill a volume V in equilibrium at temperature T. The actual motion of individual particles, and therefore also the statistical properties of the entire system, are determined by the laws of quantum mechanics. It appears, however, that, excluding the case of very low temperature, many properties of a molecular system may be described to sufficient accuracy in a purely classical manner merely by introducing some greater precision in the constants that occur in the theory. Below is a brief summary of the basic assumptions of classical statistical thermodynamics thus obtained, which we shall need later on. For a more detailed description of these problems one should refer to the special literature [1, 2, 3].

Let us first consider the simplest case of monatomic particles when the position of an individual particle is completely described by the three coordinates $q_i = (q_i^1, q_i^2, q_i^3)$ of its center of mass, and its motion by the corresponding momenta $p_i = (p_i^1, p_i^2, p_i^3)$, where i ranges from 1 to N. Let $H(q_1, \ldots, q_N; p_1, \ldots, p_N)$ be the Hamiltonian function of our system, equal to the sum of its kinetic and potential energies,

$$H(q_1, \ldots, p_N) = \sum_{1 \leq i \leq N} \frac{p_i^2}{2m} + U_N(q_1, \ldots, q_N), \quad (1.1)$$

where m is the mass of a particle. One of the basic laws of statistical physics is the statement that the probability $dW(q_1, \ldots, p_N)$ that particles of a system having positions and momenta close to certain values assigned them are asymptotically distributed, for very large N, according to the law

$$dW(q_1, \ldots, p_N) = Z_N^{-1} \exp\left[-\frac{H(q_1, \ldots, p_N)}{kT} \right] d\Gamma, \quad (1.2)$$

where k is the Boltzmann constant $k = 1.38 \cdot 10^{-16}$ erg/deg, Z_N^{-1} is the normalization constant, and $d\Gamma$ is proportional to an element of the phase space of the system

$$d\Gamma = \frac{dq_1 \ldots dq_N dp_1 \ldots dp_N}{(2\pi\hbar)^{3N}}. \quad (1.3)$$

The value $2\pi\hbar$ is the Planck constant ($\hbar = 1.05 \cdot 10^{-27}$ erg sec.). Here, and everywhere below, for the sake of brevity, we shall designate $dq_i = dq_i^1 dq_i^2 dq_i^3$ and $dp_i = dp_i^1 dp_i^2 dp_i^3$. The distribution (1.2) is called the Gibbs distribution.

The normalization condition of the Gibbs distribution is written in the form

$$\frac{1}{N!} \int \cdots \int dW(q_1, \ldots, p_N) = 1, \quad (1.4)$$

where the appearance of the factor $(N!)^{-1}$ is related to the necessity of taking into consideration the identity of all N particles of the system when integration in (1.4) takes place over the entire phase space of the system. The rearrangements of the particles among themselves, equivalent to a change in the numbering of the particles, does not result in physically differing states. Then the left-hand side of equation (1.4) corresponds to an integration only over differing states in the phase space. In connection with (1.2) this leads to the following expression for Z_N,

$$Z_N = \frac{1}{N!} \int \cdots \int \exp\left[-\frac{H(q_1, \ldots, p_N)}{kT} \right] d\Gamma, \quad (1.5)$$

where the integration is again over the whole phase space of the system.

In connection with the Hamiltonian function (1.1), where the coordinates and momenta appear to be divided among themselves, the general Gibbs distribution breaks down into two independent distributions—one for coordinates and the other for momenta. Due to the additivity of kinetic energy, the distribution of momenta in turn breaks down into N independent distributions for the momentum of each particle individually

$$dW(p_1, \ldots, p_N) = \prod_{1 \leq i \leq N} dW(p_i), \tag{1.6}$$

whereupon,

$$dW(p_i) = (2\pi m kT)^{-3/2} \exp\left(-\frac{p_i^2}{2mkT}\right) dp_i, \tag{1.7}$$

if each $dW(p_i)$ is normalized to unity. Then, for the coordinate (configurational) part of the Gibbs distribution, we obtain

$$dW(q_1, \ldots, q_N) = D_N(q_1, \ldots, q_N)\, dq_1 \ldots dq_N, \tag{1.8}$$

where

$$D_N(q_1, \ldots, q_N) = Q_N^{-1} \exp\left[-\frac{U_N(q_1, \ldots, q_N)}{kT}\right] \tag{1.9}$$

and Q_N^{-1} is the normalization constant. If $dW(q, \ldots, q_N)$ is normalized to unity without taking into consideration the identity of the particles, then for the term Q_N, called the configuration integral of the system, we obtain

$$Q_N = \int_V \cdots \int_V \exp\left[-\frac{U_N(q_1, \ldots, q_N)}{kT}\right] dq_1 \ldots dq_N. \tag{1.10}$$

From equations (1.5) to (1.10), it follows that the terms Z_N and Q_N are related to each other as follows:

$$Z_N = \left(\frac{mkT}{2\pi \hbar^2}\right)^{3N/2} \frac{Q_N}{N!}. \tag{1.11}$$

Both the terms Z_N and Q_N depend on the temperature and volume of the system, on the number of particles, and on the parameters which describe the possible external fields that act on the system. They are therefore thermodynamic functions.

The term Z_N is called the statistical integral of the system, and it plays an important role in statistical thermodynamics. If Z_N is known, then it is easy to calculate all the thermodynamic functions of the system under consideration. Thus, in statistical physics, it has been shown that the free energy of the system F is directly related to the statistical integral Z_N by means of the fundamental relationship

$$F = -kT \ln Z_N. \tag{1.12}$$

If equation (1.11) is used, we may then write

$$F = -kT \ln Q_N + NkT\left[\ln N - 1 - \tfrac{3}{2} \ln\left(\frac{mkT}{2\pi\hbar^2}\right)\right]. \tag{1.13}$$

Thus the problem of calculating the free energy of a selected system of particles amounts to the calculation of its configuration integral.

By direct differentiation of the free energy with the aid of relationships known from thermodynamics, we can find the pressure, entropy, and chemical potential of the system

$$p = -\left(\frac{\partial F}{\partial V}\right)_{T,N}, \qquad S = -\left(\frac{\partial F}{\partial T}\right)_{V,N}, \qquad \mu = \left(\frac{\partial F}{\partial N}\right)_{T,V}, \tag{1.14}$$

and also its energy

$$E = F + ST = F - T\left(\frac{\partial F}{\partial T}\right)_{V,N}. \tag{1.15}$$

By using equation (1.13) it is possible to express all these functions in terms of the configurational integral, and we obtain

$$p = kT\left(\frac{\partial \ln Q_N}{\partial V}\right)_{T,N}, \tag{1.16}$$

$$E = \tfrac{3}{2} NkT + kT^2\left(\frac{\partial \ln Q_N}{\partial T}\right)_{V,N}, \tag{1.17}$$

$$S = \tfrac{5}{2} Nk - Nk \ln N + \tfrac{3}{2} Nk \ln\left(\frac{mkT}{2\pi\hbar^2}\right) + k \ln Q_N + kT\left(\frac{\partial \ln Q_N}{\partial T}\right)_{V,N}, \tag{1.18}$$

$$\mu = -kT\left(\frac{\partial \ln Q_N}{\partial N}\right)_{V,T} + kT \ln N - \tfrac{3}{2} kT \ln\left(\frac{mkT}{2\pi\hbar^2}\right). \tag{1.19}$$

Let us consider as an example a system of non-interacting particles where $U_N = 0$. Then, from (1.10), it follows that $Q_N = V^N$ and, for the free energy, according to (1.13), we obtain

$$F_0 = -Nk \ln v - \tfrac{3}{2} NkT \ln\left(\frac{mkT}{2\pi\hbar^2}\right) - NkT, \tag{1.20}$$

where $v = V/N$ is the average volume per particle in the system. From this, for p, E, S, and μ we obtain the well-known expressions

$$p_0 = \frac{kT}{v}, \tag{1.21}$$

$$E_0 = \tfrac{3}{2} NkT, \tag{1.22}$$

$$S_0 = \tfrac{5}{2} Nk + Nk \ln v + \tfrac{3}{2} Nk \ln\left(\frac{mkT}{2\pi\hbar^2}\right), \tag{1.23}$$

$$\mu_0 = -kT \ln v - \tfrac{3}{2} kT \ln\left(\frac{mkT}{2\pi\hbar^2}\right). \tag{1.24}$$

With the aid of (1.13) and (1.20), we can represent the free energy of any system in the form of a sum of the free energy of an ideal gas F_0 (1.20) and of a supplementary contribution related to the interaction of the particles:

$$F = F_0 - kT \ln\left(\frac{Q_N}{V^N}\right). \tag{1.25}$$

All the other thermodynamic functions may be represented in an analogous manner. For example, for the entropy we easily obtain

$$T(S - S_0) = E - E_0 + kT \ln\left(\frac{Q_N}{V^N}\right). \tag{1.26}$$

But $E - E_0$ is the average value of the potential energy of the system $\bar{U}_N$, and, by using (1.9), we obtain

$$S = S_0 - k\langle \ln [V^N D_N(q_1, \ldots, q_N)] \rangle, \tag{1.27}$$

where the broken brackets ($\langle\ \rangle$) indicate averaging according to the Gibbs distribution.

Up to now we have considered that the position and motion of each particle is completely described by the position and momentum of its center of mass. In the case of complex particles that have more than three degrees of freedom the theory is easily generalized by introducing into the Hamiltonian function the necessary number of coordinates and momenta and by considering the full phase space or the full momentum and full configurational spaces, respectively. The fundamental relationship (1.12) in this case remains in force, but, in addition, Z_N should be understood as a generalization of equation (1.5) with extension of the integration to the whole of phase space. The Gibbs distribution (1.2) and its configurational part may be generalized analogously.

In fact, however, the validity of such a classical approach to the internal degrees of freedom of a particle is restricted to such high temperatures as would be uninteresting for real systems. In some cases the classical approach may be unsuitable at any temperature. In all these cases it is necessary to turn to a quantum-statistical treatment. The situation is most favorable in the case of the rotational degrees of freedom for non-spherical molecules. For heavy molecules at not too low a temperature, the classical description of their rotational motion is a reasonable approximation.

2. INTERMOLECULAR FORCES AND THE LAW OF CORRESPONDING STATES

Calculation of the configuration integral in the majority of cases presents an exceptionally complex problem. The potential energy U_N, which enters the expression (1.10) in the absence of external forces, leads to an energy of interaction of all the particles of the system. The simplest assumption that may be made concerning the function U_N is that it is pairwise additive:

$$U_N(q_1, \ldots, q_N) = \sum_{1 \leq i < j \leq N} \Phi(|q_i - q_j|). \qquad (1.28)$$

For the sake of simplicity, we have also assumed that the interaction of each pair of particles is central and depends only on the distance between their centers. The sum in (1.28) contains $N(N-1)/2$ terms; even when all simplifications are made, a precise calculation of Q_N is not possible.

The additivity of the intermolecular forces proves to be rigorously correct, for example, in the electrostatic problem of the interaction of a system of electrically charged point particles. However, it is just as easy to give an example of a system where the additivity of forces does not occur at all. Such, for example, will be the case for a system of dipolar particles which may be polarized in an external field. The interaction between the particles will depend on their dipole moments, and the latter, at each particle, will contain an inductive part depending on the total field of all the other particles which act on a given particle. For non-dipolar particles, the relationship (1.28) also cannot be strictly accurate, since it is known from the quantum-mechanical study of the interaction of three atoms that in this case a small additional term appears which depends on the mutual arrangement of all three particles. The situation is still more intricate in a condensed system of a very large number of particles, where one should expect the appearance of "collective" terms in the energy of interaction which violate the law of additivity (1.28). Nevertheless, one may assume that in a non-dipolar monoatomic liquid, and also in a non-dipolar liquid with approximately spherical molecules, the "collective" terms make only a small contribution to the full energy of the system, and in a first approximation these effects may be disregarded. The correctness of this is, to a considerable degree, confirmed by experiment [4]. Everywhere below we shall consider the relationship (1.28) to be true, although in this case the central character of the forces is not necessary.

The form of the function $\Phi(r)$ in principle may be found for each sort of particle from the corresponding quantum-mechanical calculations. In actual fact, at the present time these calculations may be made only approximately and only for the simplest atoms. Qualitatively the function $\Phi(r)$ should represent the experimentally observed attraction of particles at great distances and of their repulsion at sufficiently small distances, so that a graph of the function $\Phi(r)$ should approximately correspond to the curve in Figure 1. Essentially there is a rapid drop in $\Phi(r)$ as r increases, which expresses the short-range character of the intermolecular forces if the molecules or atoms are non-dipolar and are not electrically charged.

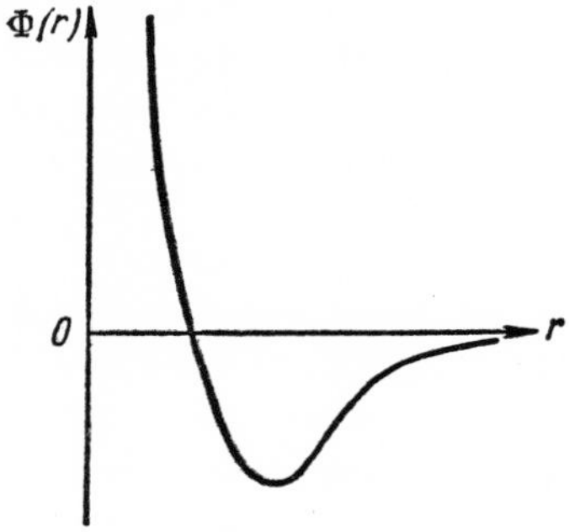

FIG. 1.—Schematic trend of the intermolecular potential $\Phi(r)$

In calculations in the theory of liquids and gases, a model intermolecular potential proposed by Lennard-Jones is often used:

$$\Phi(r) = 4\epsilon\left[\left(\frac{a}{r}\right)^{12} - \left(\frac{a}{r}\right)^{6}\right], \qquad (1.29)$$

where ϵ and a are constants having the dimensions of energy and length respectively. The length a is the effective diameter of the particle; when $r = a$ we have $\Phi(a) = 0$. The value ϵ determines the depth of the potential well of $\Phi(r)$ and, consequently, the intensity of the intermolecular forces.

But if in equation (1.29) the exponent of the 6th power in the term which describes the attraction may be considered theoretically justified and agreeing with quantum-mechanical calculations, then the exponent of the 12th power in the term describing the repulsion is selected only for reasons of convenience.

A somewhat more general model potential

$$\Phi(r) = \frac{\epsilon n}{n-6}\left(\frac{n}{6}\right)^{6/(n-6)}\left[\left(\frac{a}{r}\right)^{n} - \left(\frac{a}{r}\right)^{6}\right] \qquad (1.30)$$

(where $n > 6$ and the constants ϵ and a have the same significance as in the case of the potential eq. [1.29]) sometimes proves to be more accurate in the corresponding selection of an exponent of the nth degree (usually $n \sim 10$).

In molecular spectroscopy and in calculations connected with the application of spectroscopic data to the thermodynamics of gases, the Morse potential is often used

$$\Phi(r) = \epsilon[e^{-2\beta(r-a)} - 2e^{-\beta(r-a)}]. \tag{1.31}$$

Here a is the position of minimum of $\Phi(r)$, ϵ is the depth of this minimum, and β is a new constant which determines the slope of $\Phi(r)$ in the region of the minimum. While possessing many analytical advantages, the potential (1.31) is not plausible far from the minimum region: it decreases too rapidly when $r \to \infty$ and does not increase sufficiently rapidly when $r \to 0$. In the literature other models of the intermolecular potential have also been used; however the majority of them, as in the case of the potentials (1.29) to (1.31), cannot be considered sufficiently well founded theoretically, although they are adequate for qualitative studies and estimates.

The intermolecular potentials (1.29) and (1.30) have the interesting property of being reducible to the form of a product of the energy constant ϵ by a function of the dimensionless argument $x = r/a$:

$$\Phi(r) = \epsilon\varphi\left(\frac{r}{a}\right). \tag{1.32}$$

One may assume that the relationship (1.32) is sufficiently accurate for real atoms or molecules regardless of the choice of the exact form of the function $\varphi(x)$. If this is so, interesting thermodynamic conclusions may be obtained from it. It is easy to see that the substitution $q_i = aq_i^r$, for all $i = 1, 2, \ldots, N$ in this case gives the configuration integral (1.10) in the form

$$Q_N = a^{3N} f_N\left(\frac{kT}{\epsilon}, \frac{V}{a^3}\right), \tag{1.33}$$

where f_N is some function of the two indicated dimensionless arguments. Then for the pressure and energy of the system, in accordance with (1.16) and (1.17), we obtain

$$p = \frac{\epsilon}{a^3}\chi\left(\frac{kT}{\epsilon}, \frac{V}{a^3}\right), \qquad E = \epsilon\psi\left(\frac{kT}{\epsilon}, \frac{V}{a^3}\right). \tag{1.34}$$

If, therefore, we introduce the reduced temperature, volume, pressure, and energy T^*, V^*, p^*, and E^* defined by

$$T^* = \frac{kT}{\epsilon}, \qquad V^* = \frac{V}{a^3}, \qquad p^* = \frac{a^3 p}{\epsilon}, \qquad E^* = \frac{E}{\epsilon} \tag{1.35}$$

so that all these variables are dimensionless, one finds that

$$p^* = p^*(T^*, V^*), \qquad E^* = E^*(T^*, V^*) \qquad (1.36)$$

for all systems characterized by the common function $\varphi(x)$ and independent of the numerical values of the constants ϵ and a.

The existence of the universal functions $p^*(T^*, V^*)$ and $E^*(T^*, V^*)$ for a whole group of substances with common potential function is called the law of corresponding states, in virtue of which the thermodynamic properties of a given group, expressed on an appropriate scale, are identical.

TABLE 1

Substance	$a \cdot 10^8$ cm	$a^3 \cdot 10^{24}$ cm^3	$\epsilon \cdot 10^{15}$ erg
He.	2.56	16.8	1.41
Ne.	2.76	20.9	4.90
Ar.	3.41	39.65	16.5
Kr.	3.66	49.1	22.9
Xe.	3.95	61.5	30.3

TABLE 2

Substance	T^*_{trip}	$P^*_{trip} \cdot 10^3$	v^*_{trip}	T^*_{crit}	p^*_{crit}	v^*_{crit}
Ne.	0.690	1.882	1.292	1.247	0.1150	3.333
Ar.	0.699	1.646	1.182	1.258	0.1162	3.164
Kr.	0.698	1.556	1.161	1.26	0.1167	3.163
Xe.	0.702	1.570	1.162	1.26	0.1134	3.095
Average.	0.70	1.56	1.16	1.26	0.117	3.16

One would expect that the simplifying assumptions made in equations (1.28) to (1.32) are entirely accurate for the interaction of atoms of the noble gases. Table 1 gives the values of the constants ϵ and a obtained from a study of the properties of these substances in the gaseous state and using the assumption that the potential is correct for them (1.29) [5].

The law of corresponding states is accurately fulfilled in the case of heavy noble gases, both in the gaseous and liquefied states; examples are given in Figures 2 and 3 [5]. Figures 2 and 3 also show the corresponding experimentally determined dependence on T^* of the reduced density of gases and liquids N/V^* and of the reduced pressure p^* of the saturated vapors of argon, krypton, and xenon. Analogous graphs with comparable internal agreement are also obtained for the other thermodynamic properties of these substances. Table 2 shows the experimentally obtained values of the reduced parameters of the triple point and critical point for four noble gases. These data also illustrate the high accuracy of the law of corresponding states.

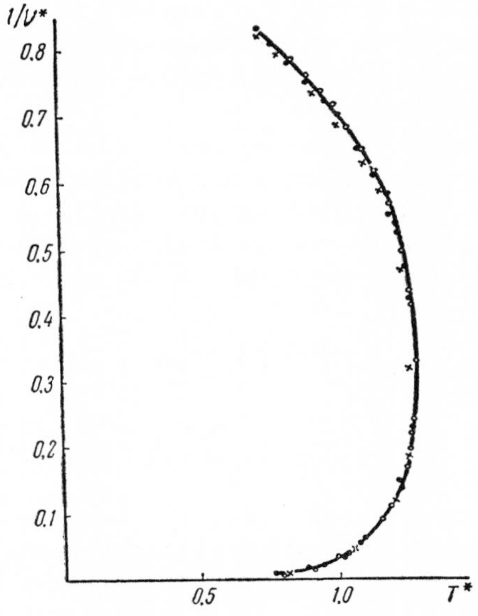

FIG. 2.—Reduced experimental values, expressed in molecular units, of the densities of gas and liquid for argon (small crosses), krypton (dots), and xenon (small circles).

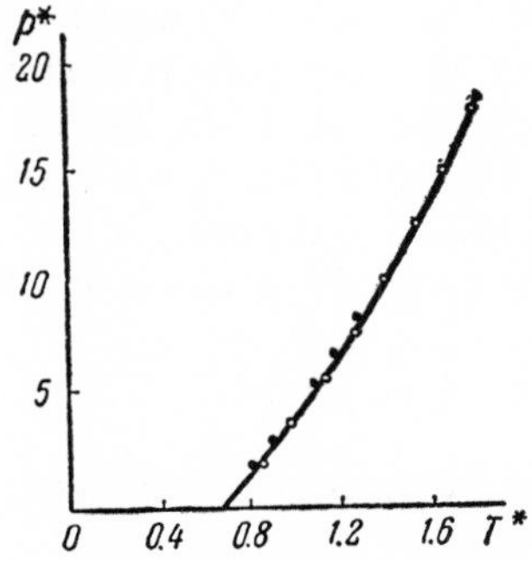

FIG. 3.—Reduced experimental melting curve, expressed in molecular units

3. QUANTUM CORRECTIONS TO THE STATISTICAL INTEGRAL AND TO THE LAW OF CORRESPONDING STATES

Inasmuch as the motions of atoms and molecules are determined by the laws of quantum mechanics, a rigorous statistical theory of atomic and molecular systems should be constructed on the basis of quantum mechanics. In this connection, it is interesting to observe to what extent quantum corrections to the classical theory set forth above are essential. In this case, we are only interested in translational degrees of freedom of the particles.

In statistical physics it has been shown that a precise quantum statistical sum of a system of interacting particles, leading in the quasi-classical approximation to the statistical integral [1, 5], may be expanded in powers of the constant $\hbar$ when quantum corrections are taken into consideration, and, in this case, the first quantum correction is proportional to $\hbar^2$ [2]:

$$Z_N = Z_N^{\text{class}}(1 + \hbar^2 \chi + \ldots). \qquad (1.37)$$

where

$$\chi = -\frac{1}{24m(kT)^2} \sum_{1 \leq i \leq N} \left(\frac{\langle \partial^2 U_N \rangle}{\partial q_i^2} \right). \qquad (1.38)$$

Here Z_N is the exact statistical sum, Z_N^{class} is its classical approximation (1.5), U_N is the full potential energy of the system, and the broken brackets indicate averaging according to the classical Gibbs distribution (1.2). From this, with the aid of (1.12), we obtain for the free energy

$$F = F^{\text{class}} + \frac{\hbar^2}{24mkT} \sum_{1 \leq i \leq N} \left(\frac{\langle \partial^2 U_N \rangle}{\partial q_i^2} \right) + \ldots . \qquad (1.39)$$

For a more detailed evaluation of the quantum effects let us assume that the system under consideration permits the introduction of a two-parameter potential of the type of (1.32). Then it is easy to see that F^{class} will always be of the order $N\epsilon T^*$, while the quantum correction according to (1.39) will be of the order of $N\hbar^2\epsilon/ma^2T^*$; therefore, the expansion of the free energy in powers of $\hbar$ will have the form

$$F = F^{\text{class}}\left[1 + \left(\frac{\Lambda}{T^*}\right)^2 \omega(T^*, V^*) + \ldots\right], \qquad (1.40)$$

where $\omega(T^*, V^*)$ is some dimensionless thermodynamic function of the order of unity, and

$$\Lambda = \frac{\hbar}{a\sqrt{(m\epsilon)}} \qquad (1.41)$$

is a new dimensionless parameter, called the De Boer parameter, which describes the magnitude of the quantum effects in statistical systems. From the expression (1.40) it can be seen that quantum effects decrease with increasing temperature, and if the region of extremely low temperatures is excluded, the smallness of the quantum effects is determined by the smallness of parameter Λ.

The values of Λ for atoms of the noble gases are given in Table 3. It is evident from this table that Λ is small for heavy atoms and in this case quantum corrections play a very small role. On the other hand, for helium, Λ is large and its behavior in the dense gaseous and especially in the liquid states is determined by quantum effects. Quantum effects should show up for neon in the liquid state, although only to a small degree, and this actually corresponds with the experimental

TABLE 3

Substance	Λ	Substance	Λ
He........	0.424	Kr.........	0.0161
Ne........	0.0939	Xe.........	0.0103
Ar........	0.0294		

facts. The appearance of a new parameter Λ in calculating quantum corrections changes the formulation of the law of corresponding states. Instead of (1.36) we now obtain

$$p^* = p^*(T^*, V^*, \Lambda), \qquad E^* = E^*(T^*, V^*, \Lambda), \quad (1.42)$$

and for substances with light atoms deviations from the universal law of corresponding states should be observed; this actually occurs.

From here on we shall be concerned only with the classical theory of liquids. We shall not be interested in quantum effects in ordinary liquids nor shall we give special attention to the theory of quantum liquids. The freezing temperature of the overwhelming majority of liquids is so high that disregarding quantum corrections within the region that the liquid phase exists in legitimate.

4. CALCULATION OF THE CONFIGURATION INTEGRAL FOR A GAS

Precise calculation of the configuration integral Q_N for a system of interacting particles is possible in only a very small number of cases. One of these is the gaseous system where, due to the large average distance between particles, it is possible to calculate successively the interactions between pairs, triplets, quadruplets, etc., of particles and to compute their contribution to the configuration integral. In this case, one obtains an expansion of Q_N and of the thermodynamic functions of the gas in powers of the density, and, for a gas which is not too dense, it is possible, in principle, to extend the calculation to any desired degree of precision. We shall touch briefly on this process below. For more precise information the corresponding literature [3, 6, 7] should be referred to.

We shall assume that the expression (1.28) for the full potential energy of the system is valid. Then the configuration integral Q_N according to (1.10) is equal to

$$\begin{aligned} Q_N &= \int_V \cdots \int_V \exp\Big[-\frac{1}{kT}\sum_{1\le i<j\le N} \Phi(|\mathbf{q}_i-\mathbf{q}_j|)\Big] d\mathbf{q}_1 \ldots d\mathbf{q}_N \\ &= \int_V \cdots \int_V \prod_{1\le i<j\le N} \exp\Big[-\frac{\Phi(|\mathbf{q}_i-\mathbf{q}_j|)}{kT}\Big] d\mathbf{q}_1 \ldots d\mathbf{q}_N . \end{aligned} \tag{1.43}$$

Let us introduce the new functions

$$f(r) = \exp\Big[-\frac{\Phi(r)}{kT}\Big] - 1 , \tag{1.44}$$

and for brevity we will designate $f_{ij} = f(|\mathbf{q}_i - \mathbf{q}_j|)$. For the case of the assumed short-range potential $\Phi(r)$, the function $f(r)$ is significantly different from zero only in a small region of the order of the radius of action of the intermolecular forces. With the aid of the function $f(r)$ we can write

$$Q_N = \int_V \cdots \int_V \prod_{1\le i<j\le N} [1 + f(|\mathbf{q}_i - \mathbf{q}_j|)] \, d\mathbf{q}_1 \ldots d\mathbf{q}_N , \tag{1.45}$$

or, expanding the product,

$$\begin{aligned} Q_N = \int_V \cdots \int_V \Big(1 &+ \sum_{1\le i<j\le N} f_{ij} \\ &+ \sum_{1\le i<j\le k<l\le N}\sum f_{ij} f_{kl} + \ldots\Big) d\mathbf{q}_1 \ldots d\mathbf{q}_N . \end{aligned} \tag{1.46}$$

In the absence of interaction, $f(r) = 0$. Therefore, the first term in the series (1.46) corresponds to the contribution in Q_N from separate non-interacting particles, as in an ideal gas. Each term of the first sum corresponds to the contribution in Q_N from the interaction of one pair of particles in the entire system, and the entire sum corresponds to the contribution from the interaction of all possible pairs one by one. Furthermore, the terms of the second sum describe the contributions in Q_N from the simultaneous interaction of two pairs of particles in the system (when the indexes i, j, k, l are all different), or even the contributions from the interaction of triplets of particles (when $j = k$). Analogously, the successive unwritten terms of the series (1.46) describe either the interaction of many pairs, triplets, etc., of particles, or even the interaction of new and still more complex groups of particles.

The contributions to the configuration integral from the interaction of $k + 1$ particles are characterized by the "irreducible integral" β_k. Single particles that do not interact with anything make a contribution to any term of the series (1.44) of

$$\int_V d\boldsymbol{q} = V\,, \tag{1.47}$$

and this determines the zeroth irreducible integral, $\beta_0 = 1$. The interaction of one pair of particles in any term of the series (1.44) corresponds to the contribution

$$\int_V \int_V f(|\boldsymbol{q} - \boldsymbol{q}'|)\,d\boldsymbol{q}\,d\boldsymbol{q}' = V \int f(|\boldsymbol{q}|)\,d\boldsymbol{q}\,, \tag{1.48}$$

and the integral obtained here is called the first irreducible integral β_1:

$$\beta_1 = \int f(|\boldsymbol{q}|)\,d\boldsymbol{q}\,. \tag{1.49}$$

The contribution from several distinct simultaneously interacting pairs will be proportional to the corresponding powers of β_1. Thus, for two pairs, for example, we have

$$\begin{aligned} &\int\int\int\int f(|\boldsymbol{q}_1 - \boldsymbol{q}_2|)\,f(|\boldsymbol{q}_3 - \boldsymbol{q}_4|)\,d\boldsymbol{q}_1 d\boldsymbol{q}_2 d\boldsymbol{q}_3 d\boldsymbol{q}_4 \\ &\qquad = [\int\int f(|\boldsymbol{q}_1 - \boldsymbol{q}_2|)\,d\boldsymbol{q}_1 d\boldsymbol{q}_2]^2 = V^2 \beta_1^2\,. \end{aligned} \tag{1.50}$$

In the case of the interaction of triplets of particles, two typical integrals in the sum (1.46) will be

$$\begin{aligned} &\int\int\int f(|\boldsymbol{q}_1 - \boldsymbol{q}_2|)\,f(|\boldsymbol{q}_2 - \boldsymbol{q}_3|)\,d\boldsymbol{q}_1 d\boldsymbol{q}_2 d\boldsymbol{q}_3\,, \\ &\int\int\int f(|\boldsymbol{q}_1 - \boldsymbol{q}_2|)\,f(|\boldsymbol{q}_2 - \boldsymbol{q}_3|)\,f(|\boldsymbol{q}_3 - \boldsymbol{q}_1|)\,d\boldsymbol{q}_1 d\boldsymbol{q}_2 d\boldsymbol{q}_3\,. \end{aligned} \tag{1.51}$$

The first case obviously again results in β_1^2, since we have

$$\begin{aligned} &\int\int\int f(|\boldsymbol{q}_1 - \boldsymbol{q}_2|)\,f(|\boldsymbol{q}_2 - \boldsymbol{q}_3|)\,d\boldsymbol{q}_1 d\boldsymbol{q}_2 d\boldsymbol{q}_3 \\ &\qquad = \int\int f(|\boldsymbol{q}_1 - \boldsymbol{q}_2|)\,d\boldsymbol{q}_1 d\boldsymbol{q}_2 \int f(|\boldsymbol{q}_2 - \boldsymbol{q}_3|)\,d\boldsymbol{q}_3 \\ &\qquad = \beta_1 \int\int f(|\boldsymbol{q}_1 - \boldsymbol{q}_2|)\,d\boldsymbol{q}_1 d\boldsymbol{q}_2 = V\beta_1^2\,. \end{aligned} \tag{1.52}$$

The second case results in a new second irreducible integral β_2:

$$\beta_2 = \tfrac{1}{2}\int\int f(|\boldsymbol{q}|) f(|\boldsymbol{q}'|) f(|\boldsymbol{q}-\boldsymbol{q}'|)\, d\boldsymbol{q}\, d\boldsymbol{q}', \quad (1.53)$$

and the integral (1.51) itself is equal to

$$\int\int\int f(|\boldsymbol{q}_1-\boldsymbol{q}_2|) f(|\boldsymbol{q}_2-\boldsymbol{q}_3|) f(|\boldsymbol{q}_3-\boldsymbol{q}_1|) \times d\boldsymbol{q}_1 d\boldsymbol{q}_2 d\boldsymbol{q}_3 = 2V\beta_2 . \quad (1.54)$$

In the case of quadruplets of particles, if they do not decompose into independent pairs or triplets plus a single particle, some types of contributions to Q_N again result in combinations of the preceding cases. Thus, for example, we have

$$\int\int\int\int f_{12} f_{23} f_{34}\, d\boldsymbol{q}_1 d\boldsymbol{q}_2 d\boldsymbol{q}_3 d\boldsymbol{q}_4 = \beta_1 \int\int\int f_{12} f_{23}\, d\boldsymbol{q}_1 d\boldsymbol{q}_2 d\boldsymbol{q}_3 = V\beta_1^3 , \quad (1.55)$$

and further

$$\int\int\int\int f_{12} f_{13} f_{23} f_{34}\, d\boldsymbol{q}_1 d\boldsymbol{q}_2 d\boldsymbol{q}_3 d\boldsymbol{q}_4 = \beta_1 \int\int\int f_{12} f_{13} f_{23}\, d\boldsymbol{q}_1 d\boldsymbol{q}_2 d\boldsymbol{q}_3 = 2V\beta_1\beta_2 . \quad (1.56)$$

Three types of integrals will be essentially new in this situation:

$$\begin{aligned} &\int\int\int\int f_{12} f_{23} f_{34} f_{41}\, d\boldsymbol{q}_1 d\boldsymbol{q}_2 d\boldsymbol{q}_3 d\boldsymbol{q}_4 , \\ &\int\int\int\int f_{12} f_{23} f_{34} f_{41} f_{13}\, d\boldsymbol{q}_1 d\boldsymbol{q}_2 d\boldsymbol{q}_3 d\boldsymbol{q}_4 , \\ &\int\int\int\int f_{12} f_{23} f_{34} f_{41} f_{13} f_{24}\, d\boldsymbol{q}_1 d\boldsymbol{q}_2 d\boldsymbol{q}_3 d\boldsymbol{q}_4 . \end{aligned} \quad (1.57)$$

For the same four particles, three variations of the integrals of the first type and six variations of the integrals of the second type are possible, differing in the rearrangements of the particles among each other. In accordance with this, the third irreducible integral is found to be equal to

$$\begin{aligned} \beta_3 = \tfrac{1}{6}\int\int\int [\, &3 f(|\boldsymbol{q}|) f(|\boldsymbol{q}-\boldsymbol{q}'|) f(|\boldsymbol{q}'-\boldsymbol{q}''|) f(|\boldsymbol{q}''|) \\ &+ 6 f(|\boldsymbol{q}|) f(|\boldsymbol{q}-\boldsymbol{q}'|) f(|\boldsymbol{q}-\boldsymbol{q}''|) f(|\boldsymbol{q}'-\boldsymbol{q}''|) f(|\boldsymbol{q}''|) \\ &+ f(|\boldsymbol{q}|) f(|\boldsymbol{q}-\boldsymbol{q}'|) f(|\boldsymbol{q}-\boldsymbol{q}''|) f(|\boldsymbol{q}'-\boldsymbol{q}''|) \\ &\times f(|\boldsymbol{q}'|) f(|\boldsymbol{q}''|)]\, d\boldsymbol{q}\, d\boldsymbol{q}'\, d\boldsymbol{q}'' . \end{aligned} \quad (1.58)$$

Then the sum of all ten, taking into consideration the rearrangements of the integrals of (1.57), will be equal to

$$6V\beta_3 . \quad (1.59)$$

All further irreducible integrals β_k are determined analogously. Their explicit expression as the number k increases becomes more and more cumbersome. All irreducible integrals are functions of the temperature of the gas but, within the limit $N \rightarrow \infty$, do not depend on the volume of the gas.

In the rigorous theory it is formally possible to sum the series (1.46) and to reduce it to a simpler series in terms of reciprocal powers of the volume $v = V/N$, which is assumed to be constant within the limiting process $N \rightarrow \infty$ and $V \rightarrow \infty$. An expression for Q_N (asymptotically true when $N \rightarrow \infty$ and $V \rightarrow \infty$) appears as a result:

$$Q_N = \left\{ V \exp\left[\sum_{k \geq 1} \frac{\beta_k}{(k+1)\, v^k} \right] \right\}^N . \qquad (1.60)$$

By placing this in the equation for the free energy (1.25), we find that

$$F = F_0 - NkT \sum_{k \geq 1} \frac{\beta_k}{(k+s)\, v^k}, \qquad (1.61)$$

where F_0 is the free energy of an ideal gas (1.20). From this it is easy to obtain expressions for all the remaining thermodynamic functions. For example, for the pressure, according to (1.14), we obtain

$$p = \frac{kT}{v}\left(1 - \sum_{1 \leq k \leq \infty} \frac{k\beta_k}{k+1} \cdot \frac{1}{v^k}\right), \qquad (1.62)$$

taking into account that the pressure of an ideal gas is equal to $p_0 = (kT)/v$.

Thus the theory leads to a "virial series" for the pressure and other thermodynamic functions. The virial coefficients B, C, . . . for the pressure

$$p = \frac{kT}{v}\left[1 - \frac{B(\mathrm{T})}{v} - \frac{C(\mathrm{T})}{v^2} - \ldots\right] \qquad (1.63)$$

are related to the irreducible integrals β_k by the relationships

$$B = \tfrac{1}{2}\beta_1 , \qquad C = \tfrac{2}{3}\beta_2, \qquad \text{etc.} \qquad (1.64)$$

5. THE FREE-VOLUME THEORY

In the case of a high-density fluid, the method described in the preceding paragraph is inapplicable. For rough approximations in the case of liquids, lattice model theories are used successfully which make it possible approximately to evaluate the configuration integral Q_N and, on this foundation, to construct a statistical theory of liquids. Many studies have been devoted to this approach to the theory of liquids, and a broad group of problems may be roughly examined with the aid of this model. In particular, corresponding methods find important applications in the theory of solutions. Below we will briefly examine the basic ideas of this approach to the theory of liquids [5, 8, 9]. A rigorous analysis and critique of the statistical foundations of lattice theories was given in a study by Kirkwood [10].

The basis of the theories being considered is the assumption of a lattice-like quasi-crystalline structure of liquids, in the sense that each particle is compelled to move in a cell in the vicinity of a virtual lattice point. For each particle a cell is formed by the presence of neighboring particles which limit the range of its movement. Although this hypothesis is introduced only for convenience of calculation and the extended order that it gives rise to is not essential for the theory and is not used in it, nevertheless, the assumed model ascribes to a liquid a much larger degree of order than in fact actually occurs. Moreover, it is clear that, inasmuch as the molecular structure of the liquid in this case is postulated in advance, the only applicability of the theory is to the statistical thermodynamics of the liquid. Problems connected with the molecular structure of liquids and the short-range order, although of physical importance, cannot be studied in this way.

The lattice theory of liquids exists in two variations: in the form of the old "cell" theory or "theory of free volume," and in the form of the later and more complete "hole" theory of liquids. In the first case, for each particle there is a one-to-one correspondence between the particle and a lattice point, so that the number of lattice points equals the number of particles. In the second case, the number of lattice points (and the number of cells equal to it) exceeds the number of particles so as clearly to allow the presence of vacant cells or "holes" in the liquid. The degree of order ascribed to the liquid is less in this case than in the cell model, and this corresponds more closely to reality.

It should be noted that the idea of the hole model of liquids and its qualitative treatment was proposed by Ya. I. Frenkel long before the development of the corresponding statistical theories.

In both variations of the lattice theory possible jumps of particles from cell to cell, which are responsible for self-diffusion and analogous processes in liquids, are disregarded. Each particle is fixed in its cell, and therefore the configuration integral of a liquid is equal to

$$Q_N = N!\, Q_N^{(1)} , \tag{1.65}$$

where $Q_N^{(1)}$ corresponds to one definite method of arrangement of the particles, one to each cell. In the cell model at high densities this is an acceptable assumption; however at low densities, when the volumes of the cells are large and jumps might indeed occur, it leads to significant errors. In the hole model the jumps of particles from cell to cell are also not clearly discussed; however, the error that results from this is partially compensated for by calculating the average distribution of holes. The possibility of the simultaneous occupation by two or more particles of one cell is not considered in the majority of studies.

The following important assumption which is made in lattice theories is the replacement of the actual interactions of all particles of the system $U_N(q_1, \ldots, q_N)$ by some self-consistent external field which acts on each particle in its cell. Let us consider this in greater detail, using the cell model as an example. First, let all particles be placed at the centers of their cells which form the nodes of some regular crystalline lattice. Let E_0 be the energy of interaction of one particle with the entire remaining system—then in this case the full statistical energy of the lattice will be equal to $\frac{1}{2} NE_0$. The energy E_0 depends on the lattice constant; the dimensions of the cells, however, determine their volume, which is equal to $v = V/N$, and therefore $E_0 = E_0(v)$. Now let us introduce, instead of the coordinates of the particles $\boldsymbol{q}_i$, new coordinates $\boldsymbol{r}_i$ measured in each cell from its center in such a way that $\boldsymbol{r}_i$ is the displacement of the ith particle from the ith lattice point. Then let $\varphi(\boldsymbol{r})$ be the average self-consistent field acting on a certain particle in its cell arising from all the remaining particles. The function $\varphi(\boldsymbol{r})$ is defined only within the limits of one cell and assumes that the dimensions of all cells are identical, so that all $\varphi(\boldsymbol{r}_i)$ are also identical. If $\varphi(\boldsymbol{r})$ is chosen in such a way that $\varphi(0) = 0$, then in the approximation under consideration we obtain

$$U_N = \tfrac{1}{2} NE_0 + \sum_{1 \leq i \leq N} \varphi(\boldsymbol{r}_i). \tag{1.66}$$

The function $\varphi(\boldsymbol{r})$ depends on the parameters (of the intermolecular potential), on the volume v, and on the temperature T of the system $\varphi(\boldsymbol{r}) = \varphi(\boldsymbol{r}; v, T)$.

From (1.66) we have

$$\exp\left(-\frac{U_N}{kT}\right) = \exp\left(-\frac{NE_0}{2kT}\right) \prod_{1 \leq i \leq N} \exp\left[-\frac{\varphi(\boldsymbol{r}_i)}{kT}\right], \tag{1.67}$$

and, in accordance with (1.63) for the configuration integral, we obtain

$$Q_N = N! \exp\left(-\frac{NE_0}{2kT}\right) \left\{\int_\Delta \exp\left[-\frac{\varphi(\boldsymbol{r})}{kT}\right] d\boldsymbol{r}\right\}^N \tag{1.68}$$

due to the identity of all the cells. The term

$$v_f = \int_\Delta \exp\left[-\frac{\varphi(\boldsymbol{r})}{kT}\right] d\boldsymbol{r}, \tag{1.69}$$

where the integration is over the volume of one cell is called the "free volume" (per particle) of the liquid. In the absence of interaction v_f would be equal to v. According to (1.69), it appears that $v_f = v_f(v, T)$, and this function is a quantitative representation of the intuitive concept of the free volume permitted for the movement of one particle in the liquid. From (1.68) and (1.69) we have

$$Q_N = N! \exp\left(-\frac{NE_0}{2kT}\right) v_f^N . \tag{1.70}$$

By placing the expression obtained for Q_N in the general expression for the statistical integral (1.11), we obtain

$$Z_N = \left(\frac{mkT}{2\pi\hbar^2}\right)^{3N/2} \exp\left(-\frac{NE_0}{2kT}\right) v_f^N . \tag{1.71}$$

On this basis it is possible to construct a complete thermodynamics of liquids. For the free energy, for example, we obtain, in accordance with (1.12),

$$F = \tfrac{1}{2} NE_0 - \tfrac{3}{2} NkT \ln\left(\frac{mkT}{2\pi\hbar^2}\right) - NkT \ln v_f . \tag{1.72}$$

In calculating other thermodynamic functions from this, it is essential to remember that E_0 and v_f depend on volume and temperature. Thus in the cell model, the problem of constructing a statistical thermodynamics of the liquid leads to the determination of the free volume (1.69). For this, in turn, it is necessary to know the self-consistent field $\varphi(r)$.

The same idea of a self-consistent field is also used in the hole theory of liquids. This leads to a generalized free volume v_f, which depends on the average portion of holes in the network $\omega : v_f = v_f(v, T, \omega)$. Also $E_0 = E_0(v, \omega)$, and, moreover, a supplementary factor is introduced into (1.70) and (1.71) which depends on v, T, and ω and approximately allows for the statistical distribution of holes [9]. The average portion of holes in the network ω is itself a function of volume, and temperature and the form of the dependence $\omega = \omega(v, T)$ may be determined from the requirement that the free energy be a minimum with respect to variations of ω.

In all variations of the lattice theories, the most important problem is the accurate determination of the self-consistent potential $\varphi(\mathbf{r}; v, T)$, which is essential for calculating the free volume. An integral equation for the approximate determination of $\varphi(\mathbf{r}; vT)$ was obtained in paper [10]. In fact, however, this equation is not used, and all theories are constructed on a very rough approximation where $\varphi(r)$ is equal to the sum of the intermolecular potentials $\Phi(r)$ of the particles most closely surrounding a given lattice point while all these particles are considered to be held stationary on their own lattice points. In addition, an average of this sum over angles is introduced so that $\varphi(r) = \varphi(|r|)$, and the elementary cell itself, where the assigned potential is $\varphi(r)$, is considered to be spherical. Due to the fact that the thermal motion of the surrounding particles is not taken into consideration, the function $\varphi(r)$ in this case depends on the volume v only trivially through the volume of the elementary cell, while the temperature dependence $\varphi(r)$ disappears.

In addition, it is usually also understood that the lattice under consideration is close-packed, face-centered, and cubic, and that the intermolecular potential $\Phi(r)$ has the form of the Lennard-Jones potential (1.29). For such a model the function v_f, determined from (1.69), is tabulated in detail, and it may be used for various calculations related to the use of both the cell and hole models. In this way, a qualitatively acceptable description of many thermodynamic properties of liquids and dense gases has been obtained [5, 8].

Lattice theories of liquids are convenient for model calculations, and they are widely used for this purpose. Due to the large number of approximations, often not well founded, they cannot be considered to be truly rigorous statistical theories. The physical model itself, which is the basis of these theories, is not well founded. In the following chapters of this book, lattice theories of liquids will not be used. A more rigorous statistical apparatus, capable in principle of leading to a more complete theory, will be described.

6. THE STATISTICAL INTEGRAL OF A ONE-DIMENSIONAL MODEL OF A LIQUID

The extraordinary difficulty of the problem of calculating the configuration integral makes it of interest to seek methods for simplifying the models of systems. The simplest such system in which, with some supplementary simplifications, a full and precise solution of the problem is possible, is a one-dimensional model of a molecular system with short-range forces between the particles. Below we shall discuss the corresponding theory, basically following paper [11].

We shall consider an equilibrium isothermal system of N particles possessing only one degree of freedom each and distributed on a segment of the axis Ox of length L. Then, analogous to the three-dimensional case, we find that

$$Z_N = \left(\frac{mkT}{2\pi\hbar^2}\right)^{(1/2)N} \frac{Q_N}{N!}, \tag{1.73}$$

where Q_N is now equal to

$$Q_N = \int_0^L \dots \int_0^L \exp\left(-\frac{U_N}{kT}\right) dx_1 \dots dx_N. \tag{1.74}$$

The connection with thermodynamics is achieved in the usual way through the free energy

$$F = -kT \ln Z_N, \tag{1.75}$$

but only on substituting everywhere the length L for the volume V. For example, we have for the pressure

$$p = -\left(\frac{\partial F}{\partial L}\right)_T = kT \frac{\partial \ln Q_N}{\partial L}. \tag{1.76}$$

We shall consider the particles to be "impenetrable." Since they cannot get off the axis Ox, the order of their arrangement along this axis remains constant, and we can enumerate them once and for all in a definite order. We shall assume that

$$0 \leq x_1 < x_2 < \dots < x_N \leq L. \tag{1.77}$$

Furthermore, as in the three-dimensional case, we assume that the total interaction in the system is composed of the interactions of individual pairs of particles described by the potential $\Phi(|x_i - x_j|)$. If we then assume in addition that the potential $\Phi(|x|)$ is so short range that each particle interacts only with the two closest neighboring particles (one from each side), we obtain

$$U_N = \sum_{1 \leq i \leq N-1} \Phi(x_{i+1} - x_i). \tag{1.78}$$

To this must be added the energy U_L of the interaction of the particles of the system with the walls which bound it. Simplifying the notation of the integral in (1.74) by means of (1.77), we then obtain

$$Q_N = N! \int_0^L dx_N \int_0^{x_N} dx_{N-1} \dots \int_0^{x_2} \exp\left(-\frac{U_L}{kT}\right) \prod_{1 \leq i \leq N-1} \times \exp\left[-\frac{\Phi(x_{i+1} - x_i)}{kT}\right] dx_1. \tag{1.79}$$

Now let us assume that the walls that bound the system are realized in the form of two particles of the same nature, and also that these particles of the same system are held immobile at the points $x = 0$ and $x = L$. Then $U_L = \Phi(x_1) + \Phi(L - x_N)$ and

$$\exp\left(-\frac{U_L}{kT}\right) = \exp\left[-\frac{\Phi(x_1)}{kT}\right]\exp\left[-\frac{\Phi(L-x_N)}{kT}\right]. \quad (1.80)$$

For the sake of brevity, let us introduce the symbol

$$f(x) \equiv \exp\left[-\frac{\Phi(x)}{kT}\right]. \quad (1.81)$$

Then, finally, we may write that

$$\bar{Q}_N = \int_0^L dx_N \int_0^{x_N} dx_{N-1} \ldots \int_0^{x_2} \times f(x_1) f(x_2 - x_1) \ldots f(x_N - x_{N-1}) f(L - x_N)\, dx_1\,, \quad (1.82)$$

where $\bar{Q}_N = Q_N/N!$.

Now let us consider the sequence of functions

$$f_1(x) \equiv f(x),$$
$$f_m(x) = \int_0^x f(\xi) f_{m-1}(x - \xi)\, d\xi, \qquad m = 2, 3, \ldots, \quad (1.83)$$

where each f_m is obtained as a convolution of the preceding function f_{m-1} with f. According to (1.82), we may then write

$$\bar{Q}_N = f_{N+1}(L). \quad (1.84)$$

Let us designate by $\varphi(s)$ the Laplace transform of the function $f(x)$:

$$\varphi(s) = \int_0^\infty e^{-sx} f(x)\, dx\,, \qquad \mathrm{Re}(s) > 0\,, \quad (1.85)$$

so that the inverse is

$$f(x) = \frac{1}{2\pi i}\int_{c-i\infty}^{c+i\infty} e^{sx}\varphi(s)\, ds\,, \quad (1.86)$$

where the positive number c is such that the path of integration lies to the right of all the poles of $\varphi(s)$. By repeated application of the convolution theorem of the Laplace transform, we then [12] obtain

$$\int_0^\infty e^{-sx} f_m(x)\, dx = [\varphi(s)]^m, \quad (1.87)$$

and, because of (1.84), we may write that

$$\int_0^\infty e^{-sL}\bar{Q}_N(L)\, dL = [\varphi(s)]^{N+1}, \qquad \mathrm{Re}(s) > 0. \quad (1.88)$$

Hence, by application of the Laplace transform we obtain

$$\bar{Q}_N(L) = \frac{1}{2\pi i}\int_{c-i\infty}^{c+i\infty} e^{sL}[\varphi(s)]^{M+1}ds, \qquad (1.89)$$

by which, in principle, the problem of the calculation of the configuration interval is also solved.

If the function $f(x)$ is finite, which for physical reasons (see [1.81]) will always be the case, it is possible to close the path of integration in (1.89) by another infinitely large circle which encloses the left-hand portion of the half-plane, and then to deform the path of integration in any closed contour which includes the origin of the coordinates and all poles of the integrand. Then

$$\bar{Q}_N(L) = \frac{1}{2\pi i}\oint_c e^{sL}[\varphi(s)]^{N+1}ds. \qquad (1.90)$$

The contour integral may be calculated by means of the theory of residues.

For our purpose, it is sufficient to have an asymptotic estimate for $\ln \bar{Q}_N$ when $N \to \infty$ and $L \to \infty$. This was carried out rigorously in paper [11]. We can obtain the same result more simply by evaluating the integral in (1.90) by the method of steepest descent [12]. Let us introduce the average length per article $l = L/(N+1)$. Then we may write

$$e^{sL}[\varphi(s)]^{N+1} = [e^{sl}\varphi(s)]^{N+1} = e^{(N+1)\chi(s)}, \qquad (1.91)$$

where

$$\chi(s) = sl + \ln \varphi(s). \qquad (1.92)$$

Hence, for the saddle point s_0, we have the conditions

$$\chi'(s_0) = l + \left[\frac{d}{ds}\ln\varphi(s)\right]_{s=s_0} = 0, \qquad (1.93)$$

so that in the vicinity of point s_0 there will be

$$\chi(s) = ls_0 + \ln\varphi(s_0) + \tfrac{1}{2}\chi''(s_0)(s-s_0)^2 + \dots. \qquad (1.94)$$

Disregarding the further terms of the expansion and placing (1.94) in (1.91) and (1.90), we obtain

$$\bar{Q}_N(L) = [e^{s_0 l}\varphi(s_0)]^{N+1} \times \frac{1}{2\pi i}\oint_c \exp[\tfrac{1}{2}(N+1)\chi''(s_0)(s-s_0)^2]ds. \qquad (1.95)$$

On integrating along the chosen path which passes through point s_0, the integral in (1.95) gives the Poisson integral and, consequently, is of the order of $(N+1)^{1/2}$. For the asymptotic evaluation of $\ln \bar{Q}_N$, when $N \to \infty$, the logarithm of this integral is unimportant in comparison with the logarithm of the factor which stands before the integral in (1.95). More precisely,

$$\lim_{N\to\infty} [\bar{Q}_N(L)]^{1/(N+1)} = e^{s_0 l}\varphi(s_0). \qquad (1.96)$$

Thus, we obtain, asymptotically,

$$\bar{Q}_N(L) = e^{s_0 L}[\varphi(s_0)]^{N+1}. \qquad (1.97)$$

By placing this in (1.76), we obtain for the pressure

$$\frac{p}{kT} = \frac{\partial \ln \bar{Q}_N}{\partial L} = s_0 + (N+1)\left[l + \frac{d}{d s_0}\ln \varphi(s_0)\right]\frac{\partial s_0}{\partial L} = s_0, \qquad (1.98)$$

where the condition (1.93) is taken into consideration. Thus it appears that $s_0 = p/(kT)$. By placing this in (1.97), we obtain

$$\bar{Q}_N(L) = \exp\left(\frac{pL}{kT}\right)\{[\varphi(s_0)]_{s_0=p/kT}\}^{N+1}. \qquad (1.99)$$

Let us designate $\varphi(s_0)$, when $s_0 = p/(kT)$, by $\varphi(p, T)$. In accordance with (1.81) and (1.85), we have

$$\varphi(p, T) = \int_0^\infty \exp\left[-\frac{px + \Phi(x)}{kT}\right]dx. \qquad (1.100)$$

Then, finally, for the configuration integral, we obtain

$$Q_N = N!\exp\left(\frac{pL}{kT}\right)[\varphi(p, T)]^{N+1}. \qquad (1.101)$$

Thus the calculation of the configuration integral of our one-dimensional system leads to a single quadrature (1.100).

7. THE THERMODYNAMICS OF A ONE-DIMENSIONAL SYSTEM

The value of the configuration integral (1.101) makes it possible to develop the complete thermodynamics of a one-dimensional system.

From (1.73), (1.75), and (1.101) we obtain for the free energy

$$F = -\tfrac{1}{2}NkT\ln\left(\frac{mkT}{2\pi\hbar^2}\right) - (N+1)kT\ln\varphi(p, T) - pL. \qquad (1.102)$$

Since we have gone over to the language of p, T variables, it is natural to proceed from the free energy F to the full thermodynamic potential $\Phi = F + pL$. From (1.102) we determine that

$$\Phi(p, T) = -NkT\ln\varphi(p, T) - \tfrac{1}{2}NkT\ln\left(\frac{mkT}{2\pi\hbar^2}\right), \qquad (1.103)$$

where we have disregarded unity in comparison with N. From this it is easy to find all the remaining thermodynamic functions of a one-dimensional system in accordance with well-known thermodynamic rules. In particular, for the equation of state $L = (\partial\Phi/\partial p)_T$, we obtain

$$l + kT \frac{\partial}{\partial p} \ln \varphi(p, T) = 0 . \tag{1.104}$$

The same result is obtained directly from (1.93) if there we take into consideration that $s_0 = p/(kT)$.

Let us consider as the simplest example a one-dimensional system of non-interacting hard spheres of diameter a for which

$$\begin{aligned} \Phi(x) &= +\infty \quad \text{when} \quad x \leq a , \\ \Phi(x) &= 0 \quad \text{when} \quad x > a . \end{aligned} \tag{1.105}$$

We find from (1.100) that in this case

$$\varphi(p, T) = \frac{kT}{p} \exp\left(-\frac{ap}{kT}\right), \tag{1.106}$$

and consequently

$$\begin{aligned} \Phi(p, T) &= Nap + NkT \ln p \\ &\quad - \tfrac{3}{2} NkT \ln T - \tfrac{1}{2} NkT \ln\left(\frac{mk}{2\pi\hbar^2}\right), \end{aligned} \tag{1.107}$$

and for the equation of state, according to (1.105), we find that

$$p = \frac{kT}{l - a} . \tag{1.108}$$

It is easy to calculate the configuration integrals for certain other simple cases, for example, the case where the potential $\Phi(x)$ is given in the form of a square well.

Let us now consider in general form the behavior of the derivative $(\partial l/\partial p)_T$. From (1.104) we find that

$$\left(-\frac{\partial l}{\partial p}\right)_T = \frac{kT}{\varphi^2} [\varphi \varphi''_{pp} - (\varphi'_p)^2] . \tag{1.109}$$

By calculating the expressions for φ'_p and φ''_{pp} from (1.100), we find, after simple transformations, that

$$\begin{aligned} \left(-\frac{\partial l}{\partial p}\right)_T &= \frac{1}{2kT\varphi^2} \int_0^\infty \int_0^\infty \\ &\times \exp\left[-\frac{px + py + \Phi(x) + \Phi(y)}{kT}\right] (x - y)^2 dx\, dy . \end{aligned} \tag{1.110}$$

From this it can be seen that, at least when $T \neq 0$ and $T \neq \infty$, the following inequalities will always be fulfilled:

$$0 < \left(-\frac{\partial l}{\partial p}\right)_T < \infty, \tag{1.111}$$

and

$$0 < \left(-\frac{\partial p}{\partial l}\right)_T < \infty. \tag{1.112}$$

Thus pressure is always a steadily decreasing function of the "volume" l and, at finite temperatures, the derivative $(\partial p/\partial l)_T$ nowhere becomes zero. In addition, it follows from (1.100), (1.104), and (1.110) that p and $(\partial p/\partial l)_T$ are continuous everywhere.

The behavior of the system when $T \to \infty$ follows directly from (1.100). By inserting $x = [(kT)/p]\xi$, we find that, when $T \to \infty$, (1.100) becomes

$$\varphi(p, T) \to \frac{kT}{p}, \tag{1.113}$$

independent of the form of the function $\Phi(x)$. Then, in accordance with (1.110), it follows that

$$p \to \frac{kT}{l} \quad \text{when} \quad T \to \infty. \tag{1.114}$$

Thus when $T \to \infty$, any system behaves like an ideal gas. In the opposite limiting case where $T \to 0$, as the analysis of [11] shows, the behavior of the pressure depends on the properties of the intermolecular potential $\Phi(x)$. If $\Phi(x)$ has the usual form (as in Fig. 1) with a minimum at the point $x = x_m$, i.e., $\Phi(x_m) = 0$, then it is possible to show that in the limit $T \to 0$ we obtain

$$p = -\Phi'(l), \quad \text{if} \quad l < x_m, \qquad p = 0, \quad \text{if} \quad l > x_m. \tag{1.115}$$

As is well known from the thermodynamics of three-dimensional systems, the appearance of a pressure isotherm with a zero derivative $[(\partial p/\partial v)_T = 0]$ is related to a phase transition of the first order. Therefore, the fact that in our case when $T \neq 0$ the derivative $(\partial p/\partial l)_T$ does not become zero at any point of the axis l must be interpreted to mean that there is no phase transition in a one-dimensional system such as condensation or crystallization. A one-dimensional system is always, as it were, in a "subcritical" region; all the p—l—T space corresponds to a common gas-liquid phase.

It appears that the result obtained does not depend on the assumption made previously regarding the extremely short-range character of the intermolecular force. A rigorous statistical analysis was carried out in paper [13] of the behavior of the derivative $(\partial p/\partial l)_T$ for a one-dimensional system with an arbitrarily large but finite radius of action of the intermolecular force, so that each particle in this case may interact immediately with many other particles. In this case, when $T \neq 0$ the derivative $(\partial p/\partial l)_T$ does not become zero at any point. Moreover, the impossibility of one-dimensional phase transitions was studied and substantiated through thermodynamic methods by Landau [2].[1]

The physical reason for this is clear. As a matter of fact, in order that it be possible, for example, for a one-dimensional gas to condense, conditions would be required in which the probability of the formation of very large aggregates of linked particles would exceed the probability of encountering particles which were free or combined in small groups. But at finite external pressure and non-zero temperature this is impossible. If one assumes that the condensed phase has already formed in some manner, some ruptures of the bonds between molecules must occur from time to time due to thermal fluctuations. But in a one-dimensional system (in contrast with a three-dimensional one) the rupture of even one bond leads to the breakdown of the entire system: to its division into two parts. The larger the system, the more frequently such ruptures will occur, so that co-existence of the two phases at equilibrium is impossible. Therefore there will be no phase transition.

REFERENCES

[1] M. A. Leontovich, *Staticheskaya fizika*, Gostekhizdat (Statistical Physics), State Technical Press, 1945.

[2] L. D. Landau and E. M. Lifshits, *Staticheskaya fizika*, Gostekhizdat (Statistical Physics), State Technical Press, 1951.

[3] J. E. Mayer and M. Goeppert-Mayer, *Statistical Mechanics*, 1940.

[4] E. R. Dobbs, B. F. Figgins, and G. O. Jones, *Nuovo Cimento, suppl.*, **9**, No. 1 (1958), 32.

[5] Zh. De-Bur, *Uspekhi Fiz. Nauk*, **51** (1953), 71.

[6] M. P. Bukalovich and I. I. Novikov, *Uravnenie sostoyaniya real'nykh gazov* (Equation of State of Real Gases), Gosenergoizdat, 1948.

[1] *Editor's note:* Recent work by Kac, Uhlenbeck, and Hemmer shows that, in a one-dimensional system characterized by a potential of infinite range and infinitesimal depth, a true phase transition occurs.

[7] B. T. Geilikman, *Statisticheskaya teoriya fazovykh prevrashchenii*, Gostekhizdat (Statistical Theory of Phase Transitions), State Technical Press, 1954.
[8] J. Rowlinson and C. Curtiss, *J. Chem. Phys.*, **19** (1951), 1519.
[9] J. O. Hirschfelder, C. F. Curtiss, and R. B. Bird, *Molecular Theory of Gases and Liquids*, New York, 1954.
[10] J. Kirkwood, *J. Chem. Phys.*, **18** (1950), 380.
[11] F. Gursey, *Proc. Cambr. Phil. Soc.*, **46** (1950), 182.
[12] V. I. Smirnov, *Kurs vyshei matematiki*, chap. 2, **3**, Gostekhizdat (Course in Higher Mathematics), State Technical Press, 1949.
[13] L. Van-Hove, *Physica*, **16**, 137, 150.

CHAPTER 2

CORRELATION FUNCTIONS

1. THE DETERMINATION OF AND GENERAL PROPERTIES OF CORRELATION FUNCTIONS

In the present chapter we shall be concerned with a mathematical formalism which will open up new possibilities in the theory of liquids. This is the formalism of molecular distribution functions, or the so-called correlation functions. Instead of attempting to calculate the configuration integral directly, the theory describes the probability of configurational groupings of two, three, and more particles; moreover, it may be shown that it is possible through the use of correlation functions to obtain the same amount of information on the properties of a system as a whole as is obtained from the study of the statistical integral. Furthermore, in this way we obtain direct information on the molecular structure of the system being studied. This method was principally developed by Kirkwood [1, 2, 3], Bogolyubov [4], Born and Green [5, 6], and Green [7]. We shall adhere closely to the notation and method of presentation of paper [4].

Consider the same isothermal equilibrium system as in the preceding chapter. Let us select within the system an arbitrary group of s particles; $s = 1, 2, 3, \ldots$, and let $dW(q_1, \ldots, q_s)$ designate the probability of finding particles of this group respectively in the small volume elements $dq_1, dq_2, \ldots, dq_s$ near the points $q_1, q_2, \ldots, q_s$ with all the remaining particles of the system in arbitrary positions. We shall call molecular distribution functions or correlation functions $F_s(q_1, \ldots, q_s)$ those which correspond to the probability densities $dW(q_1, \ldots, q_s)$, normalized in such a way that

$$dW(q_1, \ldots, q_s) = \frac{1}{V^s} F_s(q_1, \ldots, q_s)\, dq_1 \ldots dq_s. \quad (2.1)$$

The factor V^{-s} assures that the functions F_s are dimensionless. Its introduction will prove convenient later on in the limiting transition to an infinite system since, in accordance with (2.1), F_s will remain finite when $V \to \infty$.

In a system of independent and non-interacting particles, we would apparently have

$$F_s(q_1, \ldots, q_s) = \prod_{1 \leq i \leq s} F_1(q_i). \tag{2.2}$$

The differences

$$F_s(q_1, \ldots, q_s) - \prod_{1 \leq i \leq s} F_1(q_i), \qquad s = 2, 3, \ldots, \tag{2.3}$$

characterize the correlations in the positions of the particles within the system; their absolute values may serve as a measure of disorder in the distribution of particles according to their positions. In particular, the absence in a gas or liquid of long-range order may be expressed by the convergence of the differences (2.3) to zero when all s particles are separated from one another.

The conditions for the normalization of correlation functions follow from equation (2.1), where

$$\frac{1}{V^s} \int_V \cdots \int_V F_s(q_1, \ldots, q_s)\, dq_1 \ldots dq_s = 1, \tag{2.4}$$

as do the relationships between the correlation functions of various orders:

$$\frac{1}{V^{s-p}} \int_V \cdots \int_V F_s(q_1, \ldots, q_s)\, dq_{p+1} \ldots dq_s = F_p(q_1, \ldots, q_p). \tag{2.5}$$

Equivalent to (2.4) and (2.5) are the less cumbersome conditions

$$\frac{1}{V} \int_V F_1(q)\, dq = 1, \tag{2.6}$$

$$\frac{1}{V} \int_V F_s(q_1, \ldots, q_s)\, dq_s = F_{s-1}(q_1, \ldots, q_{s-1}), \qquad s \geq 2, \tag{2.7}$$

which we will use everywhere from now on; we will consider (2.6) and (2.7) as the conditions for the normalization of the correlation functions. In addition, the functions $F_s(q_1, \ldots, q_s)$, by definition, are symmetrical functions of their arguments, so that, for example,

$$F_2(q_1, q_2) = F_2(q_2, q_1), \tag{2.8}$$

etc.

Inasmuch as the system as a whole is assumed to be in equilibrium and isothermal, for the entire system of N particles the function $F_N(q_1, \ldots, q_N)$ is proportional to the configurational part of the Gibbs distribution function, where

$$F_N(q_1, \ldots, q_N) = V^N D_N(q_1, \ldots, q_N) = V^N Q_N^{-1} \exp\left[-\frac{U_N(q_1, \ldots, q_N)}{kT}\right]. \quad (2.9)$$

By using (2.5) we can then write, for any function F_s,

$$F_s(q_1, \ldots, q_s) = V^s \int_V \cdots \int_V D_N(q_1, \ldots, q_N)\, dq_{s+1} \ldots dq_N. \quad (2.10)$$

Equation (2.10), when $s = 1, 2, \ldots$, formally solves the problem of the construction of a system of F_s functions. But it is evident that here we actually encounter the same difficulties that arose in statistical thermodynamics in an effort to calculate the configuration integral.

The uniform gas or liquid represents a very important case. This occurs in the absence of external forces and far from surfaces which bound the system under consideration. Then all the positions of a single particle are equally probable, and, in connection with (2.6), we have

$$F_1(q) = 1, \quad (2.11)$$

neglecting small corrections which disappear when $V \to \infty$. Furthermore, in this case the distribution of particles in the vicinity of any selected particle will, on the average, be spherically symmetrical. Therefore, the function $F_2(q, q')$ will depend only on one argument—the relative distance between the selected pair of particles, so that

$$F_2(q, q') = g(|q - q'|), \quad (2.12)$$

again neglecting small corrections which disappear when $V \to \infty$. Analogously, all remaining correlation functions, when $s > 2$ (but $s \ll N$), will depend on the mutual arrangement of the groups of particles with which we are concerned, but will not depend on the positions occupied or the orientation of groups as a whole. As before, in the case of the homogeneous fluid, the preceding statement is valid with the exception of small corrections which vanish in the limit $V \to \infty$.

In the more general inhomogeneous fluid, the functions F_1 and F_2 do not have the simple form of (2.11) and (2.12). In this case it is sometimes convenient to express the binary function F_2, not in terms of q and q', but in terms of new arguments

$$r = q - q', \qquad R = \tfrac{1}{2}(q + q'), \tag{2.13}$$

which specify the relative positions and the position of the center of mass of a pair of particles. Then

$$F_2(q, q') = F_2(R - \tfrac{1}{2}r, R + \tfrac{1}{2}r) = F_2^*(r, R). \tag{2.14}$$

In the transition to the uniform case, the dependence on R disappears, and $F_2(r, R)$ becomes $g(|r|)$. Note that the function F_2 does not change on inversion of the coordinates relative to the point R. As a matter of fact, from (2.8) and (2.13), we obtain

$$F_2^*(r, R) = F_2(q, q') = F_2(q', q) = F_2^*(-r, R). \tag{2.15}$$

Along with the correlation functions F_s introduced above, which determine the a priori probability of the positions of groups of particles, it is sometimes necessary to consider more complex correlation functions related to the probabilities of the positions of one group of particles in the presence of given positions of another group of particles. Let $dW_{q_{s+1}, \ldots, q_{s+p}}(q_1, \ldots, q_s)$ designate the conditional probability of finding a definite configuration of a selected group of s particles when the positions of another group of p particles is already known (and fixed). Analogously with equation (2.1), we introduce the conditional correlation functions $F_s(q_1, \ldots, q_s | q_{s+1}, \ldots, q_{s+p})$ by

$$dW_{q_{s+1}, \ldots, q_{s+p}}(q_1, \ldots, q_s) = \frac{1}{V^s} F_s(q_1, \ldots, q_s | q_{s+1}, \ldots q_{s+p})\, dq_1 \ldots dq_s. \tag{2.16}$$

The second group of coordinates in F_s must be considered as parameters. From the theorem on the multiplication of probabilities, we have

$$dW(q_1, \ldots, q_s, q_{s+1}, \ldots, q_{s+p}) = dW(q_{s+1}, \ldots, q_{s+p})\, dW_{q_{s+1}, \ldots, q_{s+p}}(q_1, \ldots, q_s). \tag{2.17}$$

Then the following relation is derived from (2.1) and (2.16):

$$F_s(q_1, \ldots, q_s | q_{s+1}, \ldots, q_{s+p}) = \frac{F_{s+p}(q_1, \ldots, q_{s+p})}{F_q(q_{s+1}, \ldots, q_{s+p})}. \tag{2.18}$$

Thus, conditional correlation functions may be expressed in terms of simple correlation functions.

The case where $p = 1$ is of the greatest importance. In a homogeneous liquid or gas, from (2.11) and (2.18), we obtain

$$F_s(q_1, \dots, q_s \mid q_{s+1}) = F_{s+1}(q_1, \dots, q_{s+1}). \qquad (2.19)$$

In particular,

$$F_1(q \mid q') = F_2(q, q') = g(|q - q'|). \qquad (2.20)$$

Thus, the function $g(r)$ has the meaning not only of a binary correlation function but also of a conditional single correlation function. The probability of finding some particle at a distance between r and $r + dr$ from some other particle, in accordance with (2.16), is equal to

$$dw(r) = g(r)\frac{4\pi r^2 dr}{V}. \qquad (2.21)$$

On the basis of this, the function $g(r)$ is called the radial distribution function of the particles of a liquid or a gas.

2. THE CALCULATION OF AVERAGE VALUES

Knowledge of the correlation functions permits the calculation of average values of quantities of the type

$$M_s(q_1, \dots, q_s) = \sum_{1 \le i_1 < i_2 < \dots < i_s \le N} f(q_{i_1}, \dots, q_{i_s}), \qquad (2.22)$$

without returning to the Gibbs distribution function. As a matter of fact, we have

$$\begin{aligned}\overline{M}_s &= \int_V \cdots \int_V M_s(q_1, \dots, q_N)\, D_N(q_1, \dots, q_N)\, dq_1 \dots dq_N \\ &= \frac{N(N-1)\dots(N-s+1)}{s!} \int_V \cdots \int_V f(q_1, \dots, q_s) \\ &\times D_N(q_1, \dots, q_N)\, dq_1 \dots dq_N = \frac{N(N-1)\dots(N-s+1)}{s!} \qquad (2.23) \\ &\times \int_V \cdots \int_V f(q_1, \dots, q_s)\, dq_1 \dots dq_s \\ &\times \int_V \cdots \int_V D_N(q_1, \dots, q_N)\, dq_{s+1} \dots dq_N,\end{aligned}$$

which, together with equation (2.20), leads to the expression

$$\begin{aligned}\overline{M}_s = \frac{N(N-1)\dots(N-s+1)}{V^s s!} \int_V \cdots \int_V f(q_1, \dots, q_s) \qquad (2.24) \\ \times F_s(q_1, \dots, q_s)\, dq_1 \dots dq_s.\end{aligned}$$

Many of the most important quantities in statistical physics are additive functions of one particle coordinate, M_1, or functions of the coordinates of two particles, M_2. For these, using (2.24), we have

$$\overline{M}_1 = \frac{N}{V} \int_V f(q) F_1(q)\, dq\,, \tag{2.25}$$

$$\overline{M}_2 = \frac{N(N-1)}{2V^2} \int_V \int_V f(q,\, q') F_2(q,\, q')\, dq\, dq'\,. \tag{2.26}$$

In order to calculate the averages of these important functions, it is sufficient to know the two simplest correlation functions $F_1(q)$ and $F(q,\, q')$. In this connection it is precisely these two functions which play the most important role in the theory of liquids.

In a uniform liquid the latter expressions may be further simplified. If we introduce the average volume per particle, $v = V/N$, then when $N \to \infty$ and $V \to \infty$, we obtain from (2.11) and (2.25),

$$\overline{M}_1 = \frac{1}{v} f(q)\, dq\,, \tag{2.27}$$

where integration is over the entire space. A similar expression is also obtained, with small corrections, when the integration is over the finite volume V (at finite N).

For two particle functions, the most interesting case occurs when $f(q,\, q')$ depends only on the distance between a pair of particles $r = |q - q'|$. Changing from integration over q and q' to integration over q' and $r = q = q'$ and utilizing (2.12), we obtain, instead of (2.26),

$$\overline{M}_2 = \frac{N-1}{2vV} \int_V dq' \int f(|r|)\, g(|r|)\, dr\,. \tag{2.28}$$

But the inner integral does not depend on q'; therefore, the second integration over q' simply gives the volume V. Passing to $N \to \infty$ and $V \to \infty$, but with v finite, and introducing spherical coordinates, we finally obtain

$$\overline{M}_2 = \frac{2\pi N}{v} \int_0^\infty f(r)\, g(r)\, r^2 dr\,. \tag{2.29}$$

From (2.10) it is evident that correlation functions depend on the parameters, temperature, density, and the characteristics of external fields if the latter exist. In particular, $g(r) = g(r;\, T,\, v)$. Therefore, averaging with correlation functions leads to the thermodynamic properties of the system.

A typical problem of statistical physics is the calculation of average values from functions which depend on the coordinates and momenta of particles of the system. But in chapter 1 we saw that, at equilibrium, coordinates and momenta are statistically independent of each other, and the distribution function for momenta takes the simple form (1.6) to (1.7). Therefore, averaging over the momentum may always be carried out without difficulty, and the problem is reduced to averaging over the coordinates. In the case of functions of type (2.22) or of combinations of functions of this type, the final averaging may be carried out with the aid of correlation functions.

Let us take as an example the calculation of the internal energy of a system of N particles with the Hamiltonian function (1.1) and potential energy (1.28). Averaging of the kinetic energy with the aid of the distribution (1.6) to (1.7) gives, as is well known, $\frac{3}{2}NkT$, and we obtain

$$E = \tfrac{3}{2}\, NkT + \langle U_N(\mathbf{q}_1, \ldots \mathbf{q}_N) \rangle. \tag{2.30}$$

The potential energy (1.28) is a two particle function and may be calculated according to (2.29). As a result, we obtain

$$E = N\left[\tfrac{3}{2}\, kT + \frac{2\pi}{v}\int_0^\infty \Phi(r)\, g(r)\, r^2 dr\right]. \tag{2.31}$$

The dependence of energy on temperature and volume, $E = E(T, v)$, is determined not only by the explicit dependence displayed but also by the implicit dependence of $g(r) = g(r; T, v)$.

With the aid of well-known thermodynamic relationships it is now possible to calculate for a known function $E(T, v)$ many other thermodynamic functions of the system and to obtain a full thermodynamic description of the liquid. We will discover below that some of these thermodynamic functions may be calculated directly from $\Phi(r)$ and $g(r)$ without use of the internal energy $E = E(T, v)$. In addition, we will see that the molecular structure of simple liquids is in many respects determined by the function $g(r)$. It therefore appears that, in the theory of liquids, the distribution function $g(r)$ plays an exceptionally important role.

3. THE STRESS TENSOR AND THE EQUATION OF STATE IN LIQUIDS

Let us now consider how the pressure in a liquid or gas may be calculated starting directly from an assumed knowledge of the intermolecular potential $\Phi(r)$ and the radial distribution function $g(r)$.

First let us assume that there exists a uniform system such that

$F_1(q) = 1$ and $F_2(q, q') = g(|q - q'|)$. According to (1.16), the pressure is related to the configuration integral by the relationship

$$p = kT \frac{\partial \ln Q_N}{\partial V}. \tag{2.32}$$

Let us consider the transformation $q \to q^* = \lambda q$ for all particles bounding the system. Let $Q_N(\lambda)$ be the configuration integral of the system after such transformation. Then $Q_N(\lambda)$ is involved in (2.32) when $\lambda = 1$, and since increasing the parameter λ by $d\lambda$ results in increasing the volume of the system by $dV = 3Vd\lambda/\lambda$, we then have

$$p = kT \frac{\partial \ln Q_N(1)}{\partial V} = \frac{kT}{3VQ_N(1)} \left[\frac{\partial Q_N(\lambda)}{\partial \lambda}\right]_{\lambda=1}. \tag{2.33}$$

Clearly, we can write

$$Q_N(\lambda) = \lambda^{3N} \int_V \cdots \int_V \exp\left[-\frac{U_N(\lambda)}{kT}\right] d\mathbf{q}_1 \ldots d\mathbf{q}_N, \tag{2.34}$$

where

$$U_N(\lambda) = \sum_{1 \le i < j \le N} \Phi(\lambda |\mathbf{q}_i - \mathbf{q}_j|), \tag{2.35}$$

and, therefore,

$$\frac{\partial Q_N(\lambda)}{\partial \lambda} = \frac{3N}{\lambda} Q_N(\lambda) - \frac{\lambda^{3N}}{kT} \sum_{1 \le i < j \le N} \int_V \cdots \int_V |\mathbf{q}_i - \mathbf{q}_j| \Phi' \times (\lambda |\mathbf{q}_i - \mathbf{q}_j|) \exp\left[-\frac{U_N(\lambda)}{kT}\right] d\mathbf{q}_1 \ldots d\mathbf{q}_N. \tag{2.36}$$

Setting $\lambda = 1$ and dividing by $Q_N(1)$, we obtain

$$\frac{1}{Q_N(1)} \left[\frac{\partial Q_N(\lambda)}{\partial \lambda}\right]_{\lambda=1} = 3N - \frac{1}{kT} \sum_{1 \le i < j \le N} \int_V \cdots \int_V |\mathbf{q}_i - \mathbf{q}_j| \times \Phi'(|\mathbf{q}_i - \mathbf{q}_j|) D_N(\mathbf{q}_1, \ldots, \mathbf{q}_N) d\mathbf{q}_1 \ldots d\mathbf{q}_N, \tag{2.37}$$

where (1.9) is taken into consideration. The second member on the right in (2.37) is the average of a two-particle function, and therefore, according to equation (2.26), we have

$$\frac{1}{Q_N(1)} \left[\frac{\partial Q_N(\lambda)}{\partial \lambda}\right]_{\lambda=1} = 3N - \frac{N(N-1)}{2kTV^2} \int_V \int_V |\mathbf{q}_1 - \mathbf{q}_2| \times \Phi'(|\mathbf{q}_1 - \mathbf{q}_2|) F_2(\mathbf{q}_1, \mathbf{q}_2) d\mathbf{q}_1 d\mathbf{q}_2. \tag{2.38}$$

Substituting equation (2.33), we obtain

$$p = \frac{NkT}{V} - \frac{N(N-1)}{6V^3} \int_V \int_V |\mathbf{q}_1 - \mathbf{q}_2| \Phi'(|\mathbf{q}_1 - \mathbf{q}_2|) \times F_2(\mathbf{q}_1, \mathbf{q}_2) d\mathbf{q}_1 d\mathbf{q}_2. \tag{2.39}$$

In the uniform system under consideration, the expression obtained for pressure is easily simplified to

$$p = \frac{kT}{v} - \frac{2}{3v^2}\int_0^\infty \Phi'(r)\, g(r)\, r^3 dr\,, \tag{2.40}$$

if we use transformations analogous to those used in going from equation (2.26) to equation (2.29). This is the equation of state of a uniform system in terms of the intermolecular forces and the radial distribution function.

Now let us consider a more complex system, such as may occur in the presence of external forces or near the boundaries of the system. As is well known from hydrostatics, forces which act on a certain area in a liquid are in this case characterized by a stress tensor $\Pi_{\alpha\beta}$, $\alpha, \beta =$ 1, 2, 3, which we shall now consider.

Let G be some closed part of a liquid bounded by surface S. We can determine the stress tensor if we can calculate the rate of change of momentum of all the particles in the volume, since according to the hydrodynamic equations the latter is equal to [8]:

$$\oint_S \Pi_{\alpha\beta} n_\beta dS\,, \tag{2.41}$$

where the n_β are the components of the only external normal to surface S. The rate of change of the momentum of all particles in G itself consists of two parts: from the change of momentum in unit time owing to the entrance and exit of particles through the bounding surface S, and from the change of momentum of particles in G owing to the action on them of forces from the side of molecules beyond volume G. In this case, the liquid as a whole is assumed to be motionless, which will be clearly allowed for by the fact that the distribution of momenta will be given in the form of the equilibrium distribution (1.6) to (1.7). Let us calculate each part of the change in momentum individually.

The transfer of momentum in unit time through an element of surface dS, passing through point $\boldsymbol{q}$, accomplished by the movement through dS of particles with momenta from $\boldsymbol{p}$ to $\boldsymbol{p} + d\boldsymbol{p}$, is equal to

$$\boldsymbol{p}\,\frac{N}{V}\, dW(\boldsymbol{p})\, F_1(\boldsymbol{q})\, \frac{(\boldsymbol{p}\boldsymbol{n})}{m}\, dS\,, \tag{2.42}$$

since the density of the number of particles in the neighborhood of point $\boldsymbol{q}$ in the chosen interval of momentums is equal to

$$\frac{N}{V}\, dW(\boldsymbol{p})\, F_1(\boldsymbol{q}) \tag{2.43}$$

and p/m is the velocity of a particle. Taking into consideration the direction of the external normal $\boldsymbol{n}$, we obtain for the αth projection of the entire increment of the momentum of particles in G for unit time arising from the transfer of particles

$$-\frac{N}{mV}\oint_S F_1(q)\,dS\int p_\alpha(pn)\,dW(p), \qquad (2.44)$$

where the inner integral is over the entire range of momentum of a single particle. In agreement with (1.7), we have

$$\int p_\alpha(pn)\,dW(p) = mkTn_\beta\,\delta_{\alpha\beta}\,, \qquad (2.45)$$

where $\delta_{\alpha\beta} = 1$ when $\alpha = \beta$ and $\delta_{\alpha\beta} = 0$ when $\alpha \neq \beta$. Placing this in (2.44) and comparing with (2.41), we obtain an expression for the "kinetic" part of the stress tensor in the form

$$\Pi^{(1)}_{\alpha\beta} = -\frac{NkT}{V}F_1(q)\,\delta_{\alpha\beta}\,. \qquad (2.46)$$

Now let us consider the average force acting on some molecule in G arising from all the molecules outside of G. If the position of the selected molecule is q_1, this force will be equal to

$$-\frac{N-1}{V}\int_{V-G}\nabla_{q_1}\Phi(|q_1-q_2|)F_1(q_2|q_1)\,dq_2, \qquad (2.47)$$

where the integral is over the entire region occupied by the system excepting only region G. Therefore, the entire force acting on all the particles in G is equal to

$$-\frac{N(N-1)}{V^2}\int_G\int_{V-G}\nabla_{q_1}\Phi(|q_1-q_2|)F_1(q_1) \times F_1(q_2|q_1)\,dq_2dq_1 \qquad (2.48)$$

or, according to (2.18),

$$-\frac{N(N-1)}{V^2}\int_V\int_G\nabla_{q_1}\Phi(|q_1-q_2|)F_2(q_1, q_2)\,dq_1dq_2\,. \qquad (2.49)$$

Here we have extended the integration in terms of q_2 to the entire volume V, since the entire force between all the particles within G, added to (2.48), is exactly equal to zero. If, finally, we go from the variables q_1 and q_2 to the variables r and R in (2.13), then, for the average force acting on the particles in G due to the remaining particles, we obtain

$$-\frac{N(N-1)}{V^2}\int_V\int_G\nabla_r\Phi(|r|)F_2^*(r, R)\,dR\,dr\,. \qquad (2.50)$$

The integral over $\boldsymbol{R}$ in (2.50) may be transformed into a surface integral. For this purpose, let us set $\boldsymbol{R} = \boldsymbol{q}_1 - \frac{1}{2}\boldsymbol{r}$. Assuming that the non-uniformity of the liquid is small, we may write

$$F_2^*(\boldsymbol{r},\boldsymbol{R}) = F_2^*(\boldsymbol{r}, \boldsymbol{q}_1 - \tfrac{1}{2}\boldsymbol{r}) = F_2^*(\boldsymbol{r}, \boldsymbol{q}_1) - \tfrac{1}{2}\boldsymbol{r}\nabla_{q_1}F_2^*(\boldsymbol{r}, \boldsymbol{q}_1) + \ldots. \tag{2.51}$$

Confining ourselves to the written members, we have

$$\begin{aligned}\int_G F_2^*(\boldsymbol{r},\boldsymbol{R})\,d\boldsymbol{R} &= \int_G F_2^*(\boldsymbol{r}, \boldsymbol{q}_1)\,d\boldsymbol{q}_1 - \tfrac{1}{2}\boldsymbol{r}\int_G \nabla \boldsymbol{q}_1 F_2^*(\boldsymbol{r}, \boldsymbol{q}_1)\,d\boldsymbol{q}_1 \\ &= \int_G F_2^*(\boldsymbol{r}, \boldsymbol{q}_1)\,d\boldsymbol{q}_1 - \tfrac{1}{2}\boldsymbol{r}\oint_S \boldsymbol{n}F_2^*(\boldsymbol{r}, \boldsymbol{q})\,dS,\end{aligned} \tag{2.52}$$

where we have utilized Gauss' theorem to transform the volume integral into a surface integral and have designated a point on surface S by $\boldsymbol{q}$. Placing this in (2.50) we see that, with (2.15), the first of the two integrals becomes zero, and instead of (2.50) we obtain

$$\frac{N(N-1)}{2V^2}\oint_S dS\int_V \nabla_r\Phi(|\boldsymbol{r}|)F_2^*(\boldsymbol{r}, \boldsymbol{q})(\boldsymbol{r}\boldsymbol{n})\,d\boldsymbol{r}. \tag{2.53}$$

Comparing this with (2.41) and taking into consideration that $\nabla_r\Phi(|\boldsymbol{r}|) = \Phi'(r)(\boldsymbol{r}/r)$, we obtain for the "potential" part of the stress tensor

$$\Pi_{\alpha\beta}^{(2)} = \frac{N(N-1)}{2V^2}\int_V \Phi'(r)F_2^*(\boldsymbol{r}, \boldsymbol{q})\frac{x_\alpha x_\beta}{r}\,d\boldsymbol{r}, \tag{2.54}$$

where x_α is a component of the vector $\boldsymbol{r}$.

Collecting together (2.45) and (2.54), we finally obtain for the stress tensor the following expression:

$$\Pi_{\alpha\beta}(\boldsymbol{q}) = -\frac{NkT}{V}F_1(\boldsymbol{q})\,\delta_{\alpha\beta} + \frac{N(N-1)}{2V^2}\int_V \Phi'(r)F_2^*(\boldsymbol{r}, \boldsymbol{q})\frac{x_\alpha x_\beta}{r}\,d\boldsymbol{r}, \tag{2.55}$$

or, going over to an unlimited system and setting $(V/N) = v$,

$$\Pi_{\alpha\beta}(\boldsymbol{q}) = -\frac{kT}{v}F_1(\boldsymbol{q})\,\delta_{\alpha\beta} + \frac{1}{2v^2}\int \Phi'(r)F_2^*(\boldsymbol{r}, \boldsymbol{q})\frac{x_\alpha x_\beta}{r}\,d\boldsymbol{r}. \tag{2.56}$$

If we want to return to a uniform system it is necessary to set $F_1(q) = 1$, $F_2(r, q) = g(|r|)$. Taking into consideration that

$$\int \Phi'(r) g(r) \frac{x_\alpha x_\beta}{r} dr = \tfrac{1}{3}\delta_{\alpha\beta} \int \Phi'(r) g(r) r dr \qquad (2.57)$$

and using the well-known relationship $\Pi_{\alpha\beta} = -p\delta_{\alpha\beta}$, we again obtain equation (2.40) for the pressure.

4. FLUCTUATIONS IN THE NUMBER OF PARTICLES IN A LIQUID

By means of correlation functions, it is also easy to express fluctuations in the number of particles in a given volume and correlations of the fluctuations of the numbers of particles in different volumes. Let us again consider some closed portion of a liquid G within V. Let $f_G(q)$ be the characteristic function of region G, i.e.,

$$f_G(q) = \begin{cases} 1, & \text{if } q \text{ lies in } G, \\ 0, & \text{if } q \text{ lies outside of } G. \end{cases} \qquad (2.58)$$

Then the number of particles in G may be written in the form

$$N_G = \sum_{1 \leq i \leq N} f_G(q_i). \qquad (2.59)$$

Consequently, we have to do with an additive magnitude of type M_1 according to (2.22). According to (2.25), we have, for the average number of particles in G,

$$\bar{N}_G = \frac{N}{V} \int_V f_G(q) F_1(q)\, dq = \frac{N}{V} \int_G F_1(q)\, dq. \qquad (2.60)$$

In a uniform fluid this results in the obvious relationship

$$\bar{N}_G = N \frac{V_G}{V}. \qquad (2.61)$$

Now let us consider the square of the number of particles in G:

$$N_G^2 = \sum_{1 \leq i \leq N} f_G(q_i) + 2 \sum_{1 \leq i < j \leq N} f_G(q_i) f_G(q_j), \qquad (2.62)$$

since $[f_G(q)]^2 = f_G(q)$. We have here the sum of variables of the additive and binary types. By using equations (2.25) and (2.26) we obtain, for the average square of the number of particles in G,

$$\langle N_G^2\rangle = \frac{N}{V}\int_V f_G(\mathbf{q})F_1(\mathbf{q})\,d\mathbf{q} + \frac{N(N-1)}{V^2}\int_V\int_V f_G(\mathbf{q}) \times f_G(\mathbf{q}')F_2(\mathbf{q},\mathbf{q}')\,d\mathbf{q}d\mathbf{q}' = \bar{N}_G + \frac{N(N-1)}{V^2} \times \int_G\int_G F_2(\mathbf{q},\mathbf{q}')\,d\mathbf{q}d\mathbf{q}'. \quad (2.63)$$

From this it is easy to obtain the quadratic fluctuation in the number of particles in the volume G. Inasmuch as $\langle(\Delta N_G)^2\rangle = \langle N_G^2\rangle - \bar{N}_G^2$, from (2.61) and (2.63), we obtain

$$\langle(\Delta N_G)^2\rangle = \bar{N}_G\left(1 - \frac{\bar{N}_G}{N}\right) + \frac{N(N-1)}{V^2}\int_G\int_G [F_2(\mathbf{q},\mathbf{q}') - F_1(\mathbf{q})F_1(\mathbf{q}')]\,d\mathbf{q}d\mathbf{q}' \quad (2.64)$$

or, if $\bar{N}_G \ll N$ and $N \to \infty$, $V \to \infty$,

$$\langle(\Delta N_G)^2\rangle = \bar{N}_G + \frac{1}{v^2}\int_G\int_G \times [F_2(\mathbf{q},\mathbf{q}') - F_1(\mathbf{q})F_1(\mathbf{q}')]\,d\mathbf{q}d\mathbf{q}'. \quad (2.65)$$

In the uniform fluid the latter equation is simplified, and we may write

$$\langle(\Delta N_G)^2\rangle = \bar{N}_G + \frac{1}{v^2}\int_G\int_G [g(|\mathbf{q}-\mathbf{q}'|) - 1]\,d\mathbf{q}d\mathbf{q}'. \quad (2.66)$$

If, in addition, the linear dimensions of region G appreciably exceed the distance at which $g(r)$ still differs from unity, then one integration may be carried out in (2.26), and we obtain

$$\langle(\Delta N_G)^2\rangle = \bar{N}_G\left\{1 + \frac{4\pi}{v}\int^{\infty}[g(r) - 1]\,r^2dr\right\}, \quad (2.67)$$

if use is made of (2.61).

From this it is possible to obtain a new relation between the radial distribution function and the thermodynamic properties of the system. We will compare, for this purpose, the result of (2.67) with the well-known formula from the thermodynamic theory of fluctuations:

$$\langle(\Delta N_G)^2\rangle = \frac{\bar{N}_G kT}{v^2\left(-\frac{\partial p}{\partial v}\right)_T}. \quad (2.68)$$

Consequently, the isothermal compressibility of the system is equal to

$$\beta_T \equiv \frac{1}{v}\left(-\frac{\partial v}{\partial p}\right)_T = \frac{v}{kT}\left\{1+\frac{4\pi}{v}\int_0^\infty [g(r)-1]\,r^2 dr\right\}. \quad (2.69)$$

Now let G_1 and G_2 be two different regions in V, possibly intersecting. Then, from (2.59), we have

$$N_{G_1}N_{G_2} = \sum_{1\le i\le N} f_{G_1}(\boldsymbol{q}_i)\,f_{G_2}(\boldsymbol{q}_i) + \sum_{1\le i<j\le N} [f_{G_1}(\boldsymbol{q}_i)\,f_{G_2}(\boldsymbol{q}_j) + f_{G_1}(\boldsymbol{q}_j)\,f_{G_2}(\boldsymbol{q}_i)]. \quad (2.70)$$

The averaging of (2.70) is carried out analogously to the averaging of (2.62), and we obtain

$$\langle N_{G_1}N_{G_2}\rangle = \frac{N}{V}\int_{G*} F_1(\boldsymbol{q})\,d\boldsymbol{q} + \frac{N(N-1)}{V^2}\int_{G_1}\int_{G_2} F_2(\boldsymbol{q},\boldsymbol{q}')\,d\boldsymbol{q}\,d\boldsymbol{q}', \quad (2.71)$$

where the first integral on the right is over the region G^*, which is the intersection of regions G_1 and G_2. Together with the coefficient that stands in front, this integral is equal to the average number of particles in G^*. For the non-intersecting regions G_1 and G_2, this term in (2.71) is absent.

Inasmuch as $\langle \Delta N_{G_1}\Delta N_{G_2}\rangle = \langle N_{G_1}N_{G_2}\rangle - \langle N_{G_1}\rangle\langle N_{G_2}\rangle$, we obtain, with the aid of equations (2.61) and (2.71),

$$\langle \Delta N_{G_1}\Delta N_{G_2}\rangle = N_{G*} - \frac{N_{G_1}N_{G_2}}{N} + \frac{N(N-1)}{V^2}\int_{G_1}\int_{G_2}[F_2(\boldsymbol{q},\boldsymbol{q}') - F_1(\boldsymbol{q})F(\boldsymbol{q}')]\,d\boldsymbol{q}\,d\boldsymbol{q}'. \quad (2.72)$$

If the regions G_1 and G_2 entirely coincide, we again return to equation (2.64). In general, however, equation (2.72) determines the magnitude of the correlation of the fluctuations in the number of particles in various volumes isolated in a liquid. In a uniform fluid, when $N \to \infty$ and $V \to \infty$, we will have

$$\langle \Delta N_{G_1}\Delta N_{G_2}\rangle = N_{G*} + \frac{1}{v^2}\int_{G_1}\int_{G_2}[g(|\boldsymbol{q}-\boldsymbol{q}'|)-1]\,d\boldsymbol{q}\,d\boldsymbol{q}'. \quad (2.73)$$

Thus, the fluctuations in the number of particles and their correlations are determined by the function

$$\nu(q, q') = F_2(q, q') - F_1(q)F_1(q') \tag{2.74}$$

or, in a uniform fluid,

$$\nu(r) = g(r) - 1\,, \tag{2.75}$$

called the "correlation function." The fact that this correlation function deviates from zero shows the presence of correlations in the positions of the particles of the system. In a gas or a liquid, $\nu(r)$ rapidly tends to zero with increasing values of r; the distance at which $\nu(r)$ is significantly different from zero determines the dimensions of the region of short-range order of the system.

Analogous to the above calculations, it is also possible to calculate the average values of the higher-order functions. Let us take as an example the calculation of $\langle N_G^3 \rangle$ which we will subsequently need. From (2.59), we have

$$\begin{aligned} N_G^3 = \sum_{1 \le i \le N} f_G(q_i) + 6 \sum_{1 \le i < j \le N} f_G(q_i) f_G(q_i) \\ + 6 \sum_{1 \le i < j < k \le N} f_G(q_i) f_G(q_j) f(q_k)\,. \end{aligned} \tag{2.76}$$

Averaging this equation in accordance with (2.24) and taking into consideration the properties of the function $f_G(q)$ from (2.58), we obtain

$$\begin{aligned} \langle N_G^3 \rangle = -2\bar{N}_G + 3\bar{N}_G^2 \\ + \frac{N(N-1)(N-2)}{V^3} \int_G \int_G \int_G F_3(q, q', q'')\, dq\, dq'\, dq''\,. \end{aligned} \tag{2.77}$$

With the aid of the relationship

$$\langle (\Delta N_G)^3 \rangle = \bar{N}_G^3 - 3\bar{N}_G \langle N_G^2 \rangle + 2\bar{N}^3 \tag{2.78}$$

it is now easy to obtain an equation for $\langle (\Delta N_G)^3 \rangle$ expressed in terms of the correlation functions F_1, F_2, and F_3, which, because of its awkwardness, we will not display [9].

5. ENTROPY

The entropy is one of the most important thermodynamic characteristics of statistical systems, but unfortunately it is not an average value of any additive or binary function and, therefore, its direct expression by means of the simplest correlation functions is impossible. An expression may be obtained indirectly if the dependence of the radial distribution function, $g(r)$, on the thermodynamic parameters T and v: $g(r) = g(r; T, v)$ is known. Differentiating equation (2.31) and (2.41) with respect to the temperature, we obtain

$$\frac{\partial E}{\partial T} = \tfrac{3}{2}Nk + \frac{2\pi N}{v}\int_0^\infty \Phi(r)\frac{\partial g}{\partial T}\, r^2 dr\,, \tag{2.79}$$

$$\frac{\partial p}{\partial T} = \frac{k}{v} - \frac{2\pi}{3v^2}\int_0^\infty \Phi(r)\frac{\partial g}{\partial T}\, r^3 dr\,. \tag{2.80}$$

The entropy may be calculated by integrating one of the well-known thermodynamic relationships

$$T\left(\frac{\partial S}{\partial T}\right)_V = \left(\frac{\partial E}{\partial T}\right)_V, \qquad \left(\frac{\partial S}{\partial V}\right)_T = \left(\frac{\partial p}{\partial T}\right)_V. \tag{2.81}$$

Entropy may be simply and directly expressed only in terms of the complete correlation function F_N, determined from equation (2.9). By placing (2.9) in (1.27), we obtain

$$S = S_0 - k\langle \ln F_N(q_1, \ldots, q_N)\rangle, \tag{2.82}$$

where S_0 is the entropy of an ideal gas (1.23).

In equation (2.82) correlations between all the particles in the system are simultaneously taken into consideration. However, it is possible to decompose this expression into a "series of increasingly complex correlations" by dividing the contributions to the entropy from groups of one, two, three, etc., particles. For this purpose, let us introduce the "correlation potentials" of groups of particles, $\Psi_s(q_1, \ldots, q_s)$, by means of the equations

$$\begin{aligned} -kT\ln F_1(q) &= \Psi_1(q)\,, \\ -kT\ln F_2(q, q') &= \Psi_2(q, q') + \Psi_1(q) + \Psi_1(q'), \\ -kT\ln F_3(q, q', q'') &= \Psi_3(q, q', q'') + \Psi_2(q, q') \\ &\quad + \Psi_2(q, q'') + \Psi_2(q', q'') + \Psi_1(q) + \Psi_1(q') + \Psi_1(q''), \end{aligned} \tag{2.83}$$

etc. Subsequently solving these equations for the function Ψ_s, we find

$$\begin{aligned} \Psi_1(q) &= -kT\ln F_1(q), \\ \Psi_2(q, q') &= -kT\ln\left[\frac{F_2(q, q')}{F_1(q)F_1(q')}\right], \\ \Psi_3(q, q', q'') &= -kT\ln\left[\frac{F_3(q, q', q'')F_1(q)F_1(q')F_1(q'')}{F_2(q, q')F_2(q, q'')F_2(q', q'')}\right], \end{aligned} \tag{2.84}$$

etc.

From this it is evident that the functions Ψ_s are significantly different from zero only in the case that all s particles of the group under consideration are situated close to one another. As a matter of fact, if one of the group of s particles, for example the first, is removed sufficiently far so that, between it and the remaining $s-1$ particles, there is neither direct nor indirect (i.e., through other particles) interaction, then, because of the probabilistic nature of the functions F_s, we will have

$$\begin{aligned} F_s(q_1, \ldots, q_s) &\to F_1(q_1)F_{s-1}(q_2, \ldots, q_s), \\ F_{s-1}(q_1, \ldots, q_{s-1}) &\to F_1(q_1)F_{s-2}(q_2, \ldots, q_{s-1}), \end{aligned} \tag{2.85}$$

etc. Therefore, according to (2.84), Ψ_s returns to zero if even one of the s particles is removed sufficiently far.

Finally, from equation (2.83), there is obtained the equation

$$\begin{aligned} -kT \ln F_N(q_1, \ldots, q_N) &= \Psi_N(q_1, \ldots, q_N) \\ &+ \sum_{1\leq i\leq N} \Psi_{N-1}(q_1, \ldots, q_{i-1}, q_{i+1}, \ldots, q_N) \\ &+ \ldots + \sum_{1\leq i<j\leq N} \Psi_2(q_i, q_j) + \sum_{1\leq i\leq N} \Psi_1(q_i) \,. \end{aligned} \tag{2.86}$$

Placing this in equation (2.82), we obtain for the entropy

$$TS = TS_0 + \overline{\Psi}_N + \Sigma\overline{\Psi}_{N-1} + \ldots + \Sigma\overline{\Psi}_2 + \Sigma\overline{\Psi}_1 \,, \tag{2.87}$$

where on the right stand the average values of all members of the right-hand side of equation (2.86). Each sum here is a function of the type M_s, according to (2.22), and may be calculated according to equation (2.24), so that as a result we obtain

$$\begin{aligned} TS = TS_0 + \sum_{1\leq s\leq N} &\frac{N(N-1)\ldots(N-s+1)}{s!V^s} \\ &\times \int_V \cdots \int_V \Psi_s(q_1, \ldots, q_s) F_s(q_1, \ldots, q_s) dq_1 \ldots dq_s \,. \end{aligned} \tag{2.88}$$

Let us consider a uniform fluid. Then $\Psi_1(q) = 0$. When $s > 1$, the integrand in each term of (2.88), when $V \to \infty$, does not depend on the position of the group as a whole. Therefore, the typical integral in (2.88) is equal to

$$\begin{aligned} V \int_V \cdots \int_V \Psi_s(q_1, \ldots, q_{s-1}, 0) F_s(q_1, \ldots, q_{s-1}, 0) \\ \times dq_1 \ldots dq_{s-1} \,, \end{aligned} \tag{2.89}$$

so that each such integral is proportional to the volume V or to the number of particles N, and in this case the integral remaining in (2.89) when $s \ll N$ does not depend on volume. In (2.88), since s is small, $N - s$ may be replaced by N; proceeding to the limit $N, V \to \infty$ under the summation sign, with $v =$ const, we will have

$$TS = TS_0 + N \sum_{2 \leq s \leq \infty} \frac{1}{s!\,v^{s-1}} \int \cdots \int \Psi_s(q_1, \ldots, 0) \times F_s(q_1, \ldots, 0)\, dq_1 \ldots dq_{s-1} \,. \tag{2.90}$$

Equations (2.88) or (2.90) express a "series of increasingly complex correlations" for the entropy. Each of their members describes the contribution to the entropy from correlations in the positions of groups of particles. For example, the contribution to the entropy from binary correlations in a uniform fluid is equal to

$$-\frac{2\pi k}{v} N \int_0^\infty g(r) \ln g(r)\, r^2 dr \,. \tag{2.91}$$

6. ELASTIC PROPERTIES OF LIQUIDS

If a liquid is subjected to slowly varying external forces, then, in consequence of its fluidity, the only elastic reaction to external forces will be resistance to an over-all compression which is characterized by the coefficient of isothermal compressibility β_T (2.69) or the corresponding modulus of compression $K_T = 1/\beta_T$.

The situation is quite different in the case of very rapidly varying external forces. In this case the liquid displays elastic properties of the same type as does a solid body. Let $\boldsymbol{u}(\boldsymbol{q})$ be the displacement vector of a particle at point $\boldsymbol{q}$ which occurs due to the rapid deformation of the liquid, and let $\tilde{\Pi}_{\alpha\beta}(\boldsymbol{q})$ and $\Pi_{\alpha\beta}(\boldsymbol{q})$ be the stress tensors at the same point before and after the application of the external force. Then, just as in the case of an isotropically elastic solid body, Hooke's law [8] will be valid for small displacements (linear in $\boldsymbol{u}$):

$$\tilde{\Pi}_{\alpha\beta} - \Pi_{\alpha\beta} = \mu \left(\frac{\partial u_\alpha}{\partial q_\beta} + \frac{\partial u_\beta}{\partial q_\alpha} \right) + (K - \tfrac{2}{3}\mu) \operatorname{div} \boldsymbol{u} \cdot \delta_{\alpha\beta} \,. \tag{2.92}$$

Here μ is the shear modulus, K is the modulus of compression; both μ and K are adiabatic elastic moduli: $\mu = \mu_s$, $K = K_s$. But it is known from the theory of elasticity that $\mu_s = \mu_T$ [8]; therefore, we shall speak only of the shear modulus[1] of a liquid μ. We shall show that in a liquid

[1] The use in this paragraph of the generally accepted notation for the sheer modulus should not lead to confusion with the notation for the chemical potential.

Hooke's law is valid (2.92), and we will simultaneously obtain an expression for the shear modulus in terms of the radial distribution function.

Let q and q' be the positions of two particles of a liquid prior to deformation and $\tilde{q}$ and $\tilde{q}'$ be their positions after deformation. If r and $\tilde{r}$ are the corresponding vector distances between these particles, then, from the expressions

$$\tilde{q} = q + u(q), \qquad \tilde{q}' = q' + u(q + r), \tag{2.93}$$

we obtain

$$\tilde{r} = r + (r \cdot \nabla_q) u(q). \tag{2.94}$$

Hence, for the distance $\tilde{r} = |\tilde{r}|$, defined as in (2.93) we find, correct to terms which are quadratic in u,

$$\tilde{r} = r + \frac{1}{r} r \cdot (r \cdot \nabla_q) u. \tag{2.95}$$

The well-known expression for the relative change in volume during deformation is also obtained from (2.94):

$$\frac{\tilde{v} - v}{v} = \mathrm{div}_q\, u, \tag{2.96}$$

the derivation of which we will omit [8]. From this we have

$$\tilde{v} = v(1 + \mathrm{div}_q\, u), \qquad \frac{1}{\tilde{v}} = \frac{1}{v}(1 - \mathrm{div}_q\, u). \tag{2.97}$$

Now let us consider the stress tensor in a deformed liquid. We shall designate all values after deformation by writing tildes above them. Then, in accordance with (2.56), we have

$$\Pi_{\alpha\beta}(\tilde{q}) = -\frac{k\tilde{T}}{\tilde{v}} \tilde{F}_1(\tilde{q})\,\delta_{\alpha\beta} + \frac{1}{2\tilde{v}^2} \int \Phi'(\tilde{r}) \tilde{F}_2^*(\tilde{r}, \tilde{q}) \frac{\tilde{x}_\alpha \tilde{x}_\beta}{\tilde{r}}\, d\tilde{r}. \tag{2.98}$$

The functions $\tilde{F}_1$ and $\tilde{F}_2^*$ are very simply related to the functions F_1 and F_2^*. It is physically obvious that the probability of finding a certain particle in the vicinity of a definite point after deformation of a liquid is equal to the probability of finding it in the same neighborhood near the same point before deformation:

$$d\tilde{W}(\tilde{q}) = dW(q)$$

or

$$\tilde{F}_1(\tilde{q}) \frac{d\tilde{q}}{\tilde{v}} = F_1(q) \frac{dq}{v}. \tag{2.99}$$

But dq changes during deformation just as v does, so that $(d\tilde{q}/\tilde{v}) = (dq/v)$, and instead of (2.99) we obtain

$$\tilde{F}_1(\tilde{q}) = F_1(q) = 1 \,, \tag{2.100}$$

if the liquid is considered to be uniform before deformation. Analogously, it is possible to show also that

$$\tilde{F}_2^*(\tilde{r}, \tilde{q}) = F_2^*(r, q) = g(r) \,. \tag{2.101}$$

Let us examine each term in (2.98) individually. The temperature $\tilde{T}$ differs from temperature T by the magnitude of the increase in temperature due to adiabatic compression of the liquid, so that

$$\tilde{T} = T + \left(\frac{\partial T}{\partial v}\right)_S (\tilde{v} - v) = T + v\left(\frac{\partial T}{\partial v}\right)_S \operatorname{div} \boldsymbol{u} \,. \tag{2.102}$$

Using equations (2.97) and (2.100), we therefore have

$$-\frac{k\tilde{T}}{\tilde{v}} \tilde{F}_1(\tilde{q})\, \delta_{\alpha\beta} = -\frac{kT}{v}\, \delta_{\alpha\beta} + k\left[\frac{T}{v} - \left(\frac{\partial T}{\partial v}\right)_S\right] \operatorname{div} \boldsymbol{u}\, \delta_{\alpha\beta} \,. \tag{2.103}$$

The second term in (2.98), with the aid of equations (2.97) and (2.101), and the relationship $(d\tilde{r}/\tilde{v}) = (dr/v)$ may be rewritten in the form

$$\frac{1}{2v^2}(1 - \operatorname{div} \boldsymbol{u}) \int \frac{1}{\tilde{r}} \Phi'(\tilde{r})\, \tilde{x}_\alpha \tilde{x}_\beta\, g(r)\, dr \,. \tag{2.104}$$

Using equations (2.94) and (2.95), we find that

$$\tilde{x}_\alpha \tilde{x}_\beta = x_\alpha x_\beta + x_\alpha (\boldsymbol{r} \cdot \nabla_q) u_\beta + x_\beta (\boldsymbol{r} \cdot \nabla_q) u_\alpha \,, \tag{2.105}$$

$$\frac{1}{\tilde{r}} \Phi'(\tilde{r}) = \frac{1}{r} \Phi'(r) + \frac{1}{r}\frac{d}{dr}\left[\frac{1}{r}\Phi'(r)\right] \boldsymbol{r}(\boldsymbol{r} \cdot \nabla_q) \boldsymbol{u} \,. \tag{2.106}$$

Placing this in expression (2.104) and keeping terms linear in $\boldsymbol{u}$, instead of the second term in (2.98), we obtain

$$\begin{aligned} &\frac{1}{2v^2}(1 - \operatorname{div} \boldsymbol{u}) \int \Phi'(r)\, g(r) \frac{x_\alpha x_\beta}{r}\, dr \\ &+ \frac{1}{2v^2} \int \Phi'(r)\, g(r) \frac{1}{r} [x_\alpha (\boldsymbol{r} \cdot \nabla_q) u_\beta + x_\beta (\boldsymbol{r} \cdot \nabla_q) u_\alpha]\, dr \\ &+ \frac{1}{2v^2} \int \frac{1}{r}\frac{d}{dr}\left[\frac{1}{r}\Phi'(r)\right] g(r)\, \boldsymbol{r}(\boldsymbol{r} \cdot \nabla_q) \boldsymbol{u}\, x_\alpha x_\beta\, dr \,. \end{aligned} \tag{2.107}$$

All these three integrals may easily be calculated if we transform to spherical coordinates. The first of them has already been calculated in (2.57). For the remaining two we obtain

$$\int \Phi'(r)\,g(r)\frac{1}{r}[x_\alpha(\boldsymbol{r}\cdot\nabla_q)u_\beta + x_\beta(\boldsymbol{r}\cdot\nabla_q)u_\alpha]\,d\boldsymbol{r}$$

$$= \frac{4\pi}{3}\left(\frac{\partial u_\beta}{\partial q_\alpha}+\frac{\partial u_\alpha}{\partial q_\beta}\right)\int_0^\infty \Phi'(r)\,g(r)\,r^3 dr\,, \qquad (2.108)$$

$$\int \frac{1}{r}\frac{d}{dr}\left[\frac{1}{r}\Phi'(r)\right]g(r)\,r\,(\boldsymbol{r}\cdot\nabla_q)u x_\alpha x_\beta d\boldsymbol{r}$$

$$= \frac{4\pi}{15}\left(\operatorname{div}\boldsymbol{u}\,\delta_{\alpha\beta}+\frac{\partial u_\alpha}{\partial q_\beta}+\frac{\partial u_\beta}{\partial q_\alpha}\right)\int_0^\infty \frac{d}{dr}\left[\frac{1}{r}\Phi'(r)\right]g(r)\,r^5 dr\,. \qquad (2.109)$$

Placing this in (2.107) and combining it with (2.104), after simple transformations we obtain

$$\tilde{\Pi}_{\alpha\beta}-\Pi_{\alpha\beta}=\frac{2\pi}{15v^2}\left(\frac{\partial u_\alpha}{\partial q_\beta}+\frac{\partial u_\beta}{\partial q_\alpha}\right)\int_0^\infty \frac{d}{dr}[r^4\Phi'(r)]\,g(r)\,dr$$

$$+\left\{p-k\left(\frac{\partial T}{\partial v}\right)_S+\frac{2\pi}{15v^2}\int_0^\infty \frac{d}{dr}\left[\frac{1}{r}\Phi'(r)\right]g(r)\,r^5 dr\right\} \qquad (2.110)$$

$$\times \operatorname{div}\boldsymbol{u}\cdot\delta_{\alpha\beta}\,,$$

where we took into consideration that $\Pi_{\alpha\beta} = -p\delta_{\alpha\beta}$ and p is determined by equation (2.40). Summing up we see that deformations and forces are actually related to one another by Hooke's law. By comparing equations (2.110) and (2.92), we obtain for the shear modulus of a liquid

$$\mu=\frac{2\pi}{15v^2}\int_0^\infty \frac{d}{dr}[r^4\Phi'(r)]\,g(r)\,dr\,. \qquad (2.111)$$

For the adiabatic modulus of compression, after simple transformations, we obtain

$$K_S = k\left[\frac{T}{v}-\left(\frac{\partial T}{\partial v}\right)_S\right]+\frac{2\pi}{9v^2}\int_0^\infty \frac{d}{dr}\left[\frac{1}{r^2}\Phi'(r)\right]g(r)\,r^4 dr\,. \qquad (2.112)$$

Thus, the shear modulus of a liquid may be calculated directly from the intermolecular potential and the radial distribution function. In order to calculate the adiabatic compressibility, it is necessary in addition to know the behavior of the function $\partial g(r;T,v)/\partial T$. Then the derivative $(\partial T/\partial v)_s$ which occurs in (2.112) may be found with the aid of equations (2.79) and (2.80) according to the well-known thermodynamic formula

$$\left(\frac{\partial T}{\partial v}\right)_S = -\frac{T}{c_v}\left(\frac{\partial p}{\partial T}\right)_v. \tag{2.113}$$

Let us note that K_s may also be calculated from the well-known relationship

$$K_S = \frac{c_p}{c_v} K_T, \tag{2.114}$$

if $K_T = 1/\beta_T$ is determined from (2.69).

7. KIRKWOOD'S METHOD AND THE CHEMICAL POTENTIAL

Kirkwood proposed a generalization of the method of correlation functions to make possible the determination of further relations between these functions and the thermodynamic properties of the system. Below, for example, we give an equation for the chemical potential, expressed in terms of the radial distribution function [2].

Let us consider a system consisting of N particles, but in which one particle, the first, for example, is distinguished in that its interaction with the remaining particles is multiplied by λ. For the entire energy of interaction of all particles we then have

$$U_N(q_1, \ldots, q_N; \lambda) = \lambda \sum_{2\le i\le N} \Phi(|q_1 - q_i|) + \sum_{2\le i<j\le N} \Phi(|q_i - q_j|), \tag{2.115}$$

or, more briefly,

$$U_N(\lambda) = \lambda U^{(1)} + U_{N-1}(q_2, \ldots, q_N). \tag{2.116}$$

When $\lambda = 1$ and $\lambda = 0$, one obtains $U_N(q_1, \ldots, q_N)$ and $U_N - 1(q_2, \ldots, q_N)$ respectively for $U_N(\lambda)$, so that when $\lambda = 0$ the first particle is excluded from the general interaction of the system. The configuration integral and the Gibbs distribution function are determined for this system in the usual way:

$$Q_N(\lambda) = \int_V \cdots \int_V \exp\left[-\frac{U_N(\lambda)}{kT}\right] dq_1 \ldots dq_N. \tag{2.117}$$

$$D_N(q_1, \ldots, q_N; \lambda) = Q_N^{-1}(\lambda) \exp\left[-\frac{U_N(\lambda)}{kT}\right]. \tag{2.118}$$

In the limiting cases $\lambda = 1$ and $\lambda = 0$, we have

$$Q_N(1) = Q_N\,; \qquad Q_N(0) = VQ_{N-1}\,, \tag{2.119}$$

where Q_N and Q_{N-1} refer to a "normal" system with the respective numbers of particles.

Furthermore, it is possible to introduce into our system a set of correlation functions $F_s(\lambda)$, determining them, as before, by means of equations (2.1). In this case it is necessary to distinguish two cases depending on whether the separated particle belongs to the group under consideration or not. If the first particle does not enter the group of s particles under consideration, then $F_1(q_2, \ldots, q_{s+1}; \lambda)$ is weakly dependent on λ, and when $N \to \infty$ this dependence disappears completely. Below we shall examine the opposite situation where the particle first separated enters the group of s particles which is of interest to us. Then, analogously to equation (2.10), we have

$$F_s(q_1, \ldots, q_s; \lambda) = V^s \int_V \ldots \int_V D_N(q_1, \ldots, q_N; \lambda) \times dq_{s+1} \ldots dq_N\,, \tag{2.120}$$

and the dependence on λ is considerable. The functions $F_s(q_1, \ldots, q_s; \lambda)$ are now no longer, generally speaking, symmetrical in all their arguments due to the separation of the first particle. For the more important binary function, however, when we take into consideration the uniformity and isotropy of the liquid, we have

$$F_2(q_1, q_2; \lambda) = F_2(|q_2 - q_1|; \lambda) = g(r; \lambda), \tag{2.121}$$

where $r = |q_1 - q_2|$, so that in this case the symmetry of $F_2(\lambda)$ relative to q_1 and q_2 is retained.

Let us now consider the chemical potential of a "normal" system consisting of N identical particles. If μ_0 is the chemical potential of the corresponding ideal gas, then, according to equations (1.19) and (1.24), we have

$$\mu = \mu_0 - kT \frac{\partial}{\partial N} \ln \frac{Q_N}{V^N}. \tag{2.122}$$

Now let us take into consideration that the number of particles in the system is actually not a continuous variable but rather a discrete variable. Therefore, the derivative of any function $A(N)$ must be defined as the ratio

$$\frac{A(N) - A(N - \Delta N)}{\Delta N} \tag{2.123}$$

when $\Delta N \ll N$, but without conversion to the physically meaningless limit $\Delta N \rightarrow \infty$. If for ΔN we take its minimum possible value, $\Delta N = 1$, then for the value of $\partial A / \partial N$ we obtain the simple difference $A(N) - A(N-1)$. Having thus calculated the right half of equation (2.122), we obtain

$$\mu = \mu_0 + kT\left(\ln V - \ln \frac{Q_N}{Q_{N-1}}\right) \qquad (2.124)$$

or, taking (2.119) into consideration,

$$\mu = \mu_0 - kT \ln \frac{Q_N(1)}{Q_N(0)}. \qquad (2.125)$$

In turn, for the last term of the expression (2.125), we have the identity

$$\ln \frac{Q_N(1)}{Q_N(0)} = \int_0^1 \frac{\partial \ln Q_N(\lambda)}{\partial \lambda}\, \partial\lambda, \qquad (2.126)$$

so that the problem is reduced to the calculation of this integral. From equations (2.117) and (2.118), we have

$$\frac{\partial Q_N(\lambda)}{\partial \lambda} = -\frac{1}{kT} \int_V \cdots \int_V \Big[\sum_{2 \leq i \leq N} \Phi(|q_1 - q_i|)\Big] \times \exp\left[-\frac{U_N(\lambda)}{kT}\right] dq_1 \ldots dq_N. \qquad (2.127)$$

Integrating first over $dq_3 \ldots dq_N$ with the aid of (2.120), we obtain

$$\frac{\partial Q_N(\lambda)}{\partial \lambda} = -\frac{Q_N(\lambda)}{kT} \cdot \frac{N-1}{V^2} \int_V \int_V \Phi(|q_1 - q_2|) \times F_2(q_1 q_2; \lambda)\, dq_1 dq_2. \qquad (2.128)$$

Taking (2.121) into consideration, completing one integration and then going over to the limit $N \rightarrow \infty$ and $V \rightarrow \infty$, we obtain

$$\frac{\partial \ln Q_N(\lambda)}{\partial \lambda} = -\frac{4\pi}{v kT} \int_0^\infty \Phi(r)\, g(r; \lambda)\, r^2 dr. \qquad (2.129)$$

With the aid of equations (2.125), (2.126), and (2.129), we finally obtain for the chemical potential of the system

$$\mu = \mu_0 + \frac{4\pi}{v} \int_0^1 d\lambda \int_0^\infty \Phi(r)\, g(r; \lambda)\, r^2 dr. \qquad (2.130)$$

Thus one more very important thermodynamic function is expressed in terms of the radial distribution function.

8. THE SCATTERING OF LIGHT AND X RAYS BY LIQUIDS

It is also possible to express the angular dependence of the intensity of the Rayleigh scattering of electromagnetic waves by a liquid with the aid of the radial distribution function if multiple scattering is disregarded [10].

Let a plane monochromatic wave of wavelength λ and a direction of propagation $\boldsymbol{n}_0$ fall on a system of N particles. We will be concerned with the electromagnetic waves scattered in a certain direction $\boldsymbol{n}$ far from the scattering system so that the waves proceeding from it may be considered to be plane waves. If $\boldsymbol{E}_j e^{i\varphi_j}$ designates the complex amplitude of a wave at the point of observation which has been scattered by the jth particle of the system, then the entire intensity at the point of observation is characterized by the amplitude

$$\boldsymbol{E} = \sum_{1\leq j\leq N} \boldsymbol{E}_j e^{i\varphi_j} = \boldsymbol{E}_1 \sum_{1\leq j\leq N} e^{i\varphi_j}, \tag{2.131}$$

and all $\boldsymbol{E}_j$ are equal to each other because of the identity of the particles. Accordingly, for the intensity we have

$$I \sim \boldsymbol{E}\boldsymbol{E}^* \sim \sum_{1\leq j\leq N} \sum_{1\leq l\leq N} e^{i(\varphi_j-\varphi_l)}, \tag{2.132}$$

where complex conjugation is designated by the asterisk. Separating the terms with equal unequal j and l into a double sum, removing N from the brackets, and introducing the proportionality coefficient, we obtain

$$I = I_0 \left[1 + \frac{2}{N} \sum_{1\leq j<l\leq N} e^{i(\varphi_j-\varphi_l)}\right]. \tag{2.133}$$

Here the first term corresponds to the total intensity of scattering by a system of N independent particles. The second term describes the interference effects between the waves scattered by different particles and, naturally, it depends on the phase differences between these waves.

The expression (2.133) corresponds to the intensity of scattering of electromagnetic waves by a system for the case of definite and fixed positions of the particles of the system. The experimentally observed intensity of scattering is obtained from this by averaging over the thermal motion of the particles or, what amounts to the same thing, by averaging over the Gibbs distribution. Thus, we obtain

$$I = I_0 \left[1 + \frac{2}{N} \left\langle \sum_{1\leq j<l\leq N} e^{i(\varphi_j-\varphi_l)} \right\rangle\right). \tag{2.134}$$

The second interference term on the right side of this equation actually depends on correlations that exist between particles of the system. In a system of absolutely independent particles, when for all F_s, $s = 1, 2, 3, \ldots$, we would have $F_s \equiv 1$; the corresponding term would give a small contribution to the scattering depending on the shape and dimensions of the surface which bound the surface of the system of particles, but would not give any volume effect. The latter is physically obvious in connection with the complete independence of the differences of phase corresponding to various pairs of particles and may easily be verified by calculation. An analogously small contribution to scattering connected with the presence of boundaries of the scattering volume also appears in the presence of correlations between the particles, and we shall not calculate it any further. Let us designate by zero the averaging over a system of independent particles. For further consideration, it will be convenient to subtract from (2.134) the interference term corresponding to this averaging. For a large system this term is practically equal to zero, and instead of (2.134) we will have

$$I = I_0 \left\{1 + \frac{2}{N}\left[\left\langle \sum_{1 \le j < l \le N} e^{i(\varphi_j - \varphi_l)} \right\rangle - \left\langle \sum_{1 \le j < l \le N} e^{i(\varphi_j - \varphi_l)} \right\rangle^0 \right]\right\}. \tag{2.135}$$

Let us find the averages which figure in (2.135). From elementary geometrical construction, it follows that the difference in phase $\varphi_j - \varphi_l$ is equal to the scalar product $(\boldsymbol{k} - \boldsymbol{k}_0) \cdot (\boldsymbol{q}_j - \boldsymbol{q}_l)$, where $\boldsymbol{k}_0 = (2\pi/\lambda)\boldsymbol{n}_0$ and $\boldsymbol{k} = (2\pi/\lambda)\boldsymbol{n}$ are the wave vectors of incident and scattered waves, respectively. If ϑ is the angle of scattering (i.e., $\cos\theta = \boldsymbol{n}\boldsymbol{n}_0$), then $|\boldsymbol{n} - \boldsymbol{n}_0| = 2\sin(\vartheta/2)$ and, designating the angle between the vectors $(\boldsymbol{q}_j - \boldsymbol{q}_l)$ and $\boldsymbol{n} - \boldsymbol{n}_0$ by θ_{jl}, we obtain

$$\varphi_j - \varphi_l = \frac{4\pi}{\lambda} \sin\frac{\vartheta}{2} |\boldsymbol{q}_j - \boldsymbol{q}_l| \cos\theta_{jl}. \tag{2.136}$$

Then the first average in (2.135) is, in accordance with equation (2.26),

$$\left\langle \sum_{1 \le j < l \le N} e^{i(\varphi_j - \varphi_l)} \right\rangle = \frac{N(N-1)}{2V^2} \int_V \int_V \exp\left(i\frac{4\pi}{\lambda} \sin\frac{\vartheta}{2} |\boldsymbol{q}_1 - \boldsymbol{q}_2| \cos\theta_{12}\right) F_2(\boldsymbol{q}_1, \boldsymbol{q}_2)\, d\boldsymbol{q}_1 d\boldsymbol{q}_2. \tag{2.137}$$

The second average in (2.135) will be written the same, but now it will be necessary to set $F_2(q_1, q_2) = 1$. Therefore

$$I = I_0 \left\{ 1 + \frac{N-1}{V^2} \int_V \int_V \exp\, (is\,|\boldsymbol{q}_1 - \boldsymbol{q}_2|\cos\theta_{12}) \times [F_2(\boldsymbol{q}_1\boldsymbol{q}_2) - 1]\, d\boldsymbol{q}_1 d\boldsymbol{q}_2 \right\}, \quad (2.138)$$

where for the sake of brevity we designate

$$s = \frac{4\pi}{\lambda} \sin \frac{\vartheta}{2}. \quad (2.139)$$

Taking into consideration that $F_2(q_1, q_2) = g(|q_1 - q_2|)$ and carrying out one integration, we obtain, after transition to the limit $N \rightarrow \infty$ and $V \rightarrow \infty$,

$$I = I_0 \left\{ 1 + \frac{1}{v} \int \exp(i\,|\boldsymbol{q}|\, s \cos\theta)[g(|\boldsymbol{q}|) - 1]\, d\boldsymbol{q} \right\}. \quad (2.140)$$

Here the integral is easily simplified if we go over to spherical coordinates with the polar axis along the vector $\boldsymbol{n} - \boldsymbol{n}_0$. Since

$$\int_0^\pi \exp\,(isr\cos\theta)\sin\theta\, d\theta = 2\, \frac{\sin(sr)}{sr}, \quad (2.141)$$

we finally obtain

$$I = I_0 \left\{ 1 + \frac{4\pi}{v} \int_0^\infty [g(r) - 1] \frac{\sin(sr)}{sr}\, r^2 dr \right\}. \quad (2.142)$$

For the region of visible light or spectral regions close to it, the wavelength $1/s$ according to (2.139) is much greater than the "correlation radius" of the particles in a liquid, so that the function $g(r) - 1$ practically disappears before the oscillations of the function $\sin(sr)/sr$ set in. Therefore, under the integral in (2.142), it is possible to expand this function into a Taylor series and to good approximation confine ourselves to the first term of the expansion $\sin(sr)/sr \approx 1$. Summing up, we obtain

$$I = I_0 \left\{ 1 + \frac{4\pi}{v} \int_0^\infty [g(r) - 1]\, r^2 dr \right\}, \quad (2.143)$$

or, comparing with (2.69),

$$I = I_0 \frac{kT}{v^2 \left(-\frac{\partial p}{\partial v} \right)_T}, \quad (2.144)$$

which coincides with the result of the thermodynamic theory of scattering of light arising from fluctuations of density [11]. The coefficient I_0

in the latter expression, which is equal to the intensity of light scattering in a system of N independent particles, may be calculated on the basis of the phenomenological theory of the propagation of light in media and is equal to [11]

$$I_0 = I_{\text{in}}\ N \frac{\pi^2 v^4}{\lambda^4 R^2} \sin^2 \gamma \left(\frac{\partial \epsilon}{\partial v}\right)^2, \qquad (2.145)$$

where I_{in} is the intensity of the incident light, R is the distance from the point of observation to the scattering body, γ is the angle between the electric vector of the incident waves and the direction of scattering, and ϵ is the dielectric permeability in the region of wavelengths which is of interest to us.

In the case of X rays, the wavelength $1/s$ at these scattering angles is much smaller than for visible light, and further simplification of equation (2.142) is impossible. The value of I depends on s. The constant I_0 is equal to NI_{00}, where I_{00} is the intensity of scattering of a single particle; this value may be determined either by experiment on the scattering of X rays by a rarefied gas, or, in principle, by means of quantum-mechanical calculations. If by $i(s)$ we designate the relative intensity of scattering $i(s) = I(s)/I_0$ and rewrite equation (2.142) in the form

$$[i(s) - 1]\, s = \frac{4\pi}{v} \int_0^\infty [g(r) - 1]\, r \sin(sr)\, dr, \qquad (2.146)$$

then the left side of this equation may be integrated as a Fourier sine-transformation of the function $(4\pi/v)[g(r) - 1]r$. Using an inverse Fourier sine-transformation, we obtain

$$[g(r) - 1]\, r = \frac{v}{2\pi^2} \int_0^\infty [i(s) - 1]\, s \sin(rs)\, ds. \qquad (2.147)$$

The latter result is noteworthy in the sense that it permits the determination of the radial distribution function $g(r)$ from experimental data for the function $i(s)$. In this case it is apparently not very significant that in equation (2.147) the function $i(s)$ is required for all values of s from zero to infinity, while in connection with (2.139) the function $i(s)$ has only been experimentally determined up to $s = 4\pi/\lambda$. In connection with the rapid decrease in the function $i(s) - 1$ with increasing values of s, the cut off in integration in (2.147) at the finite upper limit nevertheless permits us to obtain sufficiently reliable data on the radial distribution function of particles in real liquids.

REFERENCES

[1] J. Kirkwood, *J. Chem. Phys.*, **7** (1935), 919.

[2] J. Kirkwood and E. Boggs, *J. Chem. Phys.*, **10** (1942), 394.

[3] J. Kirkwood and E. Monroe, *J. Chem. Phys.*, **9** (1941), 514.

[4] N. N. Bogolyubov, *Problemy dinamicheskoi teorii v statisticheskoi fizike*, Gostekhizdat (Problems of Dynamic Theory in Statistical Theory), State Technical Press, 1946.

[5] M. Born and H. Green, *Proc. Roy. Soc, ser. A*, **188** (1946), 10.

[6] M. Born and H. Green, *ibid.*, **189** (1947), 455.

[7] H. Green, *Molecular Theory of Fluids*, Amsterdam, 1952.

[8] L. D. Landau and E. M. Lifshits, *Mekhanika sploshnykh sred*, Gostekhizdat (The Mechanics of Complex Media), State Technical Press, 1953.

[9] V. K. Prokhorenko, O. Ya. Samoilov, and I. Z. Fisher, *Doklady Akad. Nauk SSSR*, **125** (1959), 396.

[10] F. Zernicke and I. Prins, *Z. Phys.*, **41** (1927), 184.

[11] M. A. Leontovich, *Statisticheskaya fizika*, Gostekhizdat (Statistical Physics), State Technical Press, 1945.

CHAPTER 3

THE STRUCTURE OF SIMPLE LIQUIDS

1. THE RADIAL DISTRIBUTION FUNCTION OF REAL LIQUIDS

In chapter 2 we showed the importance of correlation functions and, especially the radial distribution function, for describing the properties of liquids. As a matter of fact, correlation functions contain information which make it possible not only to calculate the thermodynamic properties of liquids, but also to make qualitative judgments relevant to the molecular structure of liquids, i.e., regarding the geometric interrelations between the particles of a system. The latter question is very important in many problems of the physics of liquids—no less important than the calculation of thermodynamic functions. An exhaustive description of the molecular structure of a liquid should be given, in principle, by the full set of correlation functions F_s, $s = 1, 2, 3 \ldots$. For many problems, however, it is actually sufficient to know a small number of these functions for small s. The situation is the same as in the calculation of thermodynamic functions.

In fact, the complete set of functions F_s for a liquid is unknown. Their theoretical determination for a real three-dimensional fluid involves very great difficulties, and at the present time only two functions $F_2(q, q') = g(|q - q'|)$ and $F_3(q, q', q'')$ may be calculated even approximately for a uniform system. But we have already seen that one of the correlation functions, namely the radial distribution function $g(r)$, may be determined experimentally from X-ray data. For the same purpose, and in an analogous manner, neutron scattering and electron scattering data are also used at the present time: such studies have been carried out on a large number of liquids. Therefore, for many real liquids the radial distribution function may be considered to be known. It is natural to ask what conclusions regarding the molecular structure of liquids may be deduced from this data. In this chapter we shall examine these problems in detail. However, it is essential to remember that knowledge of only the binary correlation function is inadequate to give a complete answer to many questions. It therefore appears that, despite almost thirty years of X-ray analysis of liquids, much still remains unexplained and in dispute.

Figure 4 gives a schematic representation of the radial distribution function of a liquid $g(r)$ as obtained from calculations made from X-ray data. Let us again recall that the function $g(r)$ determines the prob-

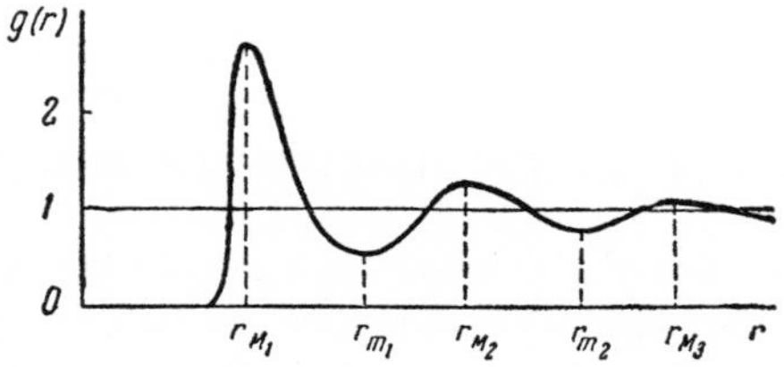

FIG. 4.—Schematic representation of the radial distribution function of particles in a monoatomic liquid.

ability of finding a molecule of the liquid at a distance from r to $r + dr$ from some other fixed molecule in accordance with the equation

$$dW(r) = g(r)\,\frac{4\pi r^2 dr}{V}. \tag{3.1}$$

The corresponding function

$$\rho(r) = \frac{1}{v}\,g(|\mathbf{r}|) \tag{3.2}$$

shows the spatial variation of the density of particles in the neighborhood of the fixed particle. Turning to Figure 4, therefore, we see that the region near the origin of the coordinates where $g(r) \approx 0$ corresponds in its dimensions to the effective diameter of a particle and represents the mutual "impenetrability" of the particles. The dimensions of this region depend on the magnitude of the pressure applied to the liquid. At a distance of several molecular diameters, the function $g(r)$ undergoes some gradually damped oscillations near the value $g(r) = 1$. The locations of the maxima of these oscillations correspond to the preferred relative distances between the neighboring particles in the liquid. Between them are located regions of comparatively low density. Finally, at still greater distances, $g(r) \approx 1$ and all the spacings of the distant particles are equally probable.

This picture is characteristic of all monoatomic liquids. In polyatomic liquids the picture is complicated due to the superposition of intermolecular and intramolecular atomic distributions, but we shall not be concerned with this now. With changes in temperature and density of the liquid, the dependence on distance of the function $g(r)$ also changes somewhat—the oscillations are sharper at low temperatures and higher densities. However, the general spatial dependence of $g(r)$ remains qualitatively the same in the liquid and in the dense gaseous states.

The specific feature of the liquid state, as described above, is characterized as the presence of "short-range order." The equation $g(r) = 1$, when the distance between the particles is large, describes the absence of "long-range order" in the liquid. The dimensions of the region of short-range order (or the region of correlation) depend on the temperature and density of the liquid and, with the exception of special cases, are always of the order of several molecular diameters. There is no doubt that, in considerable part, the short-range order observed in liquids is a density effect related to the "hardness" or impenetrability of the particles. When one such particle is fixed in position in a sufficiently dense medium, the remaining particles (on the average) will inevitably be distributed in layers regardless of the character of their interactions with each other. A similar purely geometrical effect may easily be observed, for example, in the distribution of a large number of billiard balls on a limited portion of a table. The magnitude and character of the interaction are essential for describing the finer details of the distribution of particles, but they do not influence the existence of their somewhat stratified arrangement relative to one another.

The correctness of the above interpretation of the radial distribution function $g(r)$, in terms of the effects of density and geometry in a system having a large number of particles of finite size, has been confirmed by numerous model experiments. By shaking solid spheres spread over a flat vessel or by mixing suspended spheres in a three-dimensional vessel and by subsequently analyzing statistically a large number of observations of the distances between spheres, it is possible to obtain "a radial distribution function of particles" which does not differ qualitatively from the function $g(r)$ in real liquids obtained by X-ray studies. The most complete experiments of this type were described in paper [1]. Figure 5, which was taken from this paper, shows the result of one series of measurements. The similarity of the dependences shown in Figures 4 and 5 is unmistakable. It is also possible to vary these experiments so as to imitate the forces of attraction between particles and, thus, to obtain a qualitative evaluation of the effect of interaction between particles on their mutual distribution.

2. THE RADIAL DISTRIBUTION FUNCTION OF A ONE-DIMENSIONAL MODEL OF A LIQUID

Precise theoretical calculation of the radial distribution function at high particle densities is only possible in a one-dimensional fluid. Let us briefly consider this problem and compare the results of the calculations with what has been said above regarding the radial distribution function of real liquids.

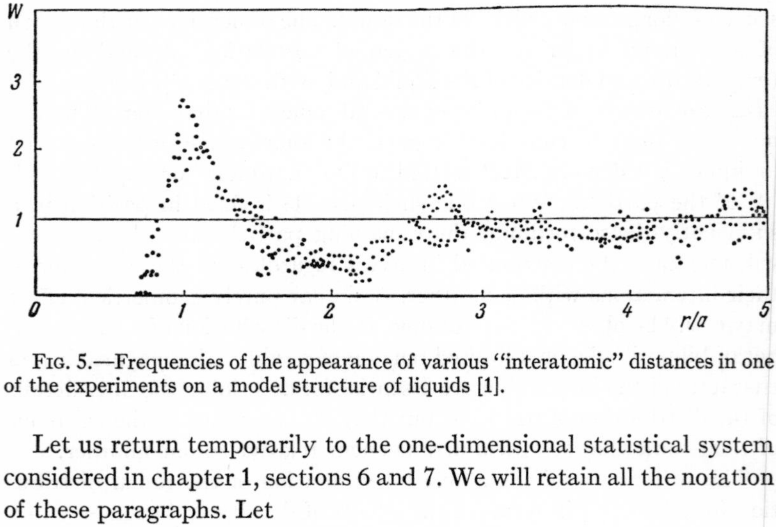

FIG. 5.—Frequencies of the appearance of various "interatomic" distances in one of the experiments on a model structure of liquids [1].

Let us return temporarily to the one-dimensional statistical system considered in chapter 1, sections 6 and 7. We will retain all the notation of these paragraphs. Let

$$dW(\xi;\, m) = \Psi_m(\xi)\, d\xi \tag{3.3}$$

designate the probability of finding some two given particles of a system, separated from one another by $m - 1$ other particles at a relative distance from ξ to $\xi + d\xi$. In this case,

$$\int_0^\infty \Psi_m(\xi)\, d\xi = 1\,. \tag{3.4}$$

If one particle has the number k, then the other will have the number $k \pm m$, and $\xi = |x_k - x_{k\pm m}|$. When $m = 1$, we seek the distribution of the closest neighbors; when $m = 2$, we seek the distribution of the second neighbors, etc.

In order to construct the function $\Psi_m(\xi)$, let us first consider the case of a large but finite system with N particles on a section of axis Ox of length L. Let one of the two particles of interest to us be the $(N + 1)$th particle in the scheme in chapter 1, section 6 so that it forms the right boundary of the system, while the other has the number $N - m$ and the coordinate x_{N-m}. Then $\xi = L - x_{N-m}$. Taking into consideration (1.77) to (1.81), the Gibbs distribution function of the system is

$$D_N(x_1, \ldots, x_N) = \bar{Q}_N^{-1} f(x_1) f(x_2 - x_1) \ldots \times f(x_N - x_{N-1}) f(L - x_N), \tag{3.5}$$

and in order to obtain the probability $dW(\xi; m)$ it is necessary to integrate this expression over all coordinates except $x_{N-m} = L - \xi$. But under the assumptions made regarding the character of interaction in this system and taking (1.77) into consideration, the fixing of the position of the $(N - m)$th particle implies the division of the entire system into two non-interacting parts: one with $N - m$ particles on the section of length $L' = L - \xi$ and the other with $m - 1$ particles on the section of length $L'' = \xi$. Therefore, the integration of expression (3.5) gives us

$$\Psi_m(\xi) = \frac{\bar{Q}_{m-1}(\xi)\bar{Q}_{N-m}(L - \xi)}{\bar{Q}_N(L)}. \tag{3.6}$$

When m is fixed and N very large, we may use for $\bar{Q}_{N-m}$ and $\bar{Q}_N$ the asymptotic evaluation of (1.81), as a result of which we obtain

$$\Psi_m(\xi) = \frac{1}{[\varphi(p, T)]^m} \exp\left(-\frac{p\xi}{kT}\right) \bar{Q}_{m-1}(\xi), \tag{3.7}$$

where

$$\bar{Q}_{m-1}(\xi) = \int_0^\xi dx_{m-1} \int_0^{x_{m-1}} dx_{m-2} \ldots \times \int_0^{x_2} f(x_1) f(x_2 - x_1) \ldots f(\xi - x_{m-1})\, dx_1. \tag{3.8}$$

When $m = 1$, we have

$$\bar{Q}_0(\xi) = f(\xi) = \exp\left[-\frac{\Phi(\xi)}{kT}\right]. \tag{3.9}$$

Consequently, the distribution of nearest neighbors in a one-dimensional liquid satisfies

$$dW(\xi; 1) = \Psi_1(\xi)\, d\xi = \frac{1}{\varphi(p, T)} \exp\left[-\frac{p\xi + \Phi(\xi)}{kT}\right] d\xi. \tag{3.10}$$

When $m > 1$, the integral (3.8) may be calculated by use of the Laplace transformation. Analogously to equation (1.90), we obtain

$$\bar{Q}_{m-1}(\xi) = \frac{1}{2\pi i} \oint_C e^{\xi s} [\varphi(s)]^m ds \,. \qquad (3.11)$$

When $m = 1$, in consequence of (1.86), we again return to (3.9). Thus we always have

$$\Psi_m(\xi) = \frac{1}{[\varphi(p, T)]^m} \exp\left(-\frac{p\xi}{kT}\right) \times \frac{1}{2\pi i} \oint_C e^{\xi s} [\varphi(s)]^m ds \,, \qquad (3.12)$$

where the path of integration encloses the poles of the integrand. The integration may be carried out according to the residue theorem if $\varphi(s)$ is known.

Now let us study the binary distribution function $F_2(x, x')$ in our one-dimensional system. As in the three-dimensional case, in the limit of an infinitely large uniform system, $F_2(x, x')$ may be replaced by $F_1(x/x')$ and treated as a conditional one particle correlation function. Because of the uniformity of the liquid it will depend only on $|x - x'|$. Thus

$$F_2(x, x') = F_1(x \mid x') = g(\,|x - x'|\,), \qquad (3.13)$$

and $g(x)$ is a one-dimensional analog of the radial distribution function. When one particle is fixed in position, the probability of finding some other (unlabeled) particle at a distance of x to $x + dx$ from the first is equal to

$$dW(x) = g(x)\frac{dx}{L}, \qquad (3.14)$$

whereupon

$$\frac{1}{L}\int_0^L g(x)\,dx = 1 \,. \qquad (3.15)$$

From equations (3.14) to (3.15) with (3.3) to 3.4), it is clear that

$$g(x) = l \sum_{1 \leq m \leq \infty} \Psi_m(x), \qquad (3.16)$$

where $l = L/N$ and it is assumed that $N \to \infty$ and $L \to \infty$. Using equation (3.12), we finally have

$$g(x) = l \exp\left(-\frac{px}{kT}\right) \sum_{1 \leq m \leq \infty} \frac{1}{2\pi i [\varphi(p, T)]^m} \times \oint_C e^{sx} [\varphi(s)]^m ds . \tag{3.17}$$

This result was first obtained in paper [2].

Let us consider, as an example, the simplest system of hard spheres of diameter a. When $\xi < am$, we have $\bar{Q}_{m-1}(\xi) = 0$, so that

$$\Psi_m(\xi) = 0 \qquad \text{when} \qquad x < am . \tag{3.18}$$

Furthermore, when $\xi \geq ma$, we have, according to (1.85),

$$\varphi(s) = \frac{e^{-as}}{s}; \qquad \varphi(p, T) = \frac{kT}{p} \exp\left(-\frac{ap}{kT}\right), \tag{3.19}$$

so that

$$\Psi_m(\xi) = \frac{\exp\left(-\frac{\xi - ma}{l - a}\right)}{(l - a)^m} \cdot \frac{1}{2\pi i} \oint_C \frac{\exp[(\xi - ma)s]}{s^m} ds , \tag{3.20}$$

while equation (1.108) is used for the pressure. The integral in this case is easily calculated using the residue theorem,

$$\frac{1}{2\pi i} \oint_C \frac{\exp[(\xi - ma)s]}{s^m} ds = \frac{(\xi - ma)^{m-1}}{(m-1)!}, \tag{3.21}$$

and we obtain

$$\Psi_m(\xi) = \frac{(\xi - ma)^{m-1}}{(m-1)!(l-a)^m} \exp\left(-\frac{\xi - ma}{l - a}\right), \quad \xi \geq ma . \tag{3.22}$$

Placing the expressions (3.18) and (3.22) in equation (3.16) we obtain the final expression for the one-dimensional analog of the radial distribution function in a system of hard spheres

$$g(x) = 0 \qquad \text{when} \qquad x < a ,$$

$$g(x) = l \sum_m{}' \frac{(x - ma)^{m-1}}{(m-1)!(l-a)^m} \exp\left(-\frac{x - ma}{l - a}\right) \quad \text{when} \quad x > a , \tag{3.23}$$

where for a given x the sum is extended over those terms for which $x - ma$ remains positive. This result was obtained for the first time by the direct use of the theory of probability in paper [3].

Figure 6 shows the function $g(x)$, according to (3.23), for two values of l. As l increases, the amplitude of the oscillations of $g(x)$ decreases and they narrow. On the other hand, as the value of $l - a$ decreases, the oscillations get stronger and extend over the whole region. The

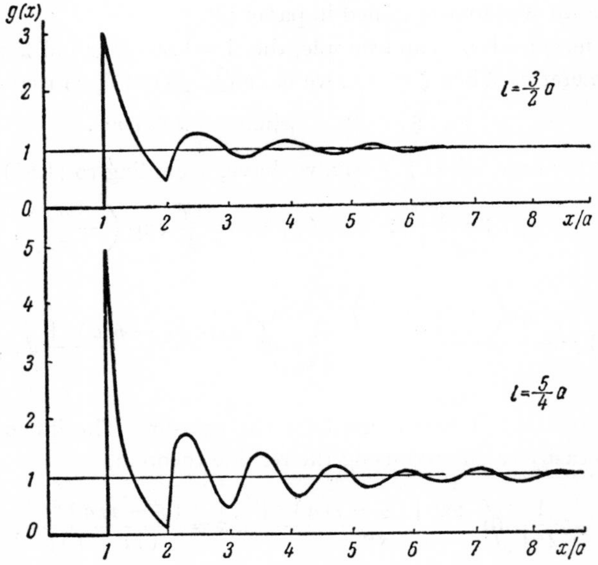

FIG. 6.—One-dimensional function $g(x)$ for a system of hard spheres at values of $l = \frac{3}{2}a$ and $l = \frac{5}{4}a$.

sharpness of the first peak of $g(x)$ is related to the discontinuous character of the intermolecular potential in the hard sphere problem and is not of significance for the problem of the general properties of $g(x)$. We are convinced by the diagram that, in the problem under consideration, a typical "liquid" picture of short-range order appears. The purely geometric and density-dependent origin of the short-range order in this problem is evident.

It is, of course, necessary to keep in mind the qualitative difference between a one-dimensional and a three-dimensional system. In particular, this was manifest above in a comparatively large region of order. It is not difficult to find from (3.23) that this region extends over a number of particles approximately equal to

$$N' \sim \left(\frac{l}{l-a}\right)^2 = \left(\frac{pl}{kT}\right)^2. \qquad (3.24)$$

When $l - a$ is sufficiently small, i.e., when pressures are sufficiently high, the number N' is extremely large. This is essentially related to the one dimensionality and has no three-dimensional analog. In real liquids the radius of correlation is always of the order of several molecular diameters.

3. COMPARISON OF THE STRUCTURES OF LIQUIDS AND CRYSTALS

Now let us proceed to a more detailed examination of the experimentally determined radial distribution functions in monoatomic liquids. In this case, we shall be interested only in a general picture of the phenomenon. More detailed information on various substances may be found in review articles [4, 5, 6].

First, let us consider some hypothetical ideal crystalline lattice with immobile atoms arranged at the lattice points. Let us take one point as the origin of the coordinates and construct about it a series of coordination spheres, i.e., spheres which pass through subsequent layers of the surrounding lattice points. Let r_k be the radius of the kth coordination sphere and n_k the number of lattice points (atoms) in it. The numbers r_k and n_k depend on the type of lattice. Then two sequences of numbers,

$$r_1, r_2, \ldots, r_k, \ldots, \qquad n_1, n_2, \ldots, n_k, \ldots, \qquad (3.25)$$

completely characterize the distribution of the atoms of the crystal relative to the selected atom. It is easy to write an expression for the radial distribution function. If we retain for $g(r)$ the former meaning and normalization (3.1), then, evidently, we will have

$$g(r) = v \sum_{1 \leq k \leq \infty} \frac{n_k}{4\pi r_k^2} \delta(r - r_k), \qquad (3.26)$$

where $\delta(x)$ is a one-dimensional δ function. In a crystal, of course, there also exists a definite angular dependence of the distribution of particles. The expression (3.26) should be considered as the result of an averaging over directions (angles) of a more precise one-body correlation function $F_1(r|r')$ when $r' = 0$:

$$\oint_{\omega} F_1(r\,|\,0)\,d\omega = g(\,|\,r\,|\,), \tag{3.27}$$

where $d\omega$ is an element of solid angle.

If we wish to calculate the thermal motion of the atoms of a crystal, it will be necessary to replace the δ functions by some continuous function $\delta^*(r - r_k;\, \Delta)$, each of which is different from zero in the narrow region Δ and identical for all k. At least for small values of k, the magnitude of Δ will be much less than the differences $r_{k+1} - r_k$ so that the individual peaks of the function $g(r)$ will remain sharply separated from one another. Then we obtain

$$g(r) = v \sum_{1 \leq k \leq \infty} \frac{n_k}{4\pi r_k^2}\, \delta^*(r - r_k;\, \Delta), \tag{3.28}$$

while the integral over the function $\delta^*(x;\, \Delta)$ is equal to unity.

Now, it is natural to attempt to interpret the behavior of the initial part of the radial distribution function of the particles of a real liquid $g(r)$, which is shown schematically in Figure 4, by analogy with the result (3.28). In this case we refrain for the present from considering the problem as to whether a function $F_1(r|0)$ underlies the radial distribution function, which is related to $g(r)$ by an equation analogous to (3.27) and which describes the anisotropy of the distribution of particles (although in small volumes).

First of all, the curves $g(r)$ for liquids and crystals differ principally in the fact that in a crystal the peaks of this function are clearly resolved and separated by intervals when $g(r) = 0$, while in a liquid even the first peak is unresolved. (In a crystal, at a finite temperature, peaks with very large k values are also unresolved due to the fact that the distance $r_{k+1} - r_k$ between two peaks may be less than the width of the peak, Δ, and, at large values of k, the coordination spheres follow one after another with ever decreasing intervals.) The minimum between the first and second peaks of $g(r)$, and also between the succeeding peaks in a liquid, does not reach zero. There is a finite probability of an individual particle appearing at any distance from the selected particle, and this corresponds to the possibility of migration of a particle from the region of the first peak into the region of the second, and vice versa. The broadness of the peaks of the radial distribution function is thus related to the translational motion of the molecules in the liquid.

Nevertheless, one or two of the first peaks of $g(r)$ in a liquid are usually comparatively sharply separated; sometimes it is possible to separate another few peaks. Therefore, in this situation it is possible to speak provisionally about coordination layers or spheres, keeping in mind the first, second, etc., layers of the environment of some particle.

Let r_{M1}, r_{M2}, . . . denote the positions of the maxima of the first peaks of $g(r)$ in a liquid: these determine the most probable distances between the nearest particles, etc., in the liquid. It is noteworthy that in very many liquids at a temperature close to the melting point, the distance r_{M1} corresponds with the distance r_1 from (3.25) in the case of the corresponding crystal, or is very close to it. With increasing temperature r_{M1} usually becomes greater, but not to a significant degree. Thus, the average distances between the nearest particles in a liquid and the corresponding crystal are approximately equal. For the distances r_{M2} and r_2 from (3.25), the correspondence is usually not so good, and in some cases there is no correspondence at all. The values of r_{M1} and r_1 for some liquids in the vicinity of the melting point are shown in Table 4.

TABLE 4

Substance	r_1 Å	r_{M1} Å	Substance	r_1 Å	r_{M1} Å
Ar	3.82	3.80	Sn	3.34	3.34
Na	3.72	3.83	Au	2.88	2.86
Pb	3.49	3.43			

From the approximate equality of r_{M1} and r_1, it follows that the expansion of the substance on melting or on heating the liquid arises predominantly from "hole formation" in the liquid, i.e., due to a decrease in the number of very close neighbors and not to an increase in the distance between them. The fact that this is actually so is evident from an analysis of the average coordination numbers in liquids z_1, z_2, . . . , which are the analogues of the numbers n_1, n_2, . . . in (3.25). Inasmuch as individual peaks of $g(r)$ in a liquid are not resolved, the average numbers of particles in successive layers of close coordination z_1, z_2, . . . are not well defined as in a crystal, and various authors use different methods for evaluating them. The very simplest method consists in determining z_k as the average number of particles in a spherical layer between two minima of the function $g(r)$. If we use the notation of Figure 4, we obtain for the first and second average coordination numbers in a liquid, according to (3.2),

$$z_1 = \frac{4\pi}{v} \int_0^{r_{m_1}} g(r) r^2 dr , \tag{3.29}$$

$$z_2 = \frac{4\pi}{v} \int_{r_{m_1}}^{r_{m_2}} g(r) r^2 dr . \tag{3.30}$$

Ordinarily, a sharp division into more than two or three coordination spheres is rare and, therefore, only two or three average coordination numbers z_k in a liquid are significant.

In simple liquids, as a rule, immediately after melting the number z_k is close to the number n_k in the corresponding crystal, although somewhat smaller than it. This corresponds to the comparatively small

TABLE 5

Substance	n_1	$\langle z_1 \rangle$	Substance	n_1	$\langle z_1 \rangle$
He.	12	8.4	K.	14	8.0
Ne.	12	8.6	Hg.	12	6.0
Ar.	12	10.5	Ge.	4	8.1
Xe.	12	8.5	Sn.	10	10.0
Li.	14	9.5	Bi.	6	7.5
Na.	14	9.3			

change in the specific volume of these substances on melting, which amounts to approximately 5 to 10 per cent. On further heating of the liquid (at constant pressure), z_1 first continues to decrease rapidly, and then more slowly. Exceptions are substances with open structures in the crystalline state, such as bismuth and germanium, which contract on melting. Then, z_1 is larger than n_1 near the melting point. On further heating these liquids behave in the ordinary manner. Table 5 gives the values of n_1 and z_1 for some monoatomic substances near the melting point.

For the alkali metals which crystallize in body-centered cubic lattices, instead of n_1, the sums of n_1 and n_2 for the first two coordination spheres, which are very close to each other, are shown. In this case, after fusion the first peak of $g(r)$ in the liquid corresponds to two peaks of $g(r)$ of the crystal.

Interesting results are obtained when attempts are made to systematize the average coordination numbers z_1 in monoatomic liquids in accordance with the periodic table [5]. We will not stop to consider this.

The similarity of some of the properties of the functions $g(r)$ in liquids and crystals, which was pointed out above, is usually described by the term "quasi-crystallinity of liquids." This term, however, is very vague; various authors give it different meanings—even to the point of making an identification between the structures of liquids and crystals. We shall return to this problem again but prefer not to use this term.

The spatial variation of $g(r)$ in a liquid is characterized not only by the arrangement of its maxima and minima and by z_k numbers, but also by the shape and width of its peaks. These questions are very interesting and important both for the analysis of the structure of liquids and also for their thermodynamic implications: in the calculation of energy and pressure in a liquid, according to (2.31) and (2.40), because of the rapid decrease in the intermolecular potential $\Phi(r)$ as r increases, it is precisely the short-range order of $g(r)$ which is significant. Unfortunately, these questions have hardly been studied at all. When the densities in the system are small (gas), the shape and width of the first (and practically the only) peak of $g(r)$ is determined by the Boltzmann factor:

$$g(r) \sim \exp\left[-\frac{\Phi(r)}{kT}\right]. \tag{3.31}$$

The average width of the kth peak, Δ_k, together with the numbers r_{Mk} and z_k, is the most important characteristic of the structure of liquids. In the following paragraph we shall consider one attempt at a theoretical determination of the Δ_k.

4. A STRUCTURAL-DIFFUSION MODEL OF A LIQUID

An interesting approximate model for the structure of a liquid was suggested by I. Prins and further developed by Ya. I. Frenkel and other authors. This is the so-called "structural-diffusion" model of liquids. From our viewpoint it has little theoretical foundation; however, it gives a very graphic picture of the structure of liquids, and we shall consider it briefly [3, 7, 8].

The translational motion of particles of a liquid is disregarded, and only their irregular vibrational motion is considered. The centers of vibration are placed on a quasi-crystalline lattice, the points of which are randomly displaced relative to each other. Therefore, the width of the peaks of the radial distribution function in a liquid arises from two sources: first, due to the vibrations of the atoms as in the usual crystal, in accordance with equation (3.28); second, due to the spatial disorder of the centers of vibration themselves. Since the latter disorder is assumed for each pair of lattice points to be independent and random, the relative separation of pairs of lattice points will be determined by the addition of independent random distances, and will grow proportional to the square root of the number of displacements from the origin. Therefore, in contrast to the lattice models considered in chapter 1, in this case the quasi-crystallinity appears to be only local (on a macroscopic scale of length) and does not result in the appearance of long-range order. The order will be lost at such a distance that the average dispersion in the position of the centers of vibration exceeds the average distance between the nearest particles.

Therefore, in the model under consideration it is assumed that the mean-square width of the kth peak of the radial distribution function $\langle \Delta_k^2 \rangle$ is proportional to the coordinate r_k of this peak in the corresponding crystal:

$$\langle \Delta_k^2 \rangle = 6\,D r_k\,. \tag{3.32}$$

By analogy with the diffusion equation, the coefficient D in this expression is called the "coefficient of structural diffusion." The radius of correlation in the liquid, i.e., the dimensions of the region of short-range order, is determined from the condition

$$\sqrt{\langle \Delta_k^2 \rangle} = \sqrt{(6 D r_k)} \sim r_1 \tag{3.33}$$

and in this theory noticeably exceeds the distance at which the function $g(r)$ becomes unity. $g(r)$ will approach unity at a distance r_k determined from the condition

$$\sqrt{\langle \Delta_k^2 \rangle} = \sqrt{(6 D r_k')} \sim r_{k+1} - r_k\,; \tag{3.34}$$

in a three-dimensional case, for not too small k, the distance between the closest coordination spheres is noticeably less than the distance between the closest particles: $r_{k+1} - r_k \ll r_1$.

If we now assume some definite form for the shape of the peaks of the radial distribution function, we obtain an expression for this function which is analogous to equation (3.28), but with the replacement of Δ by Δ_k, in accordance with (3.32). But it is evident that such a result is unacceptable, since it gives average coordination numbers, z_k, in the liquid which are identical with the coordination numbers n_k in a crystal. Therefore, it is necessary to introduce a supplementary "packing coefficient," $1 - \gamma_k$, where γ_k is equal to the fraction of "holes" in the kth coordination sphere. If we designate by $g_k(r)$ the kth peak function described in this theory, with $g_k(r)$ normalized so that the integral

$$\int_0^\infty g_k(r)\, r^2 dr = 1, \tag{3.35}$$

then, for $g(r)$, we obtain

$$g(r) = \frac{v}{4\pi} \sum_{1\leq k\leq\infty} (1-\gamma_k)\, n_k\, g_k(r). \tag{3.36}$$

It is usually assumed that all peaks have a Gaussian shape. Then

$$g_k(r) = [(6\pi D r_k)^{\frac{1}{2}}(r_k^2 + 3Dr_k)]^{-1} \exp\left[-\frac{(r-r_k)^2}{6Dr_k}\right]. \tag{3.37}$$

The corresponding calculations for some liquids have been carried out [9]. By the selection of a suitable reference crystalline lattice which determines the set of numbers r_k and n_k, and selection of the numbers γ_k and D, it is possible to obtain curves of $g(r)$ which agree satisfactorily with the experimentally determined radial distribution functions. In some cases it was possible to follow the temperature dependence of the coefficient of structural diffusion D. In this case, it appeared that for all monoatomic liquids, one should start from a structure with the densest atom packing, and in many cases these structures appeared to be completely different from the structures of the corresponding crystals before melting.

Thus, we have here a useful and graphic model of the structure of simple liquids. We should not, however, overrate it and consider it a systematic description of the structure of real liquids. First of all, it is clear that any quasi-crystalline model of a liquid may be considered applicable only in a narrow range of states close to the melting point. At some distance from it the structure of the liquid changes greatly and no links with any crystalline lattice whatsoever exist. In the model under consideration the situation is unsatisfactory even in such a narrow region. It would seem that the emergence of structural diffusion, if it is considered as a real process, might serve as a physical explanation of the act of melting, but for this it would be essential that we were considering one and the same lattice in the liquid and solid phase, and as a rule this is not so.

From a theoretical viewpoint the very idea of structural diffusion, as it is ordinarily used, must be recognized as being poorly grounded. In theories of ordinary diffusion, of Brownian movement, and of analogous processes, there always exist two time scales: the microscopic, with unit of time τ which determines the time of correlation of the microprocesses on which the observed phenomenon is based, and the macroscopic, with a unit of time much larger than τ. During a small interval of time on the macroscopic scale, the process may be considered to be independent of the details of motion during the preceding interval. It is precisely on this macroscopic time scale that the Fokker-Planck equation is valid, and under certain conditions the relation $\langle \xi^2 \rangle = 6\,Dt$ is reliable. On the microscopic time scale, however, the relation $\langle \xi^2 \rangle = f(t)$ is very complex, depends on the initial conditions, is different for various processes, and only passes over to the simple law $f(t) = 6\,Dt$ when $t \gg \tau$.

The general ideas which lead to the structural diffusion of liquids are the same as in the case of ordinary diffusion, Brownian movement, etc., only in this case the time is replaced by the distance between the particles of a liquid, while the quantity Δ_k replaces the displacement. In this case, therefore, there must be two length scales with different relations for $\langle \Delta_k^2 \rangle = f(r_k)$, and the assumption that $f(r_k) = 6\,Dr_k$ may only refer to the macroscopic scale. But in these terms, the problem of the determination of the radial distribution function from the very beginning refers to the microscopic scale of length, of order of the diameter of a particle a, or of the distance between neighboring particles r_1. If, therefore, the idea of structural diffusion is generally true, equation (3.32) may be true only for $r_k \gg r_1$ or $k \gg 1$. Meanwhile the number of observed peaks in the function $g(r)$ is very small, and condition (3.34) is satisfied even when $k = 3$ or 4, i.e., sooner than would seem justified by (3.32).

The accuracy of expression (3.32), for large values of k only, is easy to verify on a one-dimensional model (3.23). We should also note that the first peaks of the function $g(r)$ for real liquids do not have a Gaussian form (3.37).

5. FLUCTUATIONS OF THE COORDINATION NUMBERS IN SIMPLE LIQUIDS

The information which may be obtained from knowledge of the radial distribution function of real liquids may be expanded by studying not only the average coordination numbers z_k but also their fluctuations [10, 11]. For this purpose, let us consider the equation for the fluctuations of the number of particles in some volume G (2.65). If, instead of the fixed volume G, we consider some volume G' which is centered around a particle for the liquid, then in this equation one must understand by the terms F_1 and F_2 the conditional correlation functions $F_1(q|q_0)$ and $F_2(q, q'|q_0)$, where q_0 are the coordinates of the selected particle, so that we have

$$\langle(\Delta N_{G'})^2\rangle = \langle N_{G'}\rangle + \frac{1}{v^2}\int_{G'}\int_{G'}[F_2(q, q'|q_0) - F_1(q|q_0)F_1(q'|q_0)]\,dq\,dq' . \tag{3.38}$$

However, from (2.19), the conditional correlation functions may be expressed in terms of simple correlation functions, but of a higher order. If in addition to this we consider the selected particle as located at the origin of the coordinates, then, instead of (3.38), we may write

$$\langle(\Delta N_{G'})^2\rangle = \langle N_{G'}\rangle + \frac{1}{v^2}\int_{G'}\int_{G'}[F_3(q, q', 0) - F_2(q, 0)F_2(q', 0)]\,dq\,dq' . \tag{3.39}$$

Actually, the function $F_3(q, q', 0)$ is unknown and we cannot make use of this equation. But we can use the identity

$$F_3(q, q', 0) \equiv F_2(q, q')F_2(q, 0)F_2q', 0) + [F_3(q, q', 0) - F_2(q, q')F_2(q, 0)F_2(q', 0)] \tag{3.40}$$

and, taking into consideration that $F_2(q, 0) = g(|q|)$ and $F_2(q, q') = g(|q - q'|)$, we can write

$$\langle(\Delta N_{G'})^2\rangle = \langle N_{G'}\rangle + \frac{1}{v^2}\int_{G'}\int_{G'} g(|q|)g(|q'|) \times [g(|q - q'|) - 1]\,dq\,dq' + \frac{1}{v^2}\int_{G'}\int_{G'}[F_3(q, q', 0) - g(|q|)g(|q'|)g(|q - q'|)]\,dq\,dq' . \tag{3.41}$$

If for the sake of brevity we write this in the form

$$\langle(\Delta N_{G'})^2\rangle = \langle(\Delta N_{G'})^2\rangle^* + \langle(\Delta N_{G'})^2\rangle^{**} , \tag{3.42}$$

where the last term corresponds to the second integral in equation (3.41), we may attempt to evaluate each part of the fluctuation in this expression individually.

Part of the fluctuation

$$\langle(\Delta N_{G'})^2\rangle^* = \langle N_{G'}\rangle + \frac{1}{v^2}\int_{G'}\int_{G'} g(|q|)g(|q'|)[g(|q - q'|) - 1]\,dq\,dq' \tag{3.43}$$

depends only on the radial distribution function. Consequently it may be calculated directly. Thus, after simple transformations, we obtain for the first coordination sphere

$$\langle (\Delta z_1)^2 \rangle^* = \langle z_1 \rangle + \frac{8\pi^2}{v^2} \int_0^{r_{m_1}} \int_0^{r_{m_1}} g(r) g(\rho) \times \left\{ \int_{|r-\rho|}^{|r+\rho|} [g(t) - 1] t dt \right\} r\rho \, dr \, d\rho, \tag{3.44}$$

where, instead of $N_{G'}$ we write z_1, while r_{m_1} is the position of the first minimum of the function $g(r)$. For the second coordination sphere we obtain analogously

$$\langle (\Delta z_2)^2 \rangle^* = \langle z_2 \rangle + \frac{8\pi^2}{v^2} \int_{r_{m_1}}^{r_{m_2}} \int_{r_{m_1}}^{r_{m_2}} g(r) g(\rho) \times \left\{ \int_{|r-\rho|}^{|r+\rho|} [g(t) - 1] t dt \right\} r\rho \, dr \, d\rho. \tag{3.45}$$

The second part of the fluctuation

$$\langle (\Delta N_{G'})^2 \rangle^{**} = \frac{1}{v^2} \int_{G'} \int_{G'} [F_3(\mathbf{q}, \mathbf{q}', 0) - g(|\mathbf{q}|) g(|\mathbf{q}'|) g(|\mathbf{q} - \mathbf{q}'|)] d\mathbf{q} d\mathbf{q}' \tag{3.46}$$

cannot be calculated, but it may be estimated. Let us first consider the case of a dense gas. With the aid of equations (4.28), (4.35), (4.37), and (4.43) of the next chapter it is easy to calculate that the expansion of the integrand in (3.46) in powers of the density has the form

$$F_3(\mathbf{q}, \mathbf{q}', 0) - g(|\mathbf{q}|) g(|\mathbf{q}'|) g(|\mathbf{q} - \mathbf{q}'|) = \frac{1}{v} \exp\left[- \frac{\Phi(|\mathbf{q}|) + \Phi(|\mathbf{q}'|) + \Phi(|\mathbf{q} - \mathbf{q}'|)}{kT} \right] \times \int f(|\mathbf{q} - \mathbf{q}''|) f(|\mathbf{q}' - \mathbf{q}''|) f(|\mathbf{q}''|) d\mathbf{q}'' + O\left(\frac{1}{v^2}\right). \tag{3.47}$$

Therefore, for $\langle (\Delta N_{G'})^2 \rangle^{**}$, we obtain

$$\langle (\Delta N_{G'})^2 \rangle^{**} = \frac{1}{v^3} \int_{G'} \int_{G'} \exp\left[- \frac{\Phi(|\mathbf{q}|) + \Phi(|\mathbf{q}'|) + \Phi(|\mathbf{q} - \mathbf{q}'|)}{kT} \right] \times \left(\int \left\{ \exp\left[- \frac{\Phi(|\mathbf{q} - \mathbf{q}''|)}{kT} \right] - 1 \right\} \left\{ \exp\left[- \frac{\Phi(|\mathbf{q}' - \mathbf{q}''|)}{kT} \right] - 1 \right\} \times \left\{ \exp\left[- \frac{\Phi(|\mathbf{q}''|)}{kT} \right] - 1 \right\} d\mathbf{q}'' \right) d\mathbf{q} d\mathbf{q}' + O\left(\frac{1}{v^4}\right). \tag{3.}$$

The sign of the expression obtained depends on the sign of the internal integral; therefore, it is not difficult to become convinced that, at temperatures of the order of the critical temperature or below, this integral is positive. For example, let there be three points $\boldsymbol{q}$, $\boldsymbol{q}'$, and 0 far from one another. Then the internal integral in (3.48), according to (1.62), is equal to six times the second virial coefficient of the gas. It is well known that below the Boyle temperature (and even more so below the critical temperature $T_B \sim 3T_{cr}$) the second virial coefficient is positive; therefore, all these regions make a positive contribution to (3.48). If two of the three points $\boldsymbol{q}$, $\boldsymbol{q}'$, and 0 in the internal integral coincide, then it converges to the expression

$$\int \left\{ \exp\left[-\frac{\Phi(|\boldsymbol{q}''|)}{kT} \right] - 1 \right\}^2 \left\{ \exp\left[-\frac{\Phi(|\boldsymbol{q}-\boldsymbol{q}''|)}{kT} \right] - 1 \right\} d\boldsymbol{q}''$$

and it is clear that this integral is now positive in the region of the critical temperature and below. Finally, if all three points $\boldsymbol{q}$, $\boldsymbol{q}'$, and 0 coincide, the internal integral converges, roughly, to the cube of the second virial coefficient, and in the range of temperature that is of interest to us, it is again positive.

Thus, in the case of a gas $\langle(\Delta N_{G'})^2\rangle^{**} > 0$ always, if only the temperature is not too high. In the case of a liquid, the quantitative evaluation of $\langle(\Delta N_{G'})^2\rangle^{**}$ is difficult; however, it is possible to use the following expression. Complete disregard of the integrand in (3.46) corresponds in the theory of liquids to the superposition approximation, which will be examined in detail in chapter 5. This approximation has been thoroughly studied and it is known that it results in a noticeable decrease in the entropy of a liquid, i.e., it ascribes to the liquid too much order. In a real liquid, therefore, the disruption of order is greater than is calculated in only the first term in (3.42), so that now

$$\langle(\Delta N_{G'})^2\rangle^{**} > 0\,. \tag{3.49}$$

The lower limit of the fluctuations of the coordination numbers is bounded by (3.44) and (3.45), and in this case it appears that

$$\langle(\Delta z_k)^2\rangle > \langle(\Delta z_k)^2\rangle^*. \tag{3.50}$$

This inequality may be fairly great.

One may evaluate analogously the correlations of the fluctuations of the coordination numbers in various coordination spheres. Applying to equation (2.73) all the above reasoning, we obtain, for example, the correlation of the fluctuations of the first and second coordination numbers

$$\langle \Delta z_1 \Delta z_2 \rangle^* = \frac{8\pi^2}{v^2} \int_0^{r_{m_1}} \int_{r_{m_1}}^{r_{m_2}} g(r) g(\rho) \times \left\{ \int_{|r-\rho|}^{r+\rho} [g(t) - 1] t dt \right\} r \rho d r d \rho . \tag{3.51}$$

A more precise expression is again needed in the calculation of $\langle \Delta_{z_1} \Delta_{z_2} \rangle^{**}$. As above, it is not difficult to show that at least in a dense gas at not very high temperatures $\langle \Delta_{z_1} \Delta_{z_2} \rangle^{**} > 0$.

Now let us consider to what results the statement of the theory leads. Table 6 gives the results of calculations of the fluctuations of the

TABLE 6

T °K	$\langle z_1 \rangle$	δ^*_1	$\langle z_2 \rangle$	δ^*_2	η^*
84.4	10.5	0.06	3.2	0.47	....
86.3	8.9	0.11	4.0	0.56	−1.7
91.8	6.8	0.24	5.1	0.38	−0.57
126.7	6.0	0.27	4.4	0.41	−0.52
144.1	6.7	0.30	5.0	0.40	−0.12
149.3	8.5	0.26	....	....	....

first and second coordination numbers and correlations of these fluctuations in liquid argon obtained with the aid of experimental curves of $g(r)$ taken from papers [12] and [13]. The first line of the table almost coincides with the triple point, the last with the critical point. For the sake of brevity, the following notation is used:

$$\delta_1^* = \frac{\sqrt{\langle (\Delta z_1)^2 \rangle^*}}{\langle z_1 \rangle}; \qquad \delta_2^* = \frac{\sqrt{\langle (\Delta z_2)^2 \rangle^*}}{\langle z_2 \rangle}; \qquad \eta^* = \frac{\langle \Delta z_1 \Delta z_2 \rangle^*}{\sqrt{[\langle (\Delta z_1)^2 \rangle^* \langle (\Delta z_2)^2 \rangle^*]}} . \tag{3.52}$$

The data of the last lines are unreliable and are of little interest due to the relative lack of structure of the liquid at high temperatures. For example, when $T = 149.3°$ K, the first coordination sphere is very diffuse and may only be identified with difficulty, while the second does not yet exist at all. If, for the present, we discard the results relating to the immediate neighborhood of the triple point (melting point), one is struck by the very large fluctuations of the coordination numbers—of the order of 25 to 30 per cent in the first and 40 to 50 per cent in the second coordination spheres. In this case it is necessary to keep in mind that the real level of fluctuations is still higher because of the inequality (3.50). For the time being, it is impossible to assert definitely, for the same reason, that in the vicinity of the triple point of argon the fluctuations of the coordination numbers are comparatively small, as is shown in the table.

Analogous results are also obtained for other compressed noble gases, and also for liquid metals. Table 7 gives the results of calculations for liquid mercury according to the experimental data from [14] on the radial distribution function. The first line of the table coincides almost exactly with the melting temperature. The same comment as was given above in connection with Table 6 applies to the last lines.

TABLE 7

t °C	$\langle z_1 \rangle$	δ^*_1	$\langle z_2 \rangle$	δ^*_2	η^*
− 38	7.3	0.14	5.5	0.34	−1.4
0	6.4	0.21	7.5	0.28	−0.96
50	6.1	0.25	8.2	0.27	−0.61
100	4.9	0.23	6.1	0.29	−1.33
150	6.7	0.11	3.6	0.42	−2.2
200	9.2	0.07	...	...	...

It is evident that here the level of fluctuations of the coordination numbers is very high, although somewhat lower than in the case of argon. Calculations for many other metals lead to the same results. In this case in the neighborhood of the melting point the fluctuations of the coordination numbers remain comparatively large. For example, for liquid gallium supercooled by 10°, according to the data for $g(r)$ from [15], $\delta_1^* = 0.18$ is obtained.

Thus, the so-called coordination numbers in liquids $\langle z_1 \rangle$, $\langle z_2 \rangle$, . . . have an average character and differ in principle from the coordination numbers n_1, n_2, . . . in crystals. At a level of fluctuations of 50 per cent and above it is difficult to attach any definite meaning to the coordination numbers $\langle z_2 \rangle$, etc. It should be noted that in both tables the value η^* is always negative and comparatively large.

The same results are obtained for all other liquids. This indicates that the fluctuations in the first two coordination spheres occur principally with opposite signs and gives evidence of the extremely subtle structural interrelations of the fluctuations of order in liquids.

The distribution of the deviations of z_1 or z_2 from their average values is of very great interest. To study this it is necessary to evaluate the sign and magnitude of $\langle (\Delta N_{G'})^3 \rangle$. According to equations (2.77) and (2.78), we need to know the conditional correlation function $F_3(q, q', q'' \mid q_0)$ in a liquid, which is equivalent to knowing the ordinary correlation function $F_4(q, q', q'', q_0)$. It is impossible to carry out such a calculation. In very rough fashion, however, it is possible to replace the calcuation of $\langle(\Delta N_{G'})^3\rangle$ by the calculation of $\langle(\Delta N_G)^3\rangle$ if the volumes G and G' are of equal dimensions (as above G is an arbitrary volume in the liquid and G' is the volume surrounding some particle). Then, according to (2.77), it is only necessary to know the function $F^3(q, q', q'')$, and this may be approximately evaluated with the aid of identity (3.40) as was done previously. Such an evaluation for mercury and argon carried out for volume G equal to the volume of the first coordination sphere showed that $\langle(\Delta N_G)^3\rangle$ was always negative and was of the order of ten units in magnitude. This should be interpreted as an indication of the asymmetry of the fluctuations of the coordination numbers: at a given $\langle z_1\rangle$, deviations in the direction of a decrease in z_1 are more probable than an increase. For such comparatively densely packed structures as argon and mercury, this result seems natural. In liquids with an open structure, for example in the case of water, one would expect the opposite result, and this is indeed the case [16].

6. INSTANTANEOUS AND AVERAGE ORDER IN SIMPLE LIQUIDS

Let us return to the problem of the nature of short-range order in simple liquids.

Let us consider first the case of an atomic crystal. Ignoring the long-range order, let us consider only the immediate neighborhood of some selected atom. We shall not take into consideration the comparatively rare disruption of order in the form of defects of structure. Then, in this case, all the thermal motion results in small vibrations of the atoms about the regularly distributed lattice points. And although the instantaneous positions of the atoms do not correspond with the lattice points, the average volumes of the vibrations through which the positions of the atoms are "smeared" during their thermal motion are symmetrically distributed near the corresponding lattice points, and their combination also shows a completely regular structure. It is, therefore, evident that it is necessary to distinguish two things: the true, instantaneous order of the distribution of the atoms of a crystal, and their average order. The latter is perfectly regular, possesses anisotropy and translational symmetry, and is responsible for the majority of the peculiarities of the physical properties of crystals. However, the instantaneous order of the distribution of the atoms of a crystal is not so regular: straight lines carried through the centers of the closest atoms and the angles between pairs of such lines deviate from the corresponding crystallographic directions and angles. For physical processes, the characteristic time of which is markedly less than the typical period of atomic vibrations, the instantaneous disorder is significant. A well-known example of such a process is the scattering of electrons in a crystal. The finite length of the mean-free path of an electron arises from the irregularity of the instantaneous crystalline field, caused by the thermal vibrations of the atoms.

Under ordinary conditions, however, the average amplitude of the thermal vibrations of atoms in a crystal constitutes a very small fraction of the lattice constant, and therefore the degree of irregularity of the instantaneous position of the atoms is also small. Thus, in the theory of physical processes in crystals, the effects caused by the instantaneous irregularities of structure may be considered to be small and weak perturbations. In other words, the "disorder parameter" which must be assigned to crystals due to their thermal motion is small.

It is natural to take the value ϵ as such a "disorder parameter"; it is equal to the relative average-square fluctuation of the interatomic distance or of the lattice constant

$$\epsilon = \frac{1}{a}\sqrt{\langle (\Delta a)^2 \rangle}. \qquad (3.53)$$

It is apparent that $\epsilon \to 0$ when $T \to 0$ and ϵ increases with increasing temperature. The value of ϵ may be evaluated from the well-known Lindeman rule which relates the characteristic frequency of the crystal with thermodynamic parameters at the melting point [17]. In this way, by considering the experimental data for a large number of metals with densely packed atoms, the value $\epsilon_{\text{melt}} = 0.11$ was obtained, if, for the value a in (3.53), we take the lattice constant. Thus, below the melting point ϵ is indeed small: $\epsilon \lesssim 0.1$.

Now let us proceed to the case of liquids. There then exist two characteristic times: τ_0, the average period of vibration of the atoms; and τ, the average lifetime of an atom in a temporary position of equilibrium (see Intro., sec. 2). Near the melting point $\tau_0 \ll \tau$, and there it is necessary to distinguish three situations: (1) the instantaneous structure of the immediate environment of some atom, which determines processes with a characteristic time $t \ll \tau$; (2) the average structure of the immediate environment of some atom, which is important for such times t that $\tau_0 \ll t \ll \tau$ and for processes with such characteristic times; (3) the average structure of the immediate environment of some atom, for time t noticeably larger than $\tau: t \gg \tau$ for slow or equilibrium processes.

For the time being, we shall assume that the inequality $\tau_0 \ll \tau$ is satisfied and will consider the peculiarities of each of the enumerated forms of order in simple liquids.

The extraordinarily high level of fluctuations of the coordination numbers in simple liquids, which was discussed in section 5, gives evidence of the absence of any noticeable order of the crystalline type in the instantaneous positions of the particles, even in small regions. It is evident that the possibility of even approximately separating an elementary cell of the crystalline type in a liquid is directly related to the stability not only of the first, but also of the second coordination number. But, as we saw above, this number fluctuates, on the average, by 40 per cent or more. If one still requires an approximate translational recurrence of the cell structure, even if only within the limits of two or three elementary cells, it would be necessary to turn to the coordination numbers z_3, z_4, etc., for which the fluctuations increase catastrophically so that these numbers are of no significance whatever. The "disorder parameter" ϵ in liquids is large even immediately adjacent to the melting point. Evaluation of the width of the first peak of the radial distribution function of the particles of a liquid $g(r)$ near the melting point gives $\epsilon \gtrsim 0.25$. The jump in ϵ from the value $\epsilon \backsim 0.1$ to that indicated corresponds to a jump in entropy during melting of the substance. The range of the irregular thermal vibrations of the atoms of a liquid is comparable to the interatomic distances, and therefore a high degree of disorder is inherent in the instantaneous arrangement of the particles.

However, the picture is different if we are concerned not with the instantaneous but with the average positions of particles during a time much larger than τ_0. If in the vicinity of some particle we examine a small number $n(\backsim 10/20)$ of neighboring particles, then for a time greater than τ_0, but appreciably less than τ/n, the approximate centers of vibration of this group of particles remain practically stationary. The centers of the volumes of fluctuation of individual atoms are then comparatively ordered. In any case, the signs of order must appear in a much higher degree here than in an examination of the instantaneous picture of the arrangement of the same group of particles. We recall that in the case of crystals such an averaging for many periods of atomic vibrations results in perfect order at any amplitude of vibration. It is entirely probable that the average order now under consideration, especially near the melting point, has a high "quasi-crystallinity" in small volumes with traces of anisotropy and recurrence of structure. If for the structure now under consideration, within the limits of a small volume near the atom, we introduce the relative correlation function $F_1(\boldsymbol{r}|0)$ (see eq. [3.27] and the text preceding it), it will have a definite angular dependence, but one much more diffuse and irregular than in the case of crystals. However, the lifetime of this comparatively ordered structure is not great—it is of the order of τ/n. It continually changes with the passage of time.

Finally if we consider the mutual arrangement of a small group of particles, averaged for a time greater than τ, the "quasi-crystallinity" of the structure is completely lost and only the radial density-dependent short-range order remains. It is precisely this that we see on the curves of experimentally determined radial distribution functions $g(r)$. The function $F_1(\boldsymbol{r}|0)$, which corresponds to the averaged structure, is simply equal to $g(|\boldsymbol{r}|)$.

Up to this point it has been assumed that $\tau_0 \ll \tau$. This will occur only at high densities, which assures a large activation energy W for the jumps of particles from one quasi-equilibrium position to another. Near the melting point the density of particles is large and W is also large. It should be kept in mind, however, that the liquid domain is large and extends to the critical point. For simple liquids the specific volume at the critical point exceeds by a factor of approximately two the specific volume at the triple point: $v_{cr} \approx 3\, v_{tr}$. If, therefore, we exclude the very narrow region of states close to the melting-crystallization line, then, with increase in the volume v, the value of W will rapidly decline and the difference between τ_0 and τ/n will not be very important. In such states, i.e., in practically the overwhelming majority of the possible states of a liquid, the distinction between the two structures mentioned will not be apparent. There will exist only a strongly disordered instantaneous structure and a comparatively weakly developed radial short-range order for the time $t \ll \tau_0$. On further approach to the critical point the mode of thermal motion of atoms in a liquid will draw ever closer to the mode of their thermal motion in a gas, and the degree of order will still further decrease.

7. THE RELATION OF THE STRUCTURE OF LIQUIDS TO THEIR PHYSICAL PROPERTIES

The problems in the theory of thermal motion and structure of liquids, which were discussed above and also in the Introduction, have still been little studied. Meanwhile, a theory regarding these problems, which is absolutely essential for a correct understanding and description of the physical properties and the mechanisms of physical processes in liquids, has been well developed. The situation is simplest in regard to the equilibrium properties of liquids. As we have seen, it is sufficient in order to describe them to know a small number of equilibrium correlation functions F_s with small numbers s, principally the radial distribution function $g(r; v, T)$. They also precisely describe the average structure of the liquid during a very long time $t \gg \tau$.

However, the kinetic properties of liquids will also strongly depend or even be determined by the average structure of the liquid. Although in this book we are not concerned with problems of the kinetic theory of liquids, nevertheless let us make a brief aside.

The statistical theory of viscosity, of thermal conductivity, and of diffusion in liquids has been very little developed at the present time. Although the mechanism of these processes is related to atomic motions that take place during a time of the order of τ [3], nevertheless, being very slow, they depend to a very great degree on the average structure of the liquid as described by the equilibrium correlation function. The future rigorous statistical theory of these processes must result in expressions for the kinetic coefficients that will depend essentially on the correlation functions F_s and possibly only on $g(r)$. Interesting preliminary data in this direction have been obtained experimentally by Golik [18] who showed the existence of a correlation between the structure of liquids as determined by X rays and their viscosity.

The fact that the kinetic properties of liquids should depend on or even be determined by their equilibrium structure is not unexpected. If we consider the external force that makes the system deviate from equilibrium as a small perturbation, then the solution of the problem of finding non-equilibrium correlation functions may, in principle, be obtained by some procedure of successive approximations. Then the first approximation, linear in relation to the external force, will be determined by the preceding zeroth approximation which corresponds to equilibrium.

The theory of the kinetic properties of electrons in liquids is of special interest in connection with problems of the structure of liquids. Due to the large difference in the masses of electrons and atoms and the resulting differences in average rates of motion, the so-called adiabatic approximation will hold true: according to this approximation the motion of electrons may be considered as occurring in the presence of motionless atoms. Therefore, the individual motions of separate electrons will be determined not by the average but by the instantaneous structure of the liquid, and, conversely, a study of the electrical properties of liquids might be a valuable source of information about their instantaneous structure.

The motion of electrons in a medium is determined not directly by the distribution of the atoms or ions, but the distribution of the interatomic electrical field. Therefore, one must differentiate the cases of metallic and non-metallic liquids.

The instantaneous atomic structure of liquid metals is just as strongly disordered as in the case of other simple liquids. However, the presence of a large number of free electrons results in a marked smoothing of the interatomic field. Free electrons will redistribute themselves due to the thermal movement of ions in such a way as to reduce as much as possible the gradient of the potential of the interatomic field. Therefore, the field acting on an individual electron will be comparatively only weakly irregular. This irregularity may be considered as a small perturbation and one may construct a theory of electrical conductivity in close analogy to the case of a solid metal [19]. The very fact of weak irregularity of the interatomic field results in the existence of a comparatively large mean-free path for an electron. Thus, for example, for mercury under ordinary conditions, the mean-free path is of the order of ten or somewhat more interatomic distances.

The situation is somewhat different in the case of liquid dielectrics and semiconductors. The interatomic field in this case is only slightly smoothed by the deformation of the electron shells of atoms, and basically it remains in the same degree of irregularity as the atomic distribution itself. In this case the amplitude of the fluctuations of the field is large. Under these conditions, the mechanism of the motion of electrons in a liquid must differ essentially from the mechanism of their motion in a solid body.

It is well known that even in solid semiconductors near the melting point the experimentally determined mean-free path of an electron or an electron hole remains, as a rule, comparable or even less than their De Broglie wavelength. In many cases it even appears comparable with the lattice constant [20]. It is clear that under these conditions the very concept of mean-free path and quasi-plane waves, on the basis of which the usual theory of the electrical conductivity of crystals is constructed, loses its force. This is even more true of liquids with their strongly disordered instantaneous structure. The true wave functions of electrons in a liquid must characterize a very complex and irregular diffraction picture, which in no degree can be represented by individual plane waves. The concept of mean-free path in this case is of no significance. The mechanism of the motion of electrons in a liquid must in large measure be closer to the random wandering of Brownian particles than to the mechanism of motion of electrons in a crystal.

These interesting and important problems have been little studied. An excellent survey of the present state of theory and experiment in this field is given in paper [21].

REFERENCES

[1] W. M. Morrell and J. Hildebrand, *J. Chem. Phys.*, **8** (1936), 225.

[2] F. Zernicke and I. Prins, *Z. Phys.*, **41** (1927), 184.

[3] Ya. I. Frenkel, *Kineticheskaya teoriya zhidkostei*, Izd. AN SSSR, (Kinetic Theory of Liquids), Acad. Sci. USSR, 1945.

[4] N. Gingrich, *Uspekhi Khim.*, **15** (1946), 297.

[5] O. Ya. Samoilov, *Zh. Fiz. Khim.*, **20** (1946), 1411.

[6] I. V. Radchenko, *Uspekhi Fiz. Nauk*, **61** (1957), 249.

[7] I. Prins and H. Petersen, *Physica*, **3** (1936), 147.

[8] A. E. Glauberman, *Zh. Eksperim. i. Teor. Fiz.*, **22** (1952), 249.

[9] A. E. Glauberman and V. P. Tsvetkov, *Doklady Akad. Nauk. SSSR* **106** (1956), 623.

[10] I. Z. Fisher and V. K. Prokhorenko, *Zh. Fiz. Khim.*, **31** (1957), 2145.

[11] V. K. Prokhorenko and I. Z. Fisher, *Zh. Fiz. Khim.*, **33** (1959), 1852.

[12] A. Eisenstein and N. Gingrich, *Phys. Rev.*, **62** (1942), 261.

[13] D. Henshaw, D. Hurst, and N. Pope, *Phys. Rev.*, **92** (1953), 1229.

[14] S. Campbell and J. Hildebrand, *J. Chem. Phys.*, **11** (1943), 334.

[15] H. Gendus, *Z. f. Naturforsch., pt. A*, **2** (1947), 505.

[16] V. K. Prokhorenko, O. Ya. Samoilov, and I. Z. Fisher, *Doklady Akad. Nauk SSSR*, **125** (1959), 396.

[17] I. Gilvarry, *Phys. Rev.*, **103** (1956), 1700.

[18] A. Z. Golik, *Ukr. Khim. Zh.*, **14** (1949), 2; *Doklady Akad. Nauk SSSR*, **114** (1947), 361.

[19] S. P. Shubin, *Zh. Eksperim. i. Teor. Fiz.*, **3** (1933), 461.

[20] A. F. Ioffe, *Fizika poluprovodnikov*, AN SSSR (Physics of Semiconductors), Acad. Sci. USSR, 1957.

[21] A. R. Regel, *Stat'ya v sbornike "Struktura i svoistva zhidkikh metallov,"* Izd. In-ta metallurgii im. A. A. Baikova AN SSSR (Articles in the collection "Structure and Properties of Liquid Metals"), Press of the A. A. Baikov Inst. of Metallurgy, Acad. Sci. USSR, 1959.

CHAPTER 4

EQUATIONS FOR CORRELATION FUNCTIONS

1. DERIVATION OF THE BASIC EQUATIONS

In the preceding chapters we have become convinced of the importance of knowing the correlation functions for the construction of a theory of the structure and physical properties of liquids. In the present chapter we will deduce and study the integro-differential equations which in principle permit us to determine the correlation functions of a system of particles in accordance with the given intermolecular forces and thermodynamic conditions. In this case we go somewhat beyond the special theory of liquids and consider the applicability of the same methods to other interesting and important problems of statistical physics.

Let us again consider the system which we have already studied in chapter 2 and write the expressions for the configurational part of the Gibbs distribution function and for the correlation functions:

$$D_N(\boldsymbol{q}_1, \ldots, \boldsymbol{q}_N) = Q_N^{-1} \exp\left[-\frac{U_N(\boldsymbol{q}_1, \ldots, \boldsymbol{q}_N)}{kT}\right], \quad (4.1)$$

$$U_N(\boldsymbol{q}_1, \ldots, \boldsymbol{q}_N) = \sum_{1 \leq i < j \leq N} \Phi(|\boldsymbol{q}_i - \boldsymbol{q}_j|), \quad (4.2)$$

$$F_s(\boldsymbol{q}_1, \ldots, \boldsymbol{q}_s) = V^s \int_V \ldots \int_V D_N(\boldsymbol{q}_1, \ldots, \boldsymbol{q}_N)\, d\boldsymbol{q}_{s+1} \ldots d\boldsymbol{q}_N . \quad (4.3)$$

Differentiating the latter equation with respect to the coordinates of one of the selected s particles, the first for example, and making use of the explicit form of the function D_N according to (4.1), we obtain

$$\nabla_1 F_s(q_1, \ldots, q_s) = -\frac{V^s}{kT}\int_V \cdots \int_V \times \nabla_1 U_N(q_1, \ldots, q_N) D_N(q_1, \ldots, q_N)\, dq_{s+1} \ldots dq_N , \tag{4.4}$$

where ∇_1 is the gradient along q_1. But, from (4.2), we have

$$\begin{aligned} \nabla_1 U_N(q_1, \ldots, q_N) &= \sum_{2\le i\le N} \nabla_1 \Phi(|q_1 - q_i|) \\ &= \nabla_1 U_s(q_1, \ldots, q_s) + \sum_{s+1\le i\le N} \nabla_1 \Phi(|q_1 - q_i|), \end{aligned} \tag{4.5}$$

where

$$U_s(q_1, \ldots, q_s) = \sum_{1\le i<j\le s} \Phi(|q_i - q_j|) \tag{4.6}$$

is the energy of interaction of the selected group of s particles. Placing equation (4.5) in the right half of equation (4.4) and taking (4.3) into consideration results in the expression

$$\begin{aligned} V^s \int_V \cdots \int_V \nabla_1 U_N(q_1, \ldots, q_N) D_N(q_1, \ldots, q_N)\, dq_{s+1} \ldots dq_N \\ = F_s \nabla_1 U_s + (N - s) V^s \int_V \nabla_1 \Phi(|q_1 - q_{s+1}|)\, dq_{s+1} \\ \times \int_V \cdots \int_V D_N(q_1, \ldots, q_N)\, dq_{s+2} \ldots dq_N = F_s \nabla_1 U_s \\ + \frac{N - s}{V} \int_V \nabla_1 \Phi(|q_1 - q_{s+1}|) F_{s+1}(q_1, \ldots, q_{s+1})\, dq_{s+1} . \end{aligned} \tag{4.7}$$

If, therefore, we introduce the average volume per particle $v = V/N$, then equation (4.4) may be rewritten in the form

$$\begin{aligned} kT \nabla_1 F_s(q_1, \ldots, q_s) + F_s(q_1, \ldots, q_s) \nabla_1 U_s(q_1, \ldots, q_s) \\ + \frac{1 - \left(\frac{s}{N}\right)}{v} \int_V \nabla_1 \Phi(|q_1 - q_{s+1}|) \\ \times F_{s+1}(q_1, \ldots, q_{s+1})\, dq_{s+1} = 0 . \end{aligned} \tag{4.8}$$

When $s = 1, 2, 3, \ldots, N$ we thus obtain a system of N linear integro-differential equations for the correlation functions [1].

If we are interested only in the extensive properties of the system, it is expedient to go over to asymptotic expressions for the correlation functions and for the equations for these functions by taking the limit $N \to \infty$ and $V \to \infty$, when v is constant and removing all boundaries of region V to infinity. We note that such a limiting process is even necessary in equations (4.8), since the Gibbs distribution itself (4.1), as is well known from statistical physics, is true only asymptotically, when $N \to \infty$ and $V \to \infty$. Therefore, the equations in (4.8) are also true with precision only up to the small terms which disappear when $N \to \infty$ and $V \to \infty$. Therefore, placing $N \to \infty$ and $V \to \infty$ in (4.8), we obtain

$$kT\nabla_1 F_s + F_s \nabla_1 U_s + \frac{1}{v}\int \nabla_1 \Phi_{1,\, s+1} F_{s+1}\, d\boldsymbol{q}_{s+1} = 0\,, \qquad s = 1, 2, 3, \ldots . \tag{4.9}$$

For brevity we have dropped the arguments of all functions and have designated $\Phi(|q_1 - q_{s+1}|) = \Phi_{1,\, s+1}$.

In this way we obtain an infinite chain of linear integro-differential equations (4.9) for the determination of the asymptotic correlation functions F_s. We shall call them the Bogolyubov equations [1].

We obtain the simplest generalization of the basic equations (4.8) or (4.9) by considering the same system in a constant external field. If $\varphi(q)$ is the potential energy of a particle at point $\boldsymbol{q}$ in an external field, then, instead of (4.2), we will have

$$U_N(\boldsymbol{q}_1, \ldots, \boldsymbol{q}_N) = \sum_{1 \le i < j \le N} \Phi(|\boldsymbol{q}_i - \boldsymbol{q}_j|) + \sum_{1 \le i \le N} \varphi(\boldsymbol{q}_i). \tag{4.10}$$

It is easy to see that in this case equations (4.8) and (4.9) change only in the sense that it is necessary to include the energy of the external field in the potential energy of the group

$$U_s(\boldsymbol{q}_1, \ldots, \boldsymbol{q}_s) \to U_s(\boldsymbol{q}_1, \ldots, \boldsymbol{q}_s) + \varphi_s(\boldsymbol{q}_1, \ldots, \boldsymbol{q}_s), \tag{4.11}$$

where

$$\varphi_s(\boldsymbol{q}_1, \ldots, \boldsymbol{q}_s) = \sum_{1 \le i \le s} \varphi(\boldsymbol{q}_i). \tag{4.12}$$

Thus, equation (4.9) may now be rewritten in the form

$$kT\nabla_1 F_s + F_s \nabla_1 (U_s + \varphi_s) + \frac{1}{v}\int \nabla_1 \Phi_{1,\, s+1} F_{s+1}\, d\boldsymbol{q}_{s+1} = 0\,, \tag{4.13}$$

$s = 1, 2, 3, \ldots$, and analogously in the case of equations (4.8).

Equations (4.9) or (4.13) must be solved consistent with the supplementary conditions that F_s be symmetric in all the arguments $q_1, \ldots,$

q_s, and that the correlations vanish as the particles become distant from one another:

$$F_s(q_1, \ldots, q_s) \rightarrow \prod_{1 \leq i \leq s} F_1(q_i), \tag{4.14}$$

when all $|q_i - q_j| \rightarrow \infty$, $i, j = 1, 2, \ldots, s$. The normalization conditions become, after the transition to the limit $N \rightarrow \infty$ and $V \rightarrow \infty$,

$$\lim_{V\rightarrow\infty} \frac{1}{V} \int_V F_1(q)\, dq = 1, \tag{4.15}$$

$$\lim_{V\rightarrow\infty} \frac{1}{V} \int_V F_s(q_1, \ldots, q_s)\, dq_s = F_{s-1}(q_1, \ldots, q_{s-1}). \tag{4.16}$$

It is easy to see that, in the absence of an external force, the equations in (4.9) yield the solutions which describe a uniform and isotropic system. As a matter of fact, when $s = 1$, we have the equation

$$kT\nabla F_1(q) + \frac{1}{v}\int \nabla\Phi(|q - q'|)F_2(q, q')\, dq' = 0, \tag{4.17}$$

and on placing in it the function

$$F_1(q) = 1, \qquad F_2(q, q') = g(|q - q'|) \tag{4.18}$$

we recover an identity, inasmuch as the integral

$$\int \nabla\Phi(|q - q'|)\, g(|q - q'|)\, dq' = 0 \tag{4.19}$$

from considerations of symmetry.

Equation (4.17) may be interpreted as a condition on the absence of a current of particles in the system. It is well known, as a matter of fact, that the flux of particles J is related to the density of particles $n(q)$ and to the force acting on the particles $K(q)$ by the relation

$$J = -D\nabla n(q) + bn(q)K(q), \tag{4.20}$$

where D is the coefficient of diffusion and b is the mobility. The latter quantities are related to the well-known Einstein relationship

$$D = bkT. \tag{4.21}$$

In turn the particle density is related to the correlation function $F_1(q)$ by the relationship

$$n(q) = \frac{N}{V}F_1(q) = \frac{1}{v}F_1(q). \tag{4.22}$$

Therefore, the condition for the absence of a current of particles in the system, $J = 0$, may be written in the form

$$kT\nabla F_1(q) - F_1(q)K(q) = 0. \tag{4.23}$$

The full force acting on a particle at point q consists of the force of the external field, $\nabla\varphi(q)$, and of the average force arising from the remaining particles. Using the conditional probabilities and the conditional correlation functions, we obtain for the latter force

$$\begin{aligned} -(N-1)\int_V \nabla_q\Phi(|q-q'|)\,dW_q(q') \\ = -\frac{N-1}{V}\int_V \nabla\Phi(|q-q'|)F_1(q'|q)\,dq', \end{aligned} \tag{4.24}$$

so that

$$\begin{aligned} K(q) = -\nabla\varphi(q) \\ -\frac{N-1}{V}\int_V \nabla_q\Phi(|q-q'|)F_1'(q'|q)\,dq'. \end{aligned} \tag{4.25}$$

Therefore, equation (4.23) may be written in the form

$$\begin{aligned} kT\nabla_q F_1(q) + F_1(q)\nabla_q\varphi(q) \\ +\frac{N-1}{V}\int_V \nabla_q\Phi(|q-q'|)F_1(q)F_1(q'|q)\,dq' = 0. \end{aligned} \tag{4.26}$$

But $F_1(q)F_1(q'|q) = F_2(q, q')$, so that, after passing to the limit $N\to\infty$ and $V\to\infty$, we actually obtain the first equation (2.13). An analogous interpretation is also possible for all the remaining equations (4.13).

2. SOLUTION OF THE EQUATIONS FOR CORRELATION FUNCTIONS IN THE CASE OF A GAS

The equations for correlation functions (4.9) or (4.13) are very complex, and practical solution is only possible if we can find a suitable small expansion parameter. Below we shall consider some methods of solving the fundamental equations for different systems. First of all, we shall consider the case of a gaseous system where the density plays the role of the small parameter [1].

Let a be a characteristic molecular length—for example, the effective diameter of a particle. In the equations (4.9) or (4.13), let us substitute, for all q_i, $q = aq'$. Then the equations in (4.9) will be written

$$kT\nabla_1 F_s + F_s\nabla_1 U_s + \frac{a^3}{v}\int \nabla_1\Phi_{1,\,s+1}F_{s+1}\,dq'_{s+1} = 0, \tag{4.27}$$

where all functions here are assumed to be expressed in terms of reduced coordinates. The equations in (4.13) follow analogously. In the gaseous case $a^3/v \ll 1$, and it is possible to construct a solution to equations (4.27) in the form of density series, the parameter being a^3/v.

We should note that it is formally possible to operate directly with the equations in (4.9) or (4.13) instead of the equations in (4.27), considering $1/v$ directly as the small parameter. Below we shall consider only the case where external forces are absent. For later use it is convenient to complete the substitution of the unknown functions $F_s \rightarrow \Psi_s$ according to the relationships

$$F_s(q_1, \ldots, q_s) = \Psi_s(q_1, \ldots, q_s) \exp\left[\frac{-U_s(q_1, \ldots, q_s)}{kT}\right], \quad (4.28)$$

so that

$$U_{s+1}(q_1, \ldots, q_{s+1}) = U_s(q_1, \ldots, q_s) + \sum_{1 \leq i \leq s} \Phi(|q_i - q_{s+1}|); \quad (4.29)$$

and using the identity

$$\begin{aligned} &\nabla_1 \Phi_{1, s+1} \exp\left(-\frac{1}{kT} \sum_{1 \leq i \leq s} \Phi_{i, s+1}\right) \\ &\qquad = -kT \nabla_1 \left[\exp\left(-\frac{1}{kT} \sum_{1 \leq i \leq s} \Phi_{i, s+1}\right) - 1\right], \end{aligned} \quad (4.30)$$

we obtain the following equation for Ψ_s,

$$\nabla_1 \Psi_s = \frac{1}{v} \int \nabla_1 \left[\exp\left(-\frac{1}{kT} \sum_{1 \leq i \leq s} \Phi_{i, s+1}\right) - 1\right] \Psi_{s+1} dq_{s+1}. \quad (4.31)$$

It is also convenient to introduce the functions which we have already encountered,

$$f(|q|) = \exp\left[-\frac{\Phi(|q|)}{kT}\right] - 1, \quad (4.32)$$

so that the equations for Ψ_s (4.31) are reduced to the form

$$\begin{aligned} &\nabla_1 \Psi_s \\ &\quad = \frac{1}{v} \int \nabla_1 \left\{ \prod_{1 \leq i \leq s} [1 + f(|q_i - q_{s+1}|)] - 1 \right\} \Psi_{s+1} dq_{s+1}. \end{aligned} \quad (4.33)$$

In the uniform case with which we are concerned, $F_1(q) = \Psi_1(q) = 1$, as we have already noted; therefore, we can use the equations in (4.33) only when $s \geq 2$. In this case, it follows from the asymptotic conditions on F_s that

$$\Psi_s(q_1, \ldots, q_s) \rightarrow 1, \quad (4.34)$$

when all $|q_i - q_j| \to \infty$, $i, j = 1, 2, \ldots, s$, since then $U_s \to 0$. In addition, of course, the functions $\Psi_s(q_1, \ldots, q_s)$ must be symmetrical in all arguments.

Now let us assume that

$$\Psi_s = \Psi_s^{(0)} + \frac{1}{v}\Psi_s^{(1)} + \frac{1}{v^2}\Psi_s^{(2)} + \ldots \quad . \tag{4.35}$$

Let us place this in the equations of (4.33) and separate the terms with identical powers of $1/v$. In the zeroth approximation, we obtain the equation

$$\nabla_1 \Psi_s^{(0)} = 0 \ , \tag{4.36}$$

and from the conditions in (4.34), it follows that

$$\Psi_s^{(0)}(q_1, \ldots, q_s) = 1 \ , \tag{4.37}$$

for all values of s.

For all the subsequent approximations from (4.33) we obtain the equation

$$\nabla_1 \Psi_s^{(m)} = \int \nabla_1 \Big\{ \prod_{1 \leq i \leq s} [1 + f(|q_i - q_{s+1}|)] - 1 \Big\} \Psi_{s+1}^{(m-1)} dq_{s+1} , \tag{4.38}$$

and, in this case, it follows from (4.34) and (4.37) that

$$\Psi_s^{(m)}(q_1, \ldots, q_s) \to 0 \ , \tag{4.39}$$

when all $|q_i - q_j| \to \infty$, $i, j = 1, 2, \ldots, s$, for all values of $m \geq 1$.

In the first approximation, from (4.37) and (4.38), an equation follows which may be integrated at once, and we obtain

$$\Psi_s^{(1)} = \int \Big\{ \prod_{1 \leq i \leq s} [1 + f(|q_i - q_{s+1}|)] - 1 \Big\} dq_{s+1} + C_s^{(1)} . \tag{4.40}$$

The integration constants $C_s^{(1)}$ are determined from condition (4.39). Since the functions $f(|q|)$ rapidly decrease with increase in $|q|$, in the low density limit, we obtain

$$\Psi_s^{(1)} \to \sum_{1 \leq i \leq s} \int f(|q_i - q_{s+1}|) dq_{s+1} + C_s^{(1)} = s\beta_1 + C_s^{(1)} , \tag{4.41}$$

where we have introduced the first "irreducible integral" from the theory of gases (see chap 1, sec. 4)

$$\beta_1 = \int f(|q|) dq . \tag{4.42}$$

Thus, from (4.39) and (4.42), we obtain $C_s^{(1)} = -s\beta_1$, so that finally we have, for the first approximation,

$$\Psi_s^{(1)}(\mathbf{q}_1, \ldots, \mathbf{q}_s) = -s\beta_1 + \int \left\{ \prod_{1 \leq i \leq s} [1 + f(|\mathbf{q}_i - \mathbf{q}_{s+1}|)] - 1 \right\} d\mathbf{q}_{s+1}. \tag{4.43}$$

In the second approximation from (4.38), taking (4.43) into consideration, we have the original equations

$$\begin{aligned} \nabla_1 \Psi_s^{(2)} = &-(s+1)\beta_1 \nabla_1 \Psi_s^{(1)} \\ &+ \iint \nabla_1 \left\{ \prod_{1 \leq i \leq s} [1 + f(|\mathbf{q}_i - \mathbf{q}_{s+1}|)] - 1 \right\} \\ &\times \left\{ \prod_{1 \leq j \leq s} [1 + f(|\mathbf{q}_j - \mathbf{q}_{s+2}|)] - 1 \right\} d\mathbf{q}_{s+1} d\mathbf{q}_{s+2}. \end{aligned} \tag{4.44}$$

But it is possible to write

$$\begin{aligned} \prod_{1 \leq j \leq s} [1 + f(|\mathbf{q}_j - \mathbf{q}_{s+2}|)] - 1 = &f(|\mathbf{q}_{s+1} - \mathbf{q}_{s+2}|) \\ &+ [1 + f(|\mathbf{q}_{s+1} - \mathbf{q}_{s+2}|)] \\ &\times \left\{ \prod_{1 \leq j \leq s} [1 + f(|\mathbf{q}_j - \mathbf{q}_{s+2}|)] - 1 \right\}, \end{aligned} \tag{4.45}$$

so that our equations are reduced to the form

$$\begin{aligned} \nabla_1 \Psi_s^{(2)}(\mathbf{q}_1, \ldots, \mathbf{q}_s) = &-s\beta_1 \nabla_1 \Psi_s^{(1)}(\mathbf{q}_1, \ldots, \mathbf{q}_s) \\ &+ \iint \nabla_1 \left\{ \prod_{1 \leq i \leq s} [1 + f(|\mathbf{q}_i - \mathbf{q}_{s+1}|)] - 1 \right\} \\ &\times [1 + f(|\mathbf{q}_{s+1} - \mathbf{q}_{s+2}|)] \\ &\times \left\{ \prod_{1 \leq j \leq s} [1 + f(|\mathbf{q}_j - \mathbf{q}_{s+2}|)] - 1 \right\} d\mathbf{q}_{s+1} d\mathbf{q}_{s+2}. \end{aligned} \tag{4.46}$$

Symmetrizing the integrand with respect to $\mathbf{q}_{s+1}$ and $\mathbf{q}_{s+2}$, we easily reduce it to the gradient along $\mathbf{q}_1$ of a function, so that the equation may be immediately integrated, and we obtain

$$\begin{aligned} \Psi_s^{(2)} = &-s\beta_1 \Psi_s^{(1)} + \tfrac{1}{2} \iint [1 + f(|\mathbf{q}_{s+1} - \mathbf{q}_{s+2}|)] \\ &\times \left\{ \prod_{1 \leq i \leq s} [1 + f(|\mathbf{q}_i - \mathbf{q}_{s+1}|)] - 1 \right\} \\ &\times \left\{ \prod_{1 \leq j \leq s} [1 + f(|\mathbf{q}_j - \mathbf{q}_{s+2}|)] - 1 \right\} \\ &\times d\mathbf{q}_{s+1} d\mathbf{q}_{s+2} + C_s^{(2)}, \end{aligned} \tag{4.47}$$

where $C_s^{(2)}$ are new integration constants. When all the $q_1, \ldots, q_s$ separate from one another, then, due to the rapid decrease in the functions $f(|q|)$ from (4.47), we obtain

$$\Psi_s^{(2)} \to \tfrac{1}{2} s^2\beta_1^2 + s\beta_2 + C_s^{(2)}, \tag{4.48}$$

where we introduced the second "irreducible integral" from the theory of gases

$$\beta_2 = \tfrac{1}{2}\iint f(|q|)f(|q'|)f(|q-q'|)\,dq\,dq'. \tag{4.49}$$

Comparing (4.48) with (4.39), we obtain $C_s^{(2)} = -\frac{1}{2}s^2\beta_1^2 - s\beta_2$, so that, finally, in the second approximation we obtain

$$\begin{aligned}\Psi_s^{(2)}(q_1,\ldots,q_s) = &-s\beta_2 - \tfrac{1}{2}s^2\beta_1^2 - s\beta_1\Psi_s^{(1)}(q_1,\ldots,q_s)\\ &+\tfrac{1}{2}\iint\Big\{\prod_{1\le i\le s}[1+f(|q_i-q_{s+1}|)]-1\Big\}\\ &\times\Big\{\prod_{1\le j\le s}[1+f(|q_j-q_{s+2}|)]-1\Big\}\\ &\times[1+f(|q_{s+1}-q_{s+2}|)]\,dq_{s+1}dq_{s+2}.\end{aligned} \tag{4.50}$$

All the subsequent approximations for Ψ_s may be constructed analogously. In the course of this we will obtain, in each subsequent approximation, ever more cumbersome expressions.

Let us write the final result in the approximation found for the radial distribution function. Collect together (4.28), (4.35), (4.37), (4.43), and (4.50) when $s = 2$, and, after simple transformations and having set $F_2(q, q') = g(|q - q'|)$, we obtain

$$\begin{aligned}g(|q|) = \exp\left[-\frac{\Phi(|q|)}{kT}\right]\Big\{1 &+ \frac{1}{v}\int f(|q-q'|)\\ &\times f(|q'|)\,dq' + \frac{1}{2v^2}\left[\int f(|q-q'|)f(|q'|)\,dq'\right]^2\\ &+\frac{1}{v^2}\iint[f(|q-q'|)f(|q'-q''|)f(|q''|)\\ &+f(|q-q'|)f(|q-q''|)f(|q'-q''|)f(|q''|)\\ &+f(|q-q'|)f(|q'|)f(|q''|)f(|q'-q''|)\\ &+f(|q-q'|)f(|q-q''|)f(|q'|)f(|q''|)\\ &\times f(|q'-q''|)]\,dq'dq'' + O\left(\frac{1}{v^3}\right)\Big\}.\end{aligned} \tag{4.51}$$

We have obtained a "virial series" for the radial distribution function. From this, in accordance with general theory, it is not difficult to obtain the corresponding "virial series" for all the thermodynamic functions of a gas. Thus, it is not difficult to show that we obtain for the pressure

$$p=\frac{kT}{v}\left(1-\frac{\beta_1}{2v}-\frac{2\beta_2}{3v^2}-\frac{3\beta_3}{4v^3}-\ldots\right), \qquad (4.52)$$

which coincides with equation (1.60) of the theory of gases.

The method just described, which is that of Bogolyubov [1], may be considered to be a rigorous foundation of the methods and results of the theory of real gases mentioned in chapter 1, section 4.

3. MOLECULAR SYSTEM AT AN IDEAL WALL

The fundamental equations for the correlation functions, (4.9) or (4.13), correspond to an infinite system. A system whose boundaries are at a finite distance may be of special interest for the theory of surface effects. Such a system, of course, would not be uniform. In this section we shall take as an example a molecular system bounded by a wall of infinitely high potential. We shall see below that this problem is of interest for the theory of surface phenomena at the boundary between the liquid and its vapor [2].

Now then, let us consider a system in a half-space bounded by a plane, which we shall assume as the plane $z = 0$ of the Cartesian system of coordinates. The correlation functions F_s are determined only in the half-space $z \geq 0$. We may obtain the equations for the correlation functions by two methods. It is either necessary to return to equations (4.8) (before the limit $N \to \infty$, $V \to \infty$ is taken) and then to go over to the limit $N \to \infty$ and $V \to \infty$ so that one wall remains immobile and within the system the half-space is filled, or it is possible to place the following in equations (4.12) to (4.13):

$$\varphi(\boldsymbol{q}) = \varphi(x, y, z) = \begin{cases} +\infty & \text{when} \quad z < 0\,, \\ 0 & \text{when} \quad z > 0\,. \end{cases} \qquad (4.53)$$

In both cases we obtain

$$kT\nabla_1 F_s + F_s \nabla_1 U_s + \frac{1}{v}\int_{z_{s+1}>0} \nabla_1 \Phi_{1,\,s+1} F_{s+1} d\boldsymbol{q}_{s+1} = 0\,, \qquad (4.54)$$

$s = 1, 2, \ldots,$ where the integration is over the positive (in z) half-space. In this case, in F_s all $z_i \geq 0$ and $F_s \equiv 0$ when $z_i < 0$.

The functions F_s as before must be symmetrical and must satisfy the normalization and asymptotic factorization conditions. The latter may now be written in the form

$$\lim_{V\to\infty} \frac{1}{V} \int_{V\cdot z>0} F_1(q)\,dq = 1\,, \tag{4.55}$$

$$\lim_{V\to\infty} \frac{1}{V} \int_{V\cdot z_s>0} F_s(q_1,\ldots, q_s)\,dq_s = F_{s-1}(q_1,\ldots, q_{s-1}) \tag{4.56}$$

for $s \geq 2$.

Now the system is not uniform and equations (4.54) do not permit solution in the form (4.18). But if the constant vector $\boldsymbol{a}$ is parallel to the plane $z = 0$, then the translation

$$\boldsymbol{q}_i \to \boldsymbol{q}_i + \boldsymbol{a}\,, \qquad i = 1, 2, \ldots, s+1\,, \tag{4.57}$$

leaves equations (4.54) invariant. Therefore, $F_1(q)$ actually depends only on the z projection of the vector q, $F_2(q, q')$ depends only on $|q - q'|$, and the z projections of q and q', etc.

Conversely, if in (4.57) the constant vector $\boldsymbol{a}$ is normal to the plane $z = 0$ and $(\boldsymbol{a})_z > 0$, then, after the transformation of (4.57), the equations in (4.54) assume the form

$$kT\nabla_1 F_s + F_s \nabla_1 U_s + \frac{1}{v} \int_{z_{s+1}>-a} \nabla_1 \Phi_{1,\,s+1} F_{s+1}\, d\boldsymbol{q}_{s+1} = 0\,, \tag{4.58}$$

and when $a \to \infty$ these equations go over to equations (4.9) of the uniform system. Thus, $F_1(q) = F_1(z)$ and

$$F_1(z) \to 1 \qquad \text{when} \qquad z \to \infty\,. \tag{4.59}$$

Also,

$$F_2(q, q') \to g(|q - q'|) \quad \text{when} \quad z \to \infty \quad \text{and} \quad z' \to \infty; \tag{4.60}$$

the same is true of all the remaining F_s.

At the start, let us consider the case of a gas. We shall try to find a solution for the equations in (4.54) in the form of a power series in the density. We will again make use of (4.28), where $U_1(q) \equiv 0$. Then, analogous to equations (4.33), we obtain for Ψ_s the equations

$$\nabla_1 \Psi_s = \frac{1}{v} \int_{z_{s+1}>0} \nabla_1 \left\{ \prod_{1\leq i\leq s} [1 + f(|\boldsymbol{q}_i - \boldsymbol{q}_{s+1}|)] - 1 \right\} \times \Psi_{s+1}\, d\boldsymbol{q}_{s+1}\,, \qquad s = 1, 2, \ldots\,. \tag{4.61}$$

Again, assuming that

$$\Psi_s = \Psi_s^{(0)} + \frac{1}{v}\Psi_s^{(1)} + \ldots\,, \tag{4.62}$$

and, placing this in (4.61), we obtain equations for the successive determination of $\Psi_s^{(0)}$, $\Psi_s^{(1)}$, etc. It is easy to see that in the zeroth approximation, taking into consideration the conditions of normalization, we obtain

$$\Psi_s^{(0)}(\boldsymbol{q}_1, \ldots, \boldsymbol{q}_s) = 1 \,, \qquad s = 1, 2, \ldots, \tag{4.63}$$

and for all the subsequent approximations we obtain the equations

$$\nabla_1 \Psi_s^{(m)} = \int_{z_{s+1}>0} \nabla_1 \left\{ \prod_{1 \le i \le s} [1 + f(|\boldsymbol{q}_i - \boldsymbol{q}_{s+1}|)] - 1 \right\} \times \Psi_{s+1}^{(m-1)} d\boldsymbol{q}_{s+1} \,. \tag{4.64}$$

Solving the equations of the first approximation using (4.63), we obtain

$$\Psi_s^{(1)} = \int_{z_{s+1}>0} \left\{ \prod_{1 \le i \le s} [1 + f(|\boldsymbol{q}_i - \boldsymbol{q}_{s+1}|)] - 1 \right\} \times d\boldsymbol{q}_{s+1} + C_s^{(1)} \,, \tag{4.65}$$

where $C_s^{(1)}$ are the integration constants. Now, without changing the distances between particles we will let all $z_1, z_2, \ldots, z_s$ tend toward infinity. Then our $\Psi_s^{(1)}$ should go over to the $\Psi_s^{(1)}$ of the uniform problem (4.43), and we find that $C_s^{(1)} = s\beta_1$. So that finally

$$\Psi_s^{(1)} = \int_{z_{s+1}>0} \left\{ \prod_{1 \le i \le s} [1 + f(|\boldsymbol{q}_i - \boldsymbol{q}_{s+1}|)] - 1 \right\} \times d\boldsymbol{q}_{s+1} - s\beta_1 \,. \tag{4.66}$$

In an analogous manner we can also obtain higher approximations. Even in (4.66) it can be seen that $\Psi_1^{(1)} \neq 0$ and $\Psi_s^{(2)}$ do not only depend on $|\boldsymbol{q} - \boldsymbol{q}'|$. In this approximation the non-uniformity and non-isotropy of the system extend a distance from the wall, which is equal to the range of the intermolecular forces. In higher approximations one would expect some broadening of the boundary layer. For example, this is evident from the following approximation for $F_1(\boldsymbol{q})$ which, together with the two preceding approximations, gives

$$F_1(z) = 1 + \frac{1}{v}\left[\int_{z'>0} f(|\boldsymbol{q} - \boldsymbol{q}'|)\, d\boldsymbol{q}' - \beta_1\right] + \frac{1}{2v^2}\left[\iint_{z', z''>0} f(|\boldsymbol{q} - \boldsymbol{q}'|) f(|\boldsymbol{q} - \boldsymbol{q}''|) \times f(|\boldsymbol{q}' - \boldsymbol{q}''|)\, d\boldsymbol{q}' d\boldsymbol{q}'' - 2\beta_2\right] + \ldots \,, \tag{4.67}$$

where the vector $\boldsymbol{q}$ has the components $\boldsymbol{q} = \{0, 0, z\}$.

An interesting result is obtained if we place $z = 0$ in (4.67). It is not difficult to be convinced that

$$\int_{z'>0} f(|q'|)\,dq' = \tfrac{1}{2}\beta_1, \tag{4.68}$$

$$\iint_{z',z''>0} f(|q'|)f(|q''|)f(|q'-q''|)\,dq'dq'' = \tfrac{2}{3}\beta_2, \tag{4.69}$$

etc., so that from (4.67) it follows that

$$F_1(0) = 1 - \frac{\beta_1}{2v} - \frac{2\beta_2}{3v^2} - \dots . \tag{4.70}$$

But this series is identical with series (4.52), so that we obtain

$$F_1(0) = \frac{pv}{kT}. \tag{4.71}$$

Directly adjacent to the wall, the value of the function $F_1(z)$ is determined simply by the thermodynamic conditions. Above the Boyle point $F_1(0) > 1$; below this point $F_1(0) < 1$.

Equation (4.71) has a universal character and is true not only for gases but also for liquids. This follows from expression (2.56) for the stress tensor. The integral term in expression (2.56) corresponds to the forces acting through area dS on the portion of the liquid under consideration from particles located behind this area. If we select the area dS to be in the plane $z = 0$, then, in our problem of the ideal wall, this integral should be omitted since no forces act through such an area. In addition, for calculating the pressure on such an area it is necessary to assume that $p = -\Pi_{zz}(0)$, so that we again return to equation (4.71).

4. EQUATIONS FOR THE CORRELATION FUNCTIONS OF A SYSTEM OF ELECTRICALLY CHARGED PARTICLES

Now let us consider a system of equally charged point particles which interact with a Coulomb potential:

$$\Phi(|q|) = +\frac{e^2}{|q|}, \tag{4.72}$$

where e is the charge on one particle. Although this problem does not have a direct connection with the study of the liquid state, it is very important and interesting for the theory of the method of correlation functions.

The principal peculiarity of our system is the long-range nature of the Coulomb forces. As a result of this, for example, the basic equations (4.9) or (4.13) cannot be correct, inasmuch as integrals involving the potential (4.72) are not absolutely convergent and depend on the method of passing to the limit $V \to \infty$. However, in an effort to describe a semi-infinite system, it appears that integrals of the type found in equation (4.54) do not exist in the limit as $V \to \infty$. It is well known that for the stability of a system of identically charged particles it is necessary to introduce a field of uniformly distributed charge of opposite sign, which neutralizes the charge of all the particles of the system. In our equations this field is introduced externally. Therefore, let us consider the equations in (4.13) which, analogously to the equations in (4.8), are written

$$kT\nabla_1 F_s + F_s \nabla_1 U_s + F_s \nabla \varphi_s + \frac{N-s}{V}\int_V \nabla_1 \Phi_{1\ s+1} F_{s+1} dq_{s+1} = 0 . \qquad (4.73)$$

The density of the electrical charge of the neutralized background is equal to $\rho = -eN/V$, and, therefore, in accordance with the laws of electostatics, the potential energy of the point charge $+e$ in the field of charges ρdV will be equal to

$$\varphi(q) = -e^2 \frac{N}{V}\int_V \frac{dq'}{|q-q'|} . \qquad (4.74)$$

Placing this in (4.12) and taking (4.72) into consideration, we obtain

$$\nabla_1 \varphi_s = \nabla_1 \varphi(q_1) = -e^2 \frac{N}{V}\int_V \nabla_1 |q-q'|^{-1} dq' = -\frac{N}{V}\int_V \nabla_1 \Phi(|q_1 - q'|) dq' , \qquad (4.75)$$

so that equations (4.73) may be written in the form

$$kT\nabla_1 F_s + F_s \nabla_1 U_s + \frac{N-s}{V}\int_V \nabla_1 \Phi_{1,\,s+1}\left(F_{s+1} - \frac{N}{N-s} F_s\right) dq_{s+1} = 0 . \qquad (4.76)$$

Using the asymptotic properties of the correlation function, $F_{s+1} \to F_s$ when $|q_{s+1}| \to \infty$. Assuming the limit is reached rapidly, we can pass to the limit $N \to \infty$ and $V \to \infty$ in equations (4.76) thereby assuring absolute convergence of the integrals. As a result, for the asymptotic behavior of the correlation functions, we obtain equations

$$kT\nabla_1 F_s + F_s \nabla_1 U_s + \frac{1}{v}\int \nabla_1 \Phi_{1,\,s+1}(F_{s+1} - F_s)\, dq_{s+1} = 0 . \qquad (4.77)$$

In this case it is clear that the field of compensating charge is implicitly taken into consideration.

When $s = 1$, the equations in (4.77) become an identity on substituting $F_1(q) = 1$ and $F_2(q, q') = g(|q - q'|)$, so that calculation of the compensating background makes the system uniform and isotropic.

We note that solution of the equations in (4.77) by the method discussed in section 2 is impossible because of the divergence of the integrals arising from the long range of the potential $\Phi(|q|)$. In order to be able to separate in our equations another, more suitable, small parameter, we follow Bogolyubov [1] and introduce dimensionless units of length by defining

$$q \to q' = \frac{q}{D}, \qquad (4.78)$$

where

$$D = \left(\frac{v\,kT}{4\pi\,e^2}\right)^{1/2} \qquad (4.79)$$

is the well-known "Debye radius" of our system. Using the explicit form of the potential (4.72) after transition to the new coordinates, we obtain the equations

$$\nabla_1 F_s + \gamma F_s \nabla_1 \tilde{U}_s + \frac{1}{4\pi} \int \nabla_1 \psi_{1,\,s+1} (F_{s+1} - F_s)\, dq_{s+1} = 0, \qquad (4.80)$$

where the primes have been dropped and the following notation has been introduced:

$$\psi_{i\,k} \equiv \psi(q_i q_k) = \frac{1}{|q_i - q_k|}; \qquad \tilde{U}_s = \sum_{1 \leq i < j \leq s} \psi_{ij}. \qquad (4.81)$$

The parameter γ is equal to

$$\gamma = \frac{e^2}{kTD} = \left[\frac{4\pi\,e^6}{v\,(kT)^3}\right]^{1/2} \qquad (4.82)$$

and represents the ratio of the energy of interaction of a pair of particles located at a distance of the Debye radius from one another to their kinetic energy. We note that $\gamma/4\pi$ is at the same time the average volume per particle expressed in the new units of length: $\gamma = 4\pi v/D^3$.

Now let us assume that $\gamma \ll 1$ and attempt to construct a solution for equations (4.80) in the form of power series in the parameter γ:

$$F_s = F_s^{(0)} + \gamma F_s^{(1)} + \gamma^2 F_s^{(2)} + \dots \,. \qquad (4.83)$$

By placing this in (4.80) and separating the terms with identical powers of γ, we obtain the following systems of equations

$$\nabla_1 F_s^{(0)} + \frac{1}{4\pi}\int \nabla_1 \psi_{1,\,s+1}\,[F_{s+1}^{(0)} - F_s^{(0)}]\,d\boldsymbol{q}_{s+1} = 0\,, \qquad (4.84)$$

$$\nabla_1 F_s^{(1)} + F_s^{(0)} \nabla_1 \tilde{U}_s + \frac{1}{4\pi}\int \nabla_1 \psi_{1,\,s+1}\,[F_{s+1}^{(1)} - F_s^{(1)}]\,d\boldsymbol{q}_{s+1} = 0\,, \qquad (4.85)$$

etc., for the successive determination of $F_s^{(m)}$. In this case the conditions of symmetry, normalization, and asymptotic behavior of the correlation functions must all be satisfied.

The first two systems of equations are easily solved in general form. An obvious solution of the equations in (4.84), which satisfies all the necessary conditions, will be

$$F_s^{(0)}(\boldsymbol{q}_1, \ldots, \boldsymbol{q}_s) = 1\,, \qquad s = 1, 2, \ldots\,. \qquad (4.86)$$

Furthermore, it is not difficult to see that the equations in (4.85) permit "separation of variables" in the sense that one may assume that $F_1^{(1)} = 0$, and, for all the remaining,

$$F_s^{(1)} = \sum_{1 \le i < j \le s} f(|\boldsymbol{q}_i - \boldsymbol{q}_j|)\,, \qquad s = 2, 3, \ldots\,. \qquad (4.87)$$

The unknown function $f(|\boldsymbol{q}|)$, because of the asymptotic behavior of the correlation function, must behave as

$$f(|\boldsymbol{q}|) \rightarrow 0 \quad \text{when} \quad |\boldsymbol{q}| \rightarrow \infty \qquad (4.88)$$

and because of the normalization conditions should be integrable. Noting that

$$F_{s+1}^{(1)} - F_s^{(1)} = \sum_{1 \le i \le s} f(|\boldsymbol{q}_i - \boldsymbol{q}_{s+1}|) \qquad (4.89)$$

and

$$\int \nabla_1 \psi(|\boldsymbol{q}_1 - \boldsymbol{q}_{s+1}|)\, f(|\boldsymbol{q}_1 - \boldsymbol{q}_{s+1}|)\, d\boldsymbol{q}_{s+1} = 0\,, \qquad (4.90)$$

after substituting (4.87) in (4.85), we obtain

$$\sum_{1 \le i \le s}\Big[\nabla_1 f(|\boldsymbol{q}_1 - \boldsymbol{q}_i|) + \nabla_1 \psi(|\boldsymbol{q}_1 - \boldsymbol{q}_i|) + \frac{1}{4\pi}\int \nabla_1 \psi(|\boldsymbol{q}_1 - \boldsymbol{q}_{s+1}|)\, f(|\boldsymbol{q}_{s+1} - \boldsymbol{q}_i|)\, d\boldsymbol{q}_{s+1}\Big] = 0\,. \qquad (4.91)$$

Thus, equations (4.85) separate into identical equations for the function f. After integration over $\boldsymbol{q}_1$, we obtain the integral equation

$$f(|\boldsymbol{q}|) + \frac{1}{4\pi}\int \psi(|\boldsymbol{q} - \boldsymbol{q}'|)\, f(|\boldsymbol{q}'|)\, d\boldsymbol{q}' = -\psi(|\boldsymbol{q}|)\,. \qquad (4.92)$$

The integration constant in this case is set equal to zero in accordance with (4.88).

In order to solve equation (4.92) we employ a Laplace operator on both sides. Using (4.81), we obtain

$$\Delta f(|q|) - f(|q|) = 4\pi\delta(q), \tag{4.93}$$

where $\delta(q)$ is a three-dimensional δ function so that $\Delta\psi(|q|) = -4\pi\delta(q)$. This solution of this equation, which satisfies condition (4.88), is

$$f(|q|) = -\frac{1}{|q|}\, e^{-|q|}. \tag{4.94}$$

Thus, in this approximation, we obtain

$$F_s(q_1, \ldots, q_s) = 1 - \gamma \sum_{1\le i<j\le s} \frac{1}{|q_i - q_j|} \exp\{-|q_i - q_j|\} + \ldots \tag{4.95}$$

or, in the original variables,

$$F_s(q_1, \ldots, q_s) = 1 - \frac{e^2}{kT} \sum_{1\le i<j\le s} \frac{1}{|q_i - q_j|} \exp\left(-\frac{|q_i - q_j|}{D}\right) + \ldots. \tag{4.96}$$

In particular, for the radial distribution function, we have

$$g(r) = 1 - \frac{e^2}{kTr} \exp\left(-\frac{r}{D}\right) + \ldots. \tag{4.97}$$

It is possible to show that, in accordance with its thermodynamic consequences, solution (4.97) corresponds to the Debye-Hückel theory of ion interaction modified for the case of particles of one species. We note that in this case solutions (4.95) to (4.97) become useless at small distances between particles where they result in absurd negative probabilities.

5. A MORE PRECISE SOLUTION OF THE PROBLEM OF ELECTRICALLY CHARGED PARTICLES

Another and more precise solution of the preceding problem may be obtained by a different method based on special representation of the correlation functions. Bogolyubov showed that in the Coulomb interaction problem, a transition is possible from the functions F_1, F_2, F_3, . . . to the functions 1, f, g, . . . by means of the relationships:

$$F_1(q) = 1 , \tag{4.98}$$

$$F_2(q, q') = 1 + \gamma f(q, q'), \tag{4.99}$$

$$\begin{aligned} F_3(q, q', q'') = 1 + \gamma [f(q, q') + f(q, q'') \\ + f(q', q'')] + \gamma^2 g(q, q', q''), \end{aligned} \tag{4.100}$$

$$\begin{aligned} F_4(q, q', q'', q''') = 1 + \gamma [f(q, q') + f(q, q'') \\ + f(q, q''') + f(q', q'') + f(q', q''') + f(q'', q''')] \\ + \gamma^2 [f(q, q') f(q'', q''') + f(q, q'') f(q', q''') \\ + f(q, q''') f(q', q'') + g(q, q', q'') + g(q, q', q''') \\ + g(q, q'', q''') + g(q', q'', q''')] + \gamma^3 h(q, q', q'', q'''), \end{aligned} \tag{4.101}$$

etc. We cannot stop here for a proof [1]; however, the validity of the transformation will follow below from the fact that we will work out a direct solution for the functions f, g, h, ...

The functions f, g, . . . should be symmetrical and, because of the asymptotic behavior of the F_s,

$$f(q, q') \to 0 \quad \text{when} \quad |q - q'| \to \infty , \tag{4.102}$$

$$g(q, q', q'') \to 0 \text{ when } |q - q'|, |q - q''|, |q' - q''| \to \infty, \tag{4.103}$$

etc.

Substitute (4.98) to (4.101) in equation (4.80). After simple transformations we will then obtain equations for the functions f, g, etc. Below we will need only the first two of these equations, which have the form

$$\begin{aligned} \nabla_q f(q, q') + \nabla_q \psi(q, q') + \gamma f(q, q') \nabla_q \psi(q, q') \\ + \frac{1}{4\pi} \int \nabla_q \psi(q, q'') [f(q', q'') + \gamma g(q, q', q'')] dq'' = 0, \end{aligned} \tag{4.104}$$

$$\begin{aligned} \nabla_q g(q, q', q'') + [f(q', q'') + \gamma g(q, q', q'') \\ - \gamma f(q, q') f(q, q'')] \nabla_q [\psi(q, q') + \psi(q, q'')] \\ - \nabla_q [f(q, q') f(q, q'')] + \frac{1}{4\pi} \int \nabla_q \psi(q, q''') \\ \times [g(q', q'', q''') - \gamma h(q, q', q'', q''') \\ - \gamma f(q, q') g(q, q'', q''') - \gamma f(q, q'') \\ \times g(q, q', q''')] dq''' = 0 . \end{aligned} \tag{4.105}$$

We will solve these equations by expansion of the unknown functions into a series in powers of γ:

$$f(q, q') = f^{(0)}(q, q') + \gamma f^{(1)}(q, q') + \dots, \quad (4.106)$$

$$g(q, q', q'') = g^{(0)}(q, q', q'') + \gamma g^{(1)}(q, q', q'') + \dots, \quad (4.107)$$

etc. Placing this in equations (4.104) and (4.105) and grouping the terms with identical powers of γ, we obtain equations from successive powers of γ for $f^{(0)}$, $g^{(0)}$, $f^{(1)}$, etc. It is not difficult to see that the zeroth approximation equations may now be integrated immediately, and, from (4.102) and (4.103), the integration constants are zero. Thus, in the zeroth approximation for f and g, we obtain

$$f^{(0)}(q, q') + \frac{1}{4\pi}\int \psi(q, q'') f^{(0)}(q', q'') dq'' = -\psi(q, q'), \quad (4.108)$$

$$\begin{aligned} g^{(0)}(q, q', q'') &+ \frac{1}{4\pi}\int \psi(q, q''') g^{(0)}(q', q'', q''') dq''' \\ &= f^{(0)}(q, q') f^{(0)}(q, q'') - f^{(0)}(q', q'') \\ &\times [\psi(q, q') + \psi(q, q'')]. \end{aligned} \quad (4.109)$$

The first of these equations is identical with equation (4.92), and in accordance with (4.94) we obtain

$$f^{(0)}(q, q') = f^{(0)}(|q - q'|) = -\frac{1}{|q - q'|} \exp(-|q - q'|). \quad (4.110)$$

In order to solve equation (4.109), we will first consider the more general case of an equation of the form

$$\begin{aligned} \varphi[q, q', \dots, q^{(m)}] &+ \frac{1}{4\pi}\int \psi(q, p) \varphi[p, q', \dots, q^{(m)}] dp \\ &= \chi[q, q', \dots, q^{(m)}], \end{aligned} \quad (4.111)$$

where $\varphi(q, \dots, q^{(m)}$ is unknown, while $\chi[q, \dots, q^{(m)}]$ is a known symmetrical function and $\psi(q, p) = |q - p|^{-1}$. By applying the Laplace operator in q to both sides of equation (4.111), we find that this equation is equivalent to the differential equation

$$\Delta_q \varphi - \varphi = \Delta_q \chi . \quad (4.112)$$

It is easy to verify that equation (4.112) has as its solution the function

$$\begin{aligned} \varphi[q, \dots, q^{(m)}] &= \chi[q, \dots, q^{(m)}] \\ &+ \frac{1}{4\pi}\int f^{(0)}(q, p) \chi[p, q', \dots, q^{(m)}] dp \end{aligned} \quad (4.113)$$

with $f^{(0)}$ from (4.110). As a matter of fact, placing (4.113) in (4.112) turns the latter equation into an identity, if we take (4.93) into consideration.

Equation (4.109), which is of interest to us, belongs to the type of equation (4.111) and, therefore, according to (4.113), its solution may be written at once:

$$
\begin{aligned}
g^{(0)}(q, q', q'') = {} & f^{(0)}(q, q')\, f^{(0)}(q, q'') \\
& - f^{(0)}(q', q'')[\psi(q, q') + \psi(q, q'')] \\
& + \frac{1}{4\pi}\int [\, f^{(0)}(q, q''')\, f^{(0)}(q', q''')\, f^{(0)}(q'', q''') \\
& - f^{(0)}(q', q'')\, f^{(0)}(q, q''')\psi(q', q''') \\
& - f^{(0)}(q', q'')\, f^{(0)}(q, q''')\psi(q'', q''')\,]\, dq'''.
\end{aligned}
\tag{4.114}
$$

This equation may be somewhat simplified with the aid of equation (4.108), and we finally obtain

$$
\begin{aligned}
g^{(0)}(q, q', q'') = {} & f^{(0)}(q, q')\, f^{(0)}(q, q'') \\
& + f^{(0)}(q, q'')\, f^{(0)}(q', q'') + f^{(0)}(q, q')\, f^{(0)}(q', q'') \\
& + \frac{1}{4\pi}\int f^{(0)}(q, q''')\, f^{(0)}(q', q''')\, f^{(0)}(q'', q''')\, dq''' .
\end{aligned}
\tag{4.115}
$$

Now let us proceed to the next approximation for f. From (4.106) and (4.104), we obtain the following equation for $f^{(1)}$.

$$
\begin{aligned}
\nabla_q f^{(1)}(q, q') + f^{(0)}(q, q')\nabla_q \psi(q, q') & \\
+ \frac{1}{4\pi}\int \nabla_q \psi(q, q'')[\, f^{(0)}(q', q'') & \\
+ g^{(0)}(q, q', q'')\,]\, dq'' = 0 , &
\end{aligned}
\tag{4.116}
$$

which, with the calculation of (4.108) and (4.115), may be integrated in terms of q, while the integration constant is again equal to zero. We finally obtain the following integral equation for $f^{(1)}$:

$$
\begin{aligned}
f^{(1)}(q, q') + & \frac{1}{4\pi}\int \psi(q, q'')\, f^{(1)}(q', q'')\, dq'' \\
& = \tfrac{1}{2}[\, f^{(0)}(q, q')\,]^2 + \frac{1}{16\pi}\int f^{(0)}(q, q'')\, f^{(0)}(q', q'') \\
& \times [\, f^{(0)}(q, q'') + f^{(0)}(q', q'')\,]\, dq''.
\end{aligned}
\tag{4.117}
$$

It again has the form of equation (4.111), and therefore its solution, in accordance with (4.113), is

$$f^{(1)}(q, q') = \tfrac{1}{2}[f^{(0)}(q, q')]^2 + \frac{1}{8\pi}\int f^{(0)}(q, q'')$$
$$\times f^{(0)}(q', q'')[f^{(0)}(q, q'') + f^{(0)}(q', q'')]\,dq'' + \frac{1}{32\pi^2} \qquad (4.118)$$
$$\times \int\int f^{(0)}(q, q'')\,f^{(0)}(q', q''')[f^{(0)}(q'', q''')]^2 dq'' dq'''.$$

By using the explicit form of the function $f^{(0)}$, according to (4.100), it is easy to calculate all the integrals that enter in (4.118). Using the notation $r = |q - q'|$, we finally obtain

$$f^{(1)}(r) = -\frac{1}{6r}\,e^{-r} + \left(\frac{1}{2r^2} + \frac{1}{6r}\right)e^{-2r}$$
$$+ \frac{3-r}{8r}\,e^{-r}\int_r^\infty e^{-t}\,\frac{dt}{t} - \frac{3+r}{8r}\,e^{r}\int_r^\infty e^{-3t}\,\frac{dt}{t}. \qquad (4.119)$$

If, for the sake of brevity, we introduce the notation

$$\varphi(r) \equiv f^{(1)}(r) - \frac{1}{2r^2}\,e^{-2r}, \qquad (4.120)$$

then, together with the preceding approximations, we obtain for the radial distribution function

$$g(r) = 1 - \frac{\gamma}{r}\,e^{-r} + \frac{\gamma^2}{2r^2}\,e^{-2r} + \gamma^2\varphi(r) + \ldots . \qquad (4.121)$$

In this approximation $g(r) > 0$ for all values of r; however, a singularity has appeared at the point $r = 0$. The situation may be corrected if we note that to the same precision as in (4.121), we may write

$$g(r) = \exp\left(-\frac{\gamma}{r}\,e^{-r}\right)[1 + \gamma^2\varphi(r) + O(\gamma^3)] \qquad (4.122)$$

or, in the usual units of length,

$$g(r) = \exp\left(-\frac{e^2}{kTr}\,e^{-r/D}\right)\left[1 + \frac{e^4}{D^2(kT)^2}\,\varphi\left(\frac{r}{D}\right) + \ldots\right]. \qquad (4.123)$$

Now, when $r \to 0$, $g(r) \to 0$, as it should in a system of point particles. At small values of r, the exponential factor in (4.123) is the usual Boltzmann factor with a Coulomb potential. At large values of r, expression (4.123) goes over to the Debye-Hückel form of $g(r)$ together with the first correction. Therefore, one may assume that it has acceptable precision everywhere, if γ is not too large, and this expression may be used as a reasonable interpolation equation. It should be noted that a beautiful solution of the problem of determining the function $g(r)$ in the form (4.123) was given in paper [3].

By using this solution it is possible to determine the thermodynamic properties of the system being studied with great precision. For example, from general theory we obtain for the energy

$$E = \tfrac{3}{2} NkT + \tfrac{1}{2} NkTI(\gamma), \tag{4.124}$$

where

$$I(\gamma) = \int_0^\infty \left\{ \exp\left(-\frac{\gamma}{r}\, e^{-r}\right) [1 + \gamma^2 \varphi(r) + \ldots] - 1 \right\} r\, dr\,. \tag{4.125}$$

After conversion to the free energy, it is possible to develop the entire thermodynamics of our system.

6. CALCULATIONS WITH NON-CENTRAL FORCES; DIPOLE INTERACTION

As a further generalization of the method of correlation functions, let us now consider a system in which, as before, the total energy is the sum of the energies of the individual interacting pairs of particles, but for each pair the interaction is not central. Let each particle be characterized by the coordinates $\boldsymbol{q} = \{q^1, q^2, q^3\}$ of its center of mass and the set of coordinates $\omega = \{\omega^1, \ldots, \omega^n\}$, which determine the orientation of the particle. For example, for an axially symmetric particle, $n = 2$ and ω^1, ω^2 designate two spherical angles which determine the direction of the axis of the particle. In a more general case $n = 3$ and $\omega^1, \omega^2, \omega^3$ designate, for example, the Eulerian angles or the corresponding set of three other angular variables. We shall designate the element of volume in the space of the angular variables by $d\omega$, and let Ω be the total volume of this space for one particle. For an axially symmetric particle, in spherical coordinates $d\omega = \sin\vartheta d\vartheta d\varphi$ and $\Omega = 4\pi$.

We may now extend the definition of the correlation functions to include the new variables ω: $F_s = F_s(\boldsymbol{q}_1, \omega_1; \ldots; \boldsymbol{q}_s, \omega_s)$ so that the expression

$$F_s(\boldsymbol{q}_1, \omega_1; \ldots; \boldsymbol{q}_s, \omega_s) \frac{d\boldsymbol{q}_1 \ldots d\boldsymbol{q}_s d\omega_1 \ldots d\omega_s}{V^s \Omega^s} \tag{4.126}$$

is equal to the probability of some group of s particles having positions and orientations near the points $\boldsymbol{q}_1, \ldots, \boldsymbol{q}_s$ and the angles $\omega_1, \ldots, \omega_s$. It is possible to define the corresponding conditional correlation functions in a similar manner. The functions $F_s(\boldsymbol{q}_1, \omega_1; \ldots; \boldsymbol{q}_s, \omega_s)$, in accordance with the definition, are symmetrical in the arguments $\boldsymbol{q}_i$, ω_i. The normalization conditions may now be written in the form

$$\frac{1}{V\Omega}\int_V \oint_\omega F_1(\boldsymbol{q}, \omega)\, d\boldsymbol{q}\, d\omega = 1 \tag{4.127}$$

and

$$\frac{1}{V\Omega}\int_V \oint_\omega F_s(\boldsymbol{q}_1, \omega_1; \ldots; \boldsymbol{q}_s, \omega_s)\, d\boldsymbol{q}_s\, d\omega_s = F_{s-1}(\boldsymbol{q}_1\, \omega_1; \ldots; \boldsymbol{q}_{s-1}, \omega_{s-1}) \tag{4.128}$$

when $s \geq 2$. The asymptotic conditions now take the form

$$F_s(\boldsymbol{q}_1\, \omega_1; \ldots; \boldsymbol{q}_s, \omega_s) \rightarrow \prod_{1 \leq i \leq s} F_1(\boldsymbol{q}_i, \omega_i), \tag{4.129}$$

when all $|\boldsymbol{q}_i - \boldsymbol{q}_j| \rightarrow \infty$, $i, j = 1, 2, 3, \ldots, s$, thereby guaranteeing the "liquidity" of the system with respect to the positions of the particles.

The functions

$$F_s(\boldsymbol{q}_1, \ldots, \boldsymbol{q}_s) = \frac{1}{\Omega^s}\oint_\omega \cdots \oint_\omega F_s(\boldsymbol{q}_1, \omega_1; \ldots; \boldsymbol{q}_s, \omega_s) \times d\omega_1 \ldots d\omega_s\,, \tag{4.130}$$

$$F_s(\omega_1, \ldots, \omega_s) = \frac{1}{V^s}\int_V \cdots \int_V F_s(\boldsymbol{q}_1, \omega_1; \ldots; \boldsymbol{q}_s, \omega_s) \times d\boldsymbol{q}_1 \ldots d\boldsymbol{q}_s \tag{4.131}$$

are correlation functions in the coordinate space and in the orientation space of groups of particles, respectively.

The total potential energy of the system may now be written in the form

$$U_N = \sum_{1 \leq i < j \leq N} \Phi(\boldsymbol{q}_i, \omega_i; \boldsymbol{q}_j, \omega_j) + \sum_{1 \leq i \leq N} \varphi(\boldsymbol{q}_i, \omega_i), \tag{4.132}$$

where Φ is the potential between a pair of particles and φ is the potential energy of one particle in an external field, if such a field exists. The Gibbs distribution function, as before, is equal to

$$D_N(\boldsymbol{q}_1, \omega_1; \ldots; \boldsymbol{q}_N, \omega_N) = Q_N^{-1} \exp\left(-\frac{U_N}{kT}\right), \tag{4.133}$$

with U_N from (4.132), and we may write for the correlation functions

$$F_s(\boldsymbol{q}_1, \omega_1; \ldots; \boldsymbol{q}_s, \omega_s) = V^s\Omega^s \int_V \cdots \int_V \oint_\omega \cdots \oint_\omega D_N\, d\boldsymbol{q}_{s+1} \ldots d\boldsymbol{q}_N\, d\omega_{s+1} \ldots d\omega_N\,. \tag{4.134}$$

The correlation functions corresponding to (4.130) and (4.131) may be similarly expressed.

By using the latter expression, it is now possible to derive integro-differential equations for the correlation functions. Repeating the reasoning of section 1, instead of equations (4.13) after passing to the limit $N \to \infty$ and $V \to \infty$, we obtain two systems of equations for determining F_s:

$$kT\nabla_{q_1}F_s + F_s\nabla_{q_1}(U_s+\varphi_s) + \frac{1}{\Omega v}\int_V \oint_\omega \nabla_{q_1}\Phi_{1,\,s+1}F_{s+1}d\boldsymbol{q}_{s+1}d\omega_{s+1} = 0\,, \tag{4.135}$$

$$kT\frac{\partial F_s}{\partial \omega_1^a} + F_s\frac{\partial}{\partial \omega_1^a}(U_s+\varphi_s) + \frac{1}{\Omega v}\int_V \oint_\omega \frac{\partial \Phi_{1,\,s+1}}{\partial \omega_1^a}F_{s+1}d\boldsymbol{q}_{s+1}d\omega_{s+1} = 0\,, \tag{4.136}$$

$s = 1, 2, \ldots$ and $a = 1, 2$ or $1, 2, 3$; while

$$U_s = \sum_{1\le i<j\le s} \Phi(\boldsymbol{q}_i, \omega_i; \boldsymbol{q}_j, \omega_j); \qquad \varphi_s = \sum_{1\le i\le s} \varphi(\boldsymbol{q}_i, \omega_i). \tag{4.137}$$

The solutions of these equations should be symmetrical functions which satisfy the normalization conditions obtained from (4.127) and (4.128) in the limit $V \to \infty$ as well as the condition (4.129). If the infinite system of equations (4.135) to (4.136) admits an expansion parameter or several expansion parameters, solution is possible.

As an example of interest for the theory of liquids and gases where it would be possible to use the equations obtained, we draw attention to a system consisting of non-spherical molecules. In this case, if the non-sphericity is slight, we may assume that

$$\Phi(\boldsymbol{q}, \omega; \boldsymbol{q}', \omega') = \chi(|\boldsymbol{q}-\boldsymbol{q}'|)[1+\lambda\psi(\omega, \omega')], \tag{4.138}$$

where $\lambda(\ll 1)$ is the expansion parameter. Then for a gas it is possible to determine the correlation functions and to calculate the thermodynamic properties of the system by expansion into a double series in powers of $1/v$ and λ [4]. For it to be possible to expand the correlation functions into a series in powers of λ in the case of a liquid, it is necessary to have preliminary knowledge of these functions for the case of the central interaction. The latter problem may be approximately solved by the method described in chapter 5.

Another important example of the use of the theory discussed above is a system whose particles have constant electric dipole or quadrupole, etc., moments. Assume, for example, that all the particles have identical dipole moments $\boldsymbol{p}$. Designating $\boldsymbol{q}_i - \boldsymbol{q}_j = \boldsymbol{r}_{ij}$, we write in this case

$$\Phi(\boldsymbol{q}_i, \omega_i; \boldsymbol{q}_j, \omega_j) = \Phi_0(|\boldsymbol{r}_{ij}|) + \frac{\boldsymbol{p}_i\boldsymbol{p}_j}{|\boldsymbol{r}_{ij}|^3} - \frac{3(\boldsymbol{p}_i \cdot \boldsymbol{r}_{ij})(\boldsymbol{p}_j \cdot \boldsymbol{r}_{ij})}{|\boldsymbol{r}_{ij}|^5}, \tag{4.139}$$

where Φ_0 describes the usual short-range central forces, and the two remaining terms describe the dipole interaction of the two particles. In the gaseous state it is possible to find the correlation functions and thermodynamic properties of the gas by the usual expansion in powers of the density. It is possible, for example, to calculate without special difficulty some of the lower virial coefficients if a sufficiently simple function $\Phi_0(r)$ is taken, as has been done by many authors.

The case of dipolar molecules in the presence of a constant external electrical field $\boldsymbol{E}$ is more interesting. Then it is necessary to take into consideration the second group of terms in (4.132), setting

$$\varphi_N = -\sum_{1 \leq i \leq N} (\boldsymbol{p}_i \cdot \boldsymbol{E}) = -pE \sum_{1 \leq i \leq N} \cos \vartheta_i . \tag{4.140}$$

In the case of a gas in a weak external field it is possible to expand the correlation functions into a double series in terms of the parameters $1/v$ and pE/kT. As a result, a theory of the polarization of a dipolar gas can be constructed, taking into consideration the interaction of the particles, which is a generalization of the well-known Langevin theory for an ideal gas. In this case it is essential to note that the series obtained in this problem are not absolutely convergent; grouping them into series in powers of the density results in divergent expressions.

In connection with these problems, an observation should be made which limits the applicability to real systems of the preceding analysis. In a real system the necessity of calculating the polarizability of the dipolar molecules results in a breakdown of the additivity of the total energy of the system in terms of pair interactions. Now, it would be necessary to set

$$U_N = \sum_{1 \leq i < j \leq N} \Phi(\boldsymbol{q}_i, \omega_i; \boldsymbol{q}_j, \omega_j) + \sum_{1 \leq i < j < k \leq N} \Psi(\boldsymbol{q}_i, \omega_i; \boldsymbol{q}_j, \omega_j; \boldsymbol{q}_k, \omega_k) + \dots , \tag{4.141}$$

so that "collective" interactions would be taken into consideration. In this case, equations of the type of (4.13) or (4.135) to (4.136) are unsuitable, and it is necessary to derive their corresponding generalizations. In a liquid all "collective" terms are simultaneously essential, and the situation is fairly hopeless. In the case of a gas, however, the situation is somewhat simplified due to the fact that the calculation of each succeeding group of terms in (4.141) requires the expansion of the correlation functions in powers of the density in increasing orders, and for a moderately dense gas the calculation of extremely complex interactions is not required. Thus, if one speaks of the pressure of a gas, the pair interactions arise in the term of the order of $1/v^2$, the triplet interactions in the term of the order of $1/v^3$, etc. Analogous results are obtained in the calculation of other quantities. If, therefore, we limit ourselves to a small number of terms in the expansion in powers of the density, it is necessary to calculate only the three body or three and four body interactions, and this does not in principle cause essential difficulties.

7. THE CASE OF A DIPOLE LATTICE

In the examples considered above, we had doubly disordered systems—long-range order was absent in both the positions and the orientations of the particles. A new and very interesting case is a system of particles, the centers of which are ordered on a crystalline lattice, which may be oriented, for example, as dipoles. The particles now have only rotational degrees of freedom and two extreme configurations are possible: long-range order in the orientations of the particles of the system and orientational disorder of the particles, which leads to the concept of an "orientational gas" or "liquid." If both states are possible for a given type of lattice, there will also exist a phase transition between them in the form of "orientational melting" [5]. An example of such a system was examined in paper [6] by the methods of the theory of correlation functions.

Let $\boldsymbol{a_n}$ be a vector of the lattice, i.e.,

$$\boldsymbol{a_n} = \boldsymbol{a}_1 n_1 + \boldsymbol{a}_2 n_2 + \boldsymbol{a}_3 n_3 , \qquad (4.142)$$

where $\boldsymbol{a}_1$, $\boldsymbol{a}_2$, $\boldsymbol{a}_3$ are the basic vectors of the lattice and n_1, n_2, n_3 are whole positive or negative numbers or zero. For brevity we will also make use of the whole-number vector $\boldsymbol{n} = \{n_1, n_2, n_3\}$ for designating the lattice point instead of the vector $\boldsymbol{a_n}$. We now number the particles by the lattice point at which they are located so that the position and orientation of a particle is given by $\boldsymbol{n}$, ω. The correlation functions are now defined only in orientation space. We shall designate by

$$F_{\boldsymbol{n}_1,\ldots,\boldsymbol{n}_s}(\omega_1,\ldots,\omega_s)\frac{d\omega_1\ldots d\omega_s}{\Omega^s} \tag{4.143}$$

the probability of finding a group of s particles, at the lattice points $\boldsymbol{n}_1$, $\ldots$, $\boldsymbol{n}_s$, with orientations which are close to $\omega_1, \ldots, \omega_s$. From the definition, the functions $F_{\boldsymbol{n}_1,\ldots,\boldsymbol{n}_s}$ are symmetrical. The normalization of the correlation functions follows from (4.143):

$$\frac{1}{\Omega}\oint_{\omega} F_{\boldsymbol{n}}(\omega)\,d\omega = 1\,, \tag{4.144}$$

$$\frac{1}{\Omega}\oint_{\omega} F_{\boldsymbol{n}_1,\ldots,\boldsymbol{n}_s}(\omega_1,\ldots,\omega_s)\,d\omega_s = F_{\boldsymbol{n}_1,\ldots,\boldsymbol{n}_{s-1}}(\omega_1,\ldots,\omega_{s-1})\,. \tag{4.145}$$

The character of the orientational ordering of the system is determined primarily by the behavior of the singlet correlation function. In a disordered phase all orientations of one particle are equally probable, and in accordance with (4.144) we obtain $F_{\boldsymbol{n}}(\omega) = 1$ for all values of $\boldsymbol{n}$. In the ordered phase there exist directions of preferred orientation of the particles, determined by the character of the interaction of the particles and by the symmetry of the lattice, $F_{\boldsymbol{n}}(\omega) \neq \text{const}$.

We now obtain equations for the correlation function, assuming that the total potential energy of the system is equal to

$$U_N = U_{\boldsymbol{n}_1,\ldots,\boldsymbol{n}_N}(\omega_1,\ldots,\omega_N) = \sum_{1\le i<j\le N} \Phi_{\boldsymbol{n}_i,\boldsymbol{n}_j}(\omega_i,\omega_j), \tag{4.146}$$

where $\Phi_{\boldsymbol{n},\boldsymbol{n}'}(\omega, \omega')$ is the potential of the interaction of a pair of particles at the lattice points $\boldsymbol{n}$ and $\boldsymbol{n}'$. The Gibbs distribution function, as before, is equal to

$$D_{\boldsymbol{n}_1,\ldots,\boldsymbol{n}_N}(\omega_1,\ldots,\omega_N) = Q_N^{-1}\exp\left(-\frac{U_N}{kT}\right), \tag{4.147}$$

and the correlation functions are related to it by

$$F_{\boldsymbol{n}_1,\ldots,\boldsymbol{n}_s}(\omega_1,\ldots,\omega_s) = \Omega^s \oint_{\omega}\ldots\oint_{\omega} D_{\boldsymbol{n}_1,\ldots,\boldsymbol{n}_N} \times d\omega_{s+1}\ldots d\omega_N\,. \tag{4.148}$$

Differentiating (4.148) with respect to ω_1^{α}, using (4.147), and repeating the assumptions of section 1, we get a system of integro-differential equations

$$kT \frac{\partial F_{n_1,\dots,n_s}}{\partial \omega_1^a} + F_{n_1,\dots,n_s} \frac{\partial U_{n_1,\dots,n_s}}{\partial \omega_1^a} + \frac{1}{\Omega} \oint_{\omega} \sum_{n_{s+1} \neq n_1,\dots,n_s} \frac{\partial \Phi_{n_1,n_{s+1}}(\omega_1, \omega_{s+1})}{\partial \omega_1} \times F_{n_1,\dots,n_{s+1}} d\omega_{s+1} = 0 , \tag{4.149}$$

where

$$U_{n_1,\dots,n_s}(\omega_1,\dots,\omega_s) = \sum_{1 \leq j < i \leq s} \Phi_{n_i,n_j}(\omega_i,\omega_j) \tag{4.150}$$

is the energy of interaction of the s particles under consideration arranged at lattice points, and the summation in (4.149) is extended over all the remaining $N - s$ lattice points. The symmetry conditions and normalization conditions must be used in solving these equations. As "boundary conditions," it is necessary to use the periodicity of the correlation functions when the angular variables change by a full period.

In the case of an infinite lattice, only the summation is changed in the integrand of (4.147), which now extends over the whole infinite lattice, except s points represented in $F_{n_1,\dots,n_s}$. If, in addition, there is an external field, then it is necessary to add to (4.148) the term

$$\sum_{1 \leq i \leq s} \varphi_{n_i}(\omega_i), \tag{4.151}$$

where $\varphi_n(\omega)$ is the potential energy of one particle, located at $\boldsymbol{n}$, in the external field.

Consider as an example a dipole lattice. In this case

$$\Phi_{n_i n_j}(\omega_i,\omega_j) = \frac{1}{|a\boldsymbol{n}_i - a\boldsymbol{n}_j|^3}[\boldsymbol{p}_i\boldsymbol{p}_j - 3(\boldsymbol{p}_i \cdot \mathbf{a}_{ij})(\boldsymbol{p}_j \cdot \mathbf{a}_{ij})], \tag{4.152}$$

where, for brevity, we have designated by $\mathbf{a}_{ij}$ the vector $a\boldsymbol{n}_i - a\boldsymbol{n}_j$. If we also introduce the dipole moment $\boldsymbol{p} = p\boldsymbol{p}^0$ and measure distance in units of the lattice constant $\boldsymbol{a}$, then we obtain

$$\Phi_{n_i n_j} = \frac{p^2}{a^3} \chi(\boldsymbol{n}_i, \boldsymbol{n}_j)\psi(\omega_i, \omega_j, \mathbf{a}_{ij}), \tag{4.153}$$

where the dimensionless quantity $\chi(n_i, n_j)$ is equal to

$$\chi(n_i, n_j) = \left| \frac{an_i}{a} - \frac{an_j}{a} \right|^{-3} \qquad (4.154)$$

and ψ depends only on the angular variables. The orientation of the dipole may be given by the two spherical polar angles ϑ and φ, $d\omega = \sin\vartheta\, d\vartheta\, d\varphi$ and $\Omega = 4\pi$. Placing this in (4.147), we obtain

$$\frac{\partial F_{n_1,\ldots,n_s}}{\partial \omega_1^a} + \gamma F_{n_1,\ldots,n_s} \frac{\partial \tilde{U}_{n_1,\ \ ,n_s}}{\partial \omega_1^a} + \frac{\gamma}{4\pi} \oint_{\omega} \sum_{n_{s+1} \neq n_1,\ldots,n_s} \times \chi(n_1, n_{s+1}) \frac{\partial \psi(\omega_1, \omega_{s+1}, \mathbf{a}_{1,\ s+1})}{\partial \omega_1^a} \times F_{n_1,\ldots,n_{s+1}} d\omega_{s+1} = 0\,, \qquad (4.155)$$

where the dimensionless parameter γ is

$$\gamma = \frac{p^2}{a^3 kT}, \qquad (4.156)$$

$U_{n_1,\ldots,n_s}$ expressed in dimensionless form is designated by $\tilde{U}_{n_1,\ldots,n_s}$, and ω_1^a designates ϑ_1 or φ_1.

If γ is small it is possible to attempt to obtain a solution of the equations (4.155) in the form of a series in powers of γ,

$$F_{n_1,\ldots,n_s} = F^{(0)}_{n_1,\ldots,n_s} + \gamma F^{(1)}_{n_1,\ldots,n_s} + \ldots\,. \qquad (4.157)$$

Since according to (4.152),

$$\oint_{\omega} \psi(\omega_1, \omega_{s+1}, \mathbf{a}_{1,\ s+1})\, d\omega_{s+1} = 0\,, \qquad (4.158)$$

it is not difficult to verify that the first terms of the expansion will be

$$F_{n_1,\ldots,n_s} = 1 - \gamma \tilde{U}_{n_1,\ldots,n_s} + \ldots\,. \qquad (4.159)$$

It is also not difficult to obtain the higher terms of the expansion and to calculate then the thermodynamic properties of the dipolar lattice for small γ. One should notice, however, that small values of γ correspond to a "gaseous" state of the system—in the sense of orientational order—and other methods of analysis are needed for the study of the ordered phase and "orientational melting" which correspond to $\gamma \sim 1$.

More interesting results are obtained in the study of the dipolar lattice in a constant external electrical field. Supplementary calculation in equations (4.155) of the energy of the dipoles in the external field with subsequent expansion of the solutions into a series in powers of γ gives interesting results for the polarization properties of polar crystals [6].

8. EQUATIONS FOR CORRELATION FUNCTIONS IN PHASE SPACE

Up until now we have been interested only in the equilibrium states of various systems. Therefore, as was explained in chapter 1, the total distribution function of the states of particles of a system in phase space has separated into two independent distributions—one for the momenta, and the other for the coordinates

$$\rho_N(q_1, \ldots, q_N; p_1, \ldots, p_N) = D_N(q_1, \ldots, q_N) \times (2\pi mkT)^{-3N/2} \prod_{1 \leq i \leq N} \exp\left(-\frac{p_i^2}{2mkT}\right). \quad (4.160)$$

This made it possible to limit ourselves to the study of only the distributions of the configurations of groups of particles. In a more general case, where statistical equilibrium is absent, this does not occur, and the function ρ_N may depend on time t: $\rho_N = \rho_N(q_1, \ldots, q_N; p_1, \ldots, p_N; t)$. It is also possible in this more general case to introduce a set of correlation functions F_s, $s = 1, 2, \ldots, N$, defined in the phase spaces of groups of s particles, and to substitute for the problem of the study of the total distribution function ρ_N the study of the "partial" distribution functions $F_1, F_2, \ldots$. By means of these functions it is possible to study the time-dependent processes that occur in the system under consideration.

Although in this book we will not be concerned with kinetic problems, nevertheless, in this section we will briefly consider the properties of the correlation functions F_s in the phase space of groups of s particles and the integro-differential equations for them. These equations were first examined by Bogolyubov [1] and Born and Green [7] simultaneously with equations for the equilibrium correlation functions in configurational space. For the sake of simplicity, we will limit ourselves below to the case where each particle of the system has only three degrees of freedom, so that its state is completely described by the position vector q and by the momentum p; the particles interact pairwise with central forces. We will designate by $d\tau = dq dp$ the volume element in the phase space of one particle.

Thus, let $\rho_N = \rho_N(q_1, \ldots, q_N; p_1, \ldots, p_N; t)$ be the distribution function in phase space for the states of a system of N particles, so that the probabilities of different phases of the system will be equal to

$$dW(q_1, \ldots, q_N; p_1, \ldots, p_N; t) = \rho_N d\tau_1, \ldots, d\tau_N . \quad (4.161)$$

Let us determine the correlation functions $F_s(q_1, \ldots, q_s; p_1, \ldots, p_s; t)$ for a group of s particles selected from the system ($s = 1, 2, \ldots, N$); the F_s are defined in the phase spaces of s molecules by means of the relationships

$$dW(q_1, \ldots, q_s; p_1, \ldots, p_s; t) = F_s \frac{d\tau_1 \ldots d\tau_s}{V^s} . \quad (4.162)$$

Here V is the volume occupied by the system, while on the left-hand side of (4.162) is the probability of some phase of the chosen group of particles at a definite moment in time. It is obvious that the functions F_s are symmetrical with respect to the transposition of pairs of arguments q_i, p_i and satisfy the normalization conditions:

$$\frac{1}{V^s}\int \ldots \int F_s d\tau_1 \ldots d\tau_s = 1 , \quad (4.163)$$

where the integration is over the phase space of the group of particles under consideration. Integrating $F_s(q_1, \ldots, q_s; p_1, \ldots, p_s; t)$ over all q_i or all p_i, $i = 1, 2, \ldots, s$, we obtain the correlation functions for groups of particles in momentum or coordinate space, respectively.

The correlation functions F_s are related to total distribution function ρ_N by a relationship that follows from (4.161) and (4.162):

$$F_s(q_1, \ldots, q_s; p_1, \ldots, p_s; t) = V^s \int \ldots \int \rho_N d\tau_{s+1} \ldots d\tau_N . \quad (4.164)$$

At equilibrium, from (4.160), we have

$$F_s(q_1, \ldots, q_s; p_1, \ldots, p_s) = F_s(q_1, \ldots, q_s) \times (2\pi m k T)^{-3s/2} \prod_{1 \leq i \leq s} \exp\left(-\frac{p_i^2}{2mkT}\right), \quad (4.165)$$

where the usual equilibrium correlation functions in coordinate space are on the right.

In order to obtain integro-differential equations for the correlation functions in phase space, we will assume that the entire system is closed or is located in a given external-force field. Placing the entire system in a thermostat is not essential when there is a very large number of N particles in the system. In the case of a closed system the

Liouville theorem is applicable, according to which ρ_N is an integral of motion of the system, so that

$$\frac{d\rho_N}{dt}=\frac{\partial\rho_N}{\partial t}+\sum_{1\le i\le N}\nabla_{q_i}\cdot\rho_N\dot{q}_i+\sum_{1\le i\le N}\nabla_{p_i}\cdot\rho_N\dot{p}_i=0\,, \quad (4.166)$$

where the dots designate differentiation with respect to time. But $\dot{q}_i = p_i/m$, where m is the mass of one particle, and by the equations of motion, $\dot{p}_i = K_i$, where K_i is the force acting on the ith particle. This leads us to the "Liouville equation"

$$\frac{\partial\rho_N}{\partial t}+\sum_{1\le i\le N}\frac{p_i}{m}\cdot\nabla_{q_i}\rho_N+\sum_{1\le i\le N}K_i\cdot\nabla_{p_i}\rho_N=0\,. \quad (4.167)$$

Multiply equation (4.167) by $V^s d\tau_{s+1}\ldots d\tau_N$ and integrate over the phase space of the $(s+1)$th, . . . , Nth particles. The terms in the sums in (4.167) with $i > s$ disappear, so that the integrals

$$\int p_i\cdot\nabla_{q_i}\rho_N d\tau_i\,,\qquad \int K_i\cdot\nabla_{p_i}\rho_N d\tau_i$$

become zero. As a matter of fact, using the Gauss-Ostrogradskiĭ theorem, they lead to surface integrals in the coordinate or momentum space of the ith particle, and outside the limits of the volume V, and when the momentum becomes infinitely large, $\rho_N = 0$. Taking (4.164) into consideration, we then obtain

$$\frac{\partial F_s}{\partial t}+\sum_{1\le i\le s}\frac{p_i}{m}\cdot\nabla_{q_i}F_s$$
$$+\sum_{1\le i\le s}V^s\int\ldots\int K_i\cdot\nabla_{p_i}\rho_N d\tau_{s+1}\ldots d\tau_N=0\,. \quad (4.168)$$

For the sake of simplicity let the external-force fields be absent. Then K_i is the total force acting on the ith particle due to the remaining particles of the system, and it may be expressed in terms of the intermolecular potential $\Phi(|q_i - q_j|)$. We may write

$$K_i=-\nabla_{q_i}U_s-\nabla_{q_i}\sum_{s+1\le j\le N}\Phi(|q_i-q_j|)\,, \quad (4.169)$$

where U_s is the energy of interaction of the group of s particles under consideration, according to (4.6). Taking (4.164) and the identity of all particles into consideration, after substitution in (4.168) we obtain

$$\frac{\partial F_s}{\partial t}+\sum_{1\le i\le s}\frac{p_i}{m}\cdot\nabla_{q_i}F_s-\sum_{1\le i\le s}\nabla_{q_i}\cdot U_s\nabla_{p_i}F_s$$
$$=\frac{N-s}{V}\sum_{1\le i\le s}\int\nabla_{q_i}\Phi(|q_i-q_{s+1}|)\cdot\nabla_{p_i}F_{s+1}d\tau_{s+1}\,. \quad (4.170)$$

It is now possible to go over to asymptotic correlation functions, taking the limit $N \to \infty$ and $V \to \infty$ with uniform displacement of all boundaries of the volume V to infinity, but with $v = V/N$ constant.

$$\frac{\partial F_s}{\partial t} + \sum_{1 \le i \le s} \frac{p_i}{m} \cdot \nabla_{q_i} F_s - \sum_{1 \le i \le s} \nabla_{q_i} U_s \cdot \nabla_{p_i} F_s$$
$$= \frac{1}{v} \sum_{1 \le i \le s} \int \nabla_{q_i} \Phi(|q_i - q_{s+1}|) \nabla_{p_i} F_{s+1} d\tau_{s+1}, \quad (4.171)$$
$$s = 0, 1, 2, \ldots .$$

Thus, as in the equilibrium case, we obtain an infinite chain of integro-differential equations for the correlation functions. In the presence of an external-force field these equations keep the same form, but by U_s one must now understand the expression (4.11), which includes within itself the energy of a group of particles in an external field. In such a case, for example, when $s = 1$ we obtain

$$\frac{\partial F_1}{\partial t} + \frac{p}{m} \cdot \nabla_q F_1 - \nabla_q \varphi \cdot \nabla_p F_1$$
$$= \frac{1}{v} \int \nabla_q \Phi(|q - q'|) \nabla_p F_2 d\tau', \quad (4.172)$$

where $F_1 = F_1(q, p, t)$ and $F_2 = F_2(q, q'; p, p'; t)$ and $\varphi = \varphi(q)$ is the potential energy of a particle in the external field.

The equations in (4.171) must be solved using the normalization and symmetry properties as well as the asymptotic form of F_s, just as in the equilibrium case. Now, after taking the limit $N \to \infty$ and $V \to \infty$, the normalization conditions will be

$$\lim_{V \to \infty} \frac{1}{V^s} \int \ldots \int F_s d\tau_1 \ldots d\tau_s = 1, \quad (4.173)$$

which may also be written in a form analogous to equations (4.15) and (4.16). In addition, for non-stationary problems, the initial conditions on the functions F_s when $t = 0$ (which define the particular problem) must be observed.

If we substitute in the general equations (4.171) special solutions in the form of (4.165), then we easily obtain

$$\sum_{1 \le i \le s} \frac{p_i}{m} \cdot \Big(kT \nabla_{q_i} F_s + F_s \nabla_{q_i} U_s$$
$$+ \frac{1}{v} \int \nabla_{q_i} \Phi_{i\ s+1} F_{s+1} d\tau_{s+1} \Big) = 0. \quad (4.174)$$

Because the momenta p_i are independent, after separating out the momentum factors in F_s according to (4.165), we return to the Bogolyubov equations (4.9) for the equilibrium correlation functions in configurational space.

The equations in (4.171) describe the temporal changes in the distribution functions. In this form, however, they are still not able to describe directly the approach of the system to equilibrium or stationary states or irreversible processes, such as viscosity, thermal conductivity, etc. This is connected with the fact that these equations, just like the original equation (4.167), are time reversible: the substitutions $t \to -t$ and $p_i \to -p_i$ leave them invariant. In essence, they are still equations of dynamics and not of statistics. But they may serve as a basis for the derivation of "kinetic" equations, which contain directly in themselves the irreversibility of macroscopic processes in a system of a large number of particles and which are useful for the study of relaxation and irreversible processes in such systems [1, 8].

A generalization of the equations for the correlation functions F_s in phase space to the case of quantum mechanics was given by Bogolyubov and Gurov [9].

REFERENCES

[1] N. N. Bogolyubov, *Problemy dinamicheskoi teorii v statisticheskoi fizike*, Gostekhizdat (Problems of Dynamical Theory in Statistical Physics), State Technical Press, 1946.

[2] I. Z. Fisher and B. V. Bokut, *Zh. Fiz. Khim.*, **30** (1956), 2747.

[3] S. V. Tyablikov and V. V. Tolmachev, *Doklady Akad. Nauk SSSR*, **114** (1957), 1210.

[4] A. E. Glauberman, *Izv. Akad. Nauk SSSR, ser. fiz.*, **22** (1958), 254.

[5] Ya. I. Frenkel, *Kineticheskaya teoriya zhidkostei*, Izd. AN SSSR, (Kinetic Theory of Liquids), Acad. Sci. Press, 1945.

[6] A. E. Glauberman, *Doklady Akad. Nauk SSSR*, **108** (1956), 49.

[7] M. Born and H. Green, *Proc. Roy. Soc., ser. A*, **188** (1946), 10.

[8] J. G. Kirkwood, *J. Chem. Phys.*, **14** (1946), 180.

[9] N. N. Bogolyubov and K. P. Gurov, *Zh. Eksperim. i. Teor. Fiz.*, **17** (1947), 614.

CHAPTER 5

THEORY OF LIQUIDS IN THE SUPERPOSITION APPROXIMATION

1. THE BOGOLYUBOV EQUATION FOR THE RADIAL DISTRIBUTION FUNCTION

In the case of liquids, the basic equations for the correlation functions, (4.9) or (4.13), cannot be expanded in terms of a small parameter, and their solution is unusually complex. We therefore examine the possibility of replacing them by simpler equations which are capable of solution. In order to do this, it is first necessary somehow to terminate the infinite chain of equations (4.9) or (4.13). Inasmuch as the functions which are basically of interest to us are $F_1(q)$ and $F_2(q, q')$, our goal would be achieved if we could succeed in expressing with sufficient precision the function $F_3(q, q', q'')$ in terms of F_1 and F_2.

The simplest approximation of this kind is the so-called superposition approximation, first introduced by Kirkwood, which has the form

$$F_1(q)F_1(q')F_1(q'')F_3(q, q', q'') = F_2(q, q')F_2(q, q'')F_2(q', q''). \quad (5.1)$$

It does not originate from any statistical considerations and must be regarded as an assumption introduced solely for the purpose of simplifying calculations. It is immediately obvious that in this case one should not expect great precision since, with the aid of the conventional correlation functions which were considered in chapter 2, assumption (5.1) may be rewritten in the form

$$F_1(q \mid q', q'') = \frac{F_1(q \mid q')F_1(q \mid q'')}{F_1(q)}. \quad (5.2)$$

It is clear that in this case the simultaneous influence of the particles at points q' and q'' on the probable position of a third particle is not taken into consideration.

Despite the extraordinary complexity of the problems of the theory of liquids, it is possible to construct an approximate theory starting from relationship (5.1). We note that the superposition approximation satisfies all the essential formal requirements for the function F_3: (5.1) is symmetric, normalized as in (4.15) and (4.16), and has the proper asymptotic form (4.14), provided that F_1 and F_2 themselves satisfy these conditions.

For a uniform system in the absence of external forces, the superposition approximation assumes the simple form

$$F_3(\boldsymbol{q}, \boldsymbol{q}', \boldsymbol{q}'') = g(|\boldsymbol{q}-\boldsymbol{q}'|)\,g(|\boldsymbol{q}-\boldsymbol{q}''|)\,g(|\boldsymbol{q}'-\boldsymbol{q}''|). \quad (5.3)$$

In this case it is not difficult to obtain a closed integral equation for the radial distribution function $g(r)$ [1]. By placing equation (5.3) in equation (4.9) with $s = 2$, we obtain

$$\begin{aligned} &kT\nabla_1 \ln g(|\boldsymbol{q}_1-\boldsymbol{q}_2|) + \nabla_1\Phi(|\boldsymbol{q}_1-\boldsymbol{q}_2|) \\ &+\frac{1}{v}\int \nabla_1\Phi(|\boldsymbol{q}_1-\boldsymbol{q}_3|)\,g(|\boldsymbol{q}_1-\boldsymbol{q}_3|)\,g(|\boldsymbol{q}_2-\boldsymbol{q}_3|)\,d\boldsymbol{q}_3 = 0. \end{aligned} \quad (5.4)$$

Let us introduce a new function

$$E(x) = \int_{\infty}^{x} \Phi'(t)\,g(t)\,dt. \quad (5.5)$$

By using it we can write

$$\nabla_1\Phi(|\boldsymbol{q}_1-\boldsymbol{q}_3|)\,g(|\boldsymbol{q}_1-\boldsymbol{q}_3|) = \nabla_1 E(|\boldsymbol{q}_1-\boldsymbol{q}_3|), \quad (5.6)$$

and then equation (5.4) is integrated with respect to $\boldsymbol{q}_1$:

$$\begin{aligned} &kT \ln g(|\boldsymbol{q}|) + \Phi(|\boldsymbol{q}|) \\ &\qquad +\frac{1}{v}\int E(|\boldsymbol{q}-\boldsymbol{q}'|)\,g(|\boldsymbol{q}'|)\,d\boldsymbol{q}' = C, \end{aligned} \quad (5.7)$$

where C is an integration constant. In comparison with (5.4), we have simplified the recording of the arguments and functions. It follows from the asymptotic condition on F_2 that when $r \to \infty$, it is necessary that $g(r) \to 1$. Therefore, placing $|\boldsymbol{q}| \to \infty$ in (5.7), we obtain

$$C = \frac{1}{v}\int E(|\boldsymbol{q}|)\,d\boldsymbol{q}. \quad (5.8)$$

In this way, instead of (5.7), we obtain

$$kT \ln g(|q|) + \Phi(|q|) + \frac{1}{v} \int E(|q - q'|)[g(|q'|) - 1]\, dq' = 0 . \tag{5.9}$$

Simplifying the volume integral and changing the notation for the arguments and functions, we finally obtain

$$kT \ln g(r) + \Phi(r) + \frac{2\pi}{r v} \int_0^\infty [g(\rho) - 1] \Big[\int_{|r-\rho|}^{r+\rho} E(t)\, t\, dt \Big] \rho\, d\rho = 0 . \tag{5.10}$$

This is the Bogolyubov equation for the approximate determination of the radial distribution function of particles in a liquid or a gas. A similar equation for $g(r)$, in a somewhat different notation, was also obtained by Born and Green [2]. The strong non-linearity of this equation, resulting not only from the presence of a logarithmic term, but also from the fact that the "kernel" of the equation itself depends on an unknown function, should be noted.

Analogously, in a non-uniform liquid, with the aid of approximation (5.1) and the first two equations (4.9) or (4.13), it is possible to obtain a closed system of equations for the two functions $F_1(q)$ and $F_2(q, q')$, which we will not bother to write out at this point.

In all cases, where the exact equations for the correlation functions (4.9) or (4.13) are expandable in terms of a small parameter and their solution obtained in the form of a power series in this parameter, the same expansion is also possible in equation (5.10) or in its generalization for a non-uniform liquid. For a gaseous system, solution of equation (5.10) in the form of a series

$$g(r) = g^{(0)}(r) + \frac{1}{v} g^{(1)}(r) + \frac{1}{v^2} g^{(2)}(r) + \dots \tag{5.11}$$

may be easily accomplished. It is not difficult to verify that for the functions $g^{(0)}(r)$ and $g^{(1)}(r)$ precisely the same expressions are obtained as in the case of the exact theory derived from equation (4.51). But for $g^{(2)}(r)$ one does not obtain the correct result, and this is also true of all the higher terms of the expansion (5.11). In evaluating the pressure of a gas, this results in the fact that the superposition approximation gives the correct values for the second and third virial coefficients, but inexact values for the fourth and subsequent virial coefficients. When the density of a gas is not large, the error is not very large.

In an analogous manner, for particles interacting with a Coulomb potential, the superposition approximation gives the correct $g(r)$ up to and including terms of the order γ (see chap. 4, secs. 4 and 5) but does not reproduce the higher approximations.

We shall see below that the superposition approximation and the integral equation (5.10) constructed on the basis of it give a satisfactory qualitative description of all the properties of liquids, although the precision of many quantitative estimates is not great. Therefore, the development of a theory of liquids based on the superposition approximation is of definite interest as a first-order approximation. It is necessary to keep in mind, however, that the use of approximation (5.3) violates the internal consistency of the theory, since the approximation (5.3) is not based on any statistical principles. This is apparent from the fact that the calculation of a thermodynamic function, when carried out by several different methods with the aid of the superposition approximation, may give results that do not coincide.

2. SUPERPOSITION APPROXIMATION IN THE KIRKWOOD METHOD

In chapter 2, section 7, we became acquainted with the correlation functions $F_s(q_1, \ldots, q_s; \lambda)$ generalized by Kirkwood, where λ is the "coupling parameter" of some one selected particle of the s particles under consideration. When $\lambda = 1$ these functions coincide with the ordinary correlation functions; when $\lambda = 0$ the selected particle is excluded from interacting with the remaining molecules of the system, and $F_s(q_1, \ldots, q_s; 0)$ is reduced to the usual correlation function F_{s-1} for the remaining $s - 1$ particles. Using these functions, instead of the basic system of integro-differential equations (4.9), one may obtain an exact system of simple integral equations for F_s. By using the superposition approximation, it is further possible to obtain an approximate closed integral equation for the radial distribution function which is different from the Bogolyubov equation (5.10).

Let us assign the number 1 to the selected particle. In accordance with the definition of the functions $F_s(\lambda)$, we find (see chap. 2, sec. 7)

$$F_s(q_1, \ldots, q_s; \lambda) = V^s \int_V \cdots \int_V D_N(q_1, \ldots, q_N; \lambda)\, dq_{s+1} \ldots dq_N, \tag{5.12}$$

where

$$D_N(q_1, \ldots, q_N; \lambda)$$
$$= Q_N^{-1}(\lambda) \exp\left\{-\frac{1}{kT}\left[U_{N-1} + \lambda \sum_{2 \le i \le N} \Phi(|q_1 - q_i|)\right]\right\}, \tag{5.13}$$

$$Q_N(\lambda) = \int_V \cdots \int_V \exp\left\{-\frac{1}{kT}\left[U_{N-1} + \lambda \sum_{2 \le i \le N} \Phi(|q_1 - q_i|)\right]\right\} dq_1 \ldots dq_N, \tag{5.14}$$

while U_{N-1} designates the full energy of interaction of the particles of the system with the first particle decoupled. For the sake of simplicity we shall limit ourselves to the deduction of the integral equation for the function $F_2(\lambda)$ only.

Placing $s = 2$ in (5.12), differentiating this equation with respect to λ, and using (5.13) and (5.14), we obtain, after simple manipulations analogous to those carried out in chapter 4 and used in deducing equation (4.8),

$$kT \frac{\partial g(|q_1 - q_2|; \lambda)}{\partial \lambda} + g(|q_1 - q_2|; \lambda)\left[\Phi(|q_1 - q_2|) + kT \frac{\partial \ln Q_N(\lambda)}{\partial \lambda}\right] + \frac{N-2}{V} \int_V \Phi(|q_1 - q_3|) F_3(q_1, q_2, q_3; \lambda)\, dq_3 = 0, \tag{5.15}$$

where the fact that $F_2(q, q'; \lambda) = g(|q - q'|; \lambda)$ is taken into consideration. But, from (2.128), we have

$$kT \frac{\partial \ln Q_N(\lambda)}{\partial \lambda} = -\frac{N-1}{V} \int_V \Phi(|q_1 - q_3|)\, g(|q_1 - q_3|)\, dq_3, \tag{5.16}$$

so that equation (5.15) may be written in the form

$$kT \frac{\partial g(|q_1 - q_2|; \lambda)}{\partial \lambda} + \Phi(|q_1 - q_2|)\, g(|q_1 - q_2|; \lambda) + \frac{N-2}{V} \int_V \Phi(|q_1 - q_3|)\left[F_3(q_1, q_2, q_3; \lambda) - \frac{N-1}{N-2} g(|q_1 - q_2|; \lambda)\, g(|q_1 - q_3|; \lambda)\right] dq_3 = 0. \tag{5.17}$$

Dividing each term of the last equation by $g(|q_1 - q_2|; \lambda)$ and proceeding to the limit $N \to \infty$ and $V \to \infty$, such that $v = V/N = \text{const}$, we obtain

$$kT \frac{\partial \ln g(|q_1 - q_2|; \lambda)}{\partial \lambda} + \Phi(|q_1 - q_2|) + \frac{1}{v} \int \Phi(|q_1 - q_3|) \left[\frac{F_3(q_1, q_2, q_3; \lambda)}{g(|q_1 - q_2|; \lambda)} - g(|q_1 - q_3|; \lambda) \right] dq_3 = 0, \tag{5.18}$$

where the integration is over all space. Now, when $\lambda = 0$, it is necessary that $F_2(q, q'; \lambda) = F_1(q')$, i.e., in our case, $g(|q_1 - q_2|; 0) = 1$. Therefore, integrating equation (5.18) with respect to λ, from $\lambda = 0$ to λ, we finally obtain

$$kT \ln g(|q_1 - q_2|; \lambda) + \lambda\Phi(|q_1 - q_2|) + \frac{1}{v} \int \Phi(|q_1 - q_3|) \left\{ \int_0^\lambda \left[\frac{F_3(q_1, q_2, q_3; \lambda)}{g(|q_1 - q_2|; \lambda)} - g(|q_1 - q_3|; \lambda) \right] d\lambda \right\} dq_3 = 0. \tag{5.19}$$

Analogous equations may also be obtained for all the remaining functions $F_s(q_1, \ldots, q_s; \lambda)$, and we obtain, as in the Bogolyubov method, an infinite system of non-linear integral equations for the correlation functions.

Let us now use the superposition approximation for $F_3(\lambda)$. Assuming, as in (5.3), that with adequate accuracy

$$F_3(q_1, q_2, q_3; \lambda) = g(|q_1 - q_2|; \lambda)\, g(|q_2 - q_3|; \lambda)\, g(|q_2 - q_3|; \lambda), \tag{5.20}$$

placing (5.20) in equation (5.19), and simplifying the notation of the arguments, we obtain the closed equation

$$kT \ln g(|q|; \lambda) + \lambda\Phi(|q|) + \frac{1}{v} \int \Phi(|q - q'|) \times \left\{ \int_0^\lambda (|q - q'|; \lambda)[g(|q'|; \lambda) - 1]\, d\lambda \right\} dq' = 0. \tag{5.21}$$

By carrying out the same simplification as in the transition from equation (5.9) to equation (5.10), we finally obtain the Kirkwood equation for the radial distribution function [3].

$$kT \ln g(r, \lambda) + \lambda\Phi(r) + \frac{2\pi}{rv} \int_0^\infty \int_0^\lambda [g(\rho; \lambda) - 1] \left[\int_{|r-\rho|}^{r+\rho} \Phi(t)\, g(t; \lambda)\, t\, dt \right] d\lambda\, \rho\, d\rho\,. \tag{5.22}$$

This equation is of the same type as the Bogolyubov equation (5.10); however, it is somewhat complicated by the dependence of an unknown function on the auxiliary parameter λ. After solution of this equation it is necessary to set $\lambda = 1$.

The Bogolyubov and Kirkwood equations contain two thermodynamic parameters v and T, so that their complete solutions have the form $g(r) = g(r, v, T)$ or $g(r; \lambda) = g(r, v, T; \lambda)$, respectively. Knowledge of these functions for all three or four arguments, according to the general theory described in chapter 2, completely determines the structure and thermodynamic properties of the liquid.

3. GENERAL EXAMINATION OF THE BOGOLYUBOV EQUATION

Equations (5.10) or (5.22) for the radial distribution function are still very complex, and their solution involves great difficulties. Therefore, as a preliminary, we shall try to evaluate qualitatively the procedure used in solving these equations. To be definite, we shall examine equation (5.10), although all the results will also be applicable to equation (5.22).

It is convenient to write the basic equation (5.10) in somewhat different form. Let us make the substitution

$$g(r) = \exp\left[-\frac{\Phi(r)}{kT}\right]u(r) \tag{5.23}$$

and, moreover, let us transform to dimensionless coordinates by placing $q = aq'$, where a is some characteristic molecular length. If we introduce the function

$$\bar{E}(x) = \int_{\infty}^{x} \left\{\exp\left[-\frac{\Phi(t)}{kT}\right]\right\}' u(t)\,dt = -\frac{1}{kT}E(x), \tag{5.24}$$

where $E(x)$ is determined by (5.5), then equation (5.10) may be rewritten in the form

$$r \ln u(r) = \lambda \int_0^{\infty} \left\{\exp\left[-\frac{\Phi(\rho)}{kT}\right]u(\rho) - 1\right\} \times \left[\int_{|r-\rho|}^{r+\rho} \bar{E}(t)\,t\,dt\right]\rho\,d\rho, \tag{5.25}$$

where the primes on the arguments are dropped and the dimensionless parameter

$$\lambda = \frac{2\pi a^3}{v}, \tag{5.26}$$

which characterizes the density of the system, is introduced. In equation (5.25) λ is a typical "parameter of the integral equation." Temperature enters into this equation in a complex manner but only in combination with the intermolecular potential, so that only the ratio need be assigned.

The average values of physical quantities may be expressed in terms of the function $u(r)$ instead of $g(r)$. For pressure, for example, we find, from (2.40) and (5.23), that

$$\frac{pv}{kT} = 1 + \frac{\lambda}{3}\int_0^\infty \left\{\exp\left[-\frac{\Phi(r)}{kT}\right]\right\}' u(r)\, r^3 dr. \qquad (5.27)$$

Let us now examine the behavior of the function $u(r)$ at small and at large distances. It is easy to see that the expansion of the right side of equation (5.25) into a series in powers of r has the form $Ar + Br^3 + \ldots$ and, therefore, the function $u(r)$ at small values of r is equal to

$$u(r) = u(0)(1 + cr^2 + \ldots). \qquad (5.28)$$

Corresponding to this, we have for the radial distribution function

$$g(r) \approx u(0)\exp\left[-\frac{\Phi(r)}{kT}\right]. \qquad (5.29)$$

If the intermolecular potential $\Phi(r)$ increases sharply when $r \to 0$, as occurs, for example, in the case of the Lennard-Jones potential (1.29), then, for practical purposes, $g(r) = 0$ approximately up to $r \approx a$ because of the "impenetrability" of the particles. In the region of the minimum of the function $\Phi(r)$, the radial distribution function has a maximum, the exact position and shape of which depend on the function $u(r)$.

Let us now proceed to an examination of the behavior of $u(r)$ at large distances. Let us assume that the potential $\Phi(r)$ has a short-range character and that the values of r which are now of interest to us exceed the radius of action of the intermolecular forces. It follows from equation (5.25) that when $r \to \infty$ we have $u(r) \to 1$. It is not difficult to determine the general form of the function $u(r)$ at large values of r and to define more accurately the law according to which $u(r)$ tends toward unity [4].

Let us assume for large values of r that

$$u(r) = 1 + \frac{\varphi(r)}{r}, \qquad (5.30)$$

while $[\varphi(r)/r] \to 0$ when $r \to \infty$. Let us place this in equation (5.25) and linearize the equation in $\varphi(r)$. Then on the left-hand side in (5.25) we obtain simply $\varphi(r)$, while on the right-hand side, due to the rapid decrease of $\Phi(\rho)$ and $\bar{E}(\rho)$ with an increase in ρ, only the values of ρ which are close to r are essential in the integral. At large values of r, the upper limit in the internal integral may be changed to infinity and the exponent, $\exp[-\Phi(\rho)/kT]$, may be replaced by unity. Finally, for large values of r, we obtain

$$\varphi(r) = \lambda \int_0^\infty \left[\int_{|r-\rho|}^\infty \bar{E}(t)\, t\, dt \right] \varphi(\rho)\, d\rho \,. \qquad (5.31)$$

For brevity, let us introduce the notation

$$\begin{aligned} K(x) &= \int_{|x|}^\infty \bar{E}(t)\, t\, dt \\ &= \tfrac{1}{2} \int_{|x|}^\infty \left\{ \exp\left[-\frac{\Phi(t)}{kT} \right] \right\}' u(t)(x^2 - t^2)\, dt \,, \end{aligned} \qquad (5.32)$$

where the right half of the equation was obtained by the partial integration of (5.24). Furthermore, the function $K(x)$ decreases rapidly with increasing values of x; therefore, at large values of r it is possible to substitute in (5.31) for the lower limit of integration $-\infty$. Equation (5.31) finally assumes the form

$$\varphi(r) = \lambda \int_{-\infty}^\infty K(|r-\rho|)\, \varphi(\rho)\, d\rho \,. \qquad (5.33)$$

This is the equation for the determination of the asymptotic form of the radial distribution function (large distances). The kernel of this equation, according to (5.32), itself depends on the values of $g(r)$ at small distances, and later on in analyzing equation (5.33) we will suppose that these values of $g(r)$ are known.

Equation (5.32) is easily solved. Let us assume that

$$\varphi(r) \sim e^{i\gamma r} \,. \qquad (5.34)$$

Then, by substituting in equation (5.33), we obtain an equation for the determination of γ,

$$\lambda L(\gamma) = 1 \,, \qquad (5.35)$$

where $L(\gamma)$ is the Fourier transform of the kernel $K(x)$:

$$L(\gamma) = \int_{-\infty}^\infty K(x)\, e^{i\gamma x} dx \,. \qquad (5.36)$$

At each value of $\lambda > 0$, equation (5.35) in general has several or even infinitely many roots which may be represented in a general case by the complex numbers

$$\gamma_n = \beta_n + i\alpha_n \,, \qquad n = 1, 2, \ldots \,. \qquad (5.37)$$

Because λ is positive, and using the parity and positive nature of the function $K(x)$, it follows that these roots may be grouped in fours: $\pm\beta_n \pm i\alpha_n$. However, the roots with negative imaginary members clearly do not satisfy the condition $u(r) \to 1$ when $r \to \infty$ and must be discarded, so that a pair of roots $\pm\beta_n + i|\alpha_n|$ remains. To each such pair there corresponds in real form a solution of equation (5.33) of the form

$$\varphi_n(r) = A_n \exp(-|\alpha_n| r)\cos(\beta_n r + \delta_n), \tag{5.38}$$

where the numbers A_n and δ_n remain undetermined in the approximation under consideration. Since at large values of r (5.23) implies that $u(r)$ and $g(r)$ coincide, then from (5.31) and (5.38) we finally find that

$$g(r) = 1 + \frac{1}{r}\sum_n A_n \exp(-|\alpha_n| r)\cos(\beta_n r + \delta_n). \tag{5.39}$$

Expression (5.39) gives us a general picture of the radial distribution function when the distances between particles are large. In fact, in the series (5.39) only the term with the lowest value of $|\alpha_n|$ is important, and if it is designated by $|\alpha_1|$, then, instead of (5.39), we may write

$$g(r) \approx 1 + \frac{A_1}{r}\exp(-|\alpha_1| r)\cos(\beta_1 r + \delta_1). \tag{5.40}$$

This result agrees with the behavior of the experimentally obtained functions $g(r)$: with increasing values of r the radial distribution function oscillates, decreases in magnitude, and approaches unity.

It should be noted, in conclusion, that in accordance with the general theory, the solution of equation (5.10) should be subjected to the normalization condition

$$\lim_{r\to\infty} \frac{1}{R^3} \int_0^R [g(r) - 1]\, r^2 dr = 0. \tag{5.41}$$

However, it is evident from (5.39) that this condition is automatically fulfilled at any values of A_n, α_n, β_n, and δ_n. Therefore, once the asymptotic condition $q(r) \to 1$ when $r \to \infty$ is fulfilled the condition of normalization (5.41) places no further limitations on the solution of equation (5.10).

4. ACCURACY OF THE BOGOLYUBOV EQUATION FOR THE RADIAL DISTRIBUTION FUNCTION

The Bogolyubov equation (5.10) is a complex non-linear integral equation, a study of which from a formal mathematical point of view is of independent interest. For the theory of liquids, this equation is important and interesting only to the extent that its solution $g(r)$ describes the binary correlation function of the particles of a liquid:

$$g(|q-q'|)=F_2(q,q'). \qquad (5.42)$$

Therefore, it is interesting to examine the problem of whether or not correspondence with (5.42) will always occur in solving equation (5.10).

Equation (5.10), owing to the limit $N\to\infty$ and $V\to\infty$, asymptotically describes the extensive properties of a uniform system with $F_1(q) = 1$. Without fulfilment of the condition $F_1(q) = 1$, fulfilment of condition (5.42) also appears impossible. But it is physically obvious that the possibility of isolating a uniform volume as part of a real system depends on the ultimate thickness of the surface layer at its boundaries, where surely $F_1(q) \neq 1$. If one assumes the system to be semi-infinite and bounded by the plane $z = 0$ as in chapter 4, section 3, we come to the conclusion that the condition for the correctness of equation (5.42) is

$$F_1(z)\to 1 \quad \text{when} \quad z\to\infty, \qquad (5.43)$$

which itself defines the ultimate thickness of the boundary layer of the system. In addition to this, the limiting value unity (5.43) must be reached sufficiently rapidly. This condition may be expressed directly in terms of the properties of the function $g(r)$ [4].

For this purpose let us examine the equation, when $s = 1$, for the correlation functions of a semi-infinite system bounded by an ideal wall (4.54):

$$kT\frac{\partial F_1(z)}{\partial z}+\frac{1}{v}\int_{z'>0}\frac{\partial\Phi(|q-q'|)}{\partial z}F_2(q,q')\,dq'=0, \qquad (5.44)$$

where $z > 0$ and $q = \{0, 0, z\}$ may be computed. The approximation

$$F_2(q,q') = g(|q-q'|)F_1(z)F_1(z') \qquad (5.45)$$

will now correspond to the superposition approximation (5.3). As a matter of fact, with the aid of the conditional correlation functions, the superposition approximation (5.3) may be written not only in the form (5.2), but also in the form

$$F_2(q,q'|q'') = g(|q-q'|)F_1(q|q'')F_2(q'|q''), \qquad (5.46)$$

where q'' is the position of the arbitrarily chosen and fixed particle. In our problem it is not the third particle which is fixed, but the wall, and equation (5.46) is transformed to (5.45).

By placing (5.45) in equation (5.44) and transforming to dimensionless coordinates, we obtain the equation

$$\frac{\partial \ln F_1(z)}{\partial z} = \frac{\lambda}{2\pi} \int_{z'>0} \frac{\partial \bar{E}(|q-q'|)}{\partial z} F_1(z')\,dq', \quad (5.47)$$

where the symbols of (5.24) and (5.26) are used. By integrating this equation with respect to z and determining the integration constant from the condition that $F_1(z) \to 1$ when $z \to \infty$, we obtain

$$\ln F_1(z) = \frac{\lambda}{2\pi} \int_{z'>0} \bar{E}(|q-q'|) F_1(z')\,dq' - \frac{\lambda}{2\pi} \int \bar{E}(|q-q'|)\,dq', \quad (5.48)$$

where the second integral is over all space and does not depend on the position of point q. Let us separate it into two integrals, one for the positive and one for the negative regions, respectively. Then

$$\ln F_1(z) = -\frac{\lambda}{2\pi} \int_{z'>0} \bar{E}(|q-q'|)\,dq' + \frac{\lambda}{2\pi} \int_{z'>0} \bar{E}(|q-q'|)[F_1(z')-1]\,dq'. \quad (5.49)$$

These integrals are easily simplified by the introduction of cylindrical coordinates. We have

$$\int_{z'>0} \bar{E}(|q-q'|)[F_1(z')-1]\,dq' = 2\pi \int_0^\infty \int_0^\infty \times \bar{E}\{\sqrt{[\rho^2+(z-z')^2]}\}[F_1(z')-1]\,dz'\rho\,d\rho = 2\pi \int_0^\infty [F_1(z')-1]\left[\int_{|z-z'|}^\infty \bar{E}(t)\,t\,dt\right] dz' \quad (5.50)$$

and analogously for the first integral in (5.49). By introducing notation in accordance with (5.32) for the internal integral, we obtain an equation for $F_1(z)$ in the form

$$\ln F_1(z) = -\lambda f(z) + \lambda \int_0^\infty K(|z-z'|)[F_1(z')-1]\,dz', \quad (5.51)$$

where the function $f(z)$ is equal to

$$f(z) = \int_z^\infty K(x)\,dx. \quad (5.52)$$

We shall now concern ourselves with the behavior of $F_1(z)$ far from the walls, at distances exceeding the radius of action of the molecular forces. Then we may assume that

$$F_1(z) = 1 + \psi(z), \tag{5.53}$$

whereupon $\psi(z) \to 0$ when $z \to \infty$. Now linearize equation (5.51) in terms of $\psi(z)$. Taking into consideration the rapid decrease in the functions $K(x)$ and $f(z)$ with increase in the arguments, for large values of z, we obtain

$$\psi(z) = \lambda \int_{-\infty}^{\infty} K(|z - z'|)\psi(z')dz', \tag{5.54}$$

where we have set the lower limit of integration equal to $-\infty$, an approximation which at large values of z is unimportant.

On comparison, equations (5.54) and (5.33) are found to be identical. Consequently the functions

$$\varphi(r) = r[g(r) - 1], \qquad \psi(z) = F_1(z) - 1 \tag{5.55}$$

behave the same at large values of their arguments. From this it follows that (5.43) may be formulated in terms of the function $g(r)$ by requiring that

$$r[g(r) - 1] \to 0 \quad \text{when} \quad r \to \infty. \tag{5.56}$$

In this way, we obtain an unusual "boundary condition" for the integral equation (5.10). Its satisfaction is essential to the interpretation of the solutions of equation (5.10) as the binary distribution function of some system (see eq. [5.42]). It is possible that solutions of equation (5.10) for which condition (5.56) is not fulfilled are physically absurd. Turning our attention to expression (5.39), we see that condition (5.56) is always fulfilled if no α_n is reduced to zero. We shall see below that this condition is intimately connected with the conditions for the thermodynamic stability of the system.

The analysis of the behavior of $F_1(z)$ at large distances from the walls may now be carried to a conclusion. Applying to equation (5.54) the same reasoning as was applied to equation (5.33), we find, analogously to (5.39), that at large values of z

$$F_1(z) = 1 + \sum_n A'_n \exp(-|\alpha_n| z)\cos(\beta_n z + \delta'_n). \tag{5.57}$$

The quantities α_n and β_n are the same in this case as in (5.39) and are determined by equation (5.35). Generally speaking, however, the quantities A'_n and δ'_n are different from A_n and δ_n in (5.39).

5. THE PROBLEM OF A SYSTEM OF HARD SPHERES

The simplest system to which it would be possible to attempt to apply the theory of correlation functions developed in this and the preceding chapters is a system of rigid spheres of diameter a. In this case, the function $\Phi(r)$ is equal to

$$\begin{aligned} \Phi(r) &= +\infty \quad \text{when} \quad r < a\,, \\ \Phi(r) &= 0 \quad \text{when} \quad r > a\,. \end{aligned} \tag{5.58}$$

The solution of this problem is of great methodological interest. In chapter 3 its solution was examined for a one-dimensional case.

In the rigorous three-dimensional theory, the problem of finding the correlation functions and thermodynamic properties of the system may be solved by the expansion of all quantities in a power series in the density. This has been done by many authors; finding high-order approximations, however, involves extremely cumbersome calculations. The best results were obtained in paper [5] where the pressure was successfully calculated correct up to the fifth virial coefficient, inclusive:

$$\begin{aligned} \frac{pv}{kT} = 1 + 4\left(\frac{v_0}{v}\right) + 10\left(\frac{v_0}{v}\right)^2 + 18.36\left(\frac{v_0}{v}\right)^3 \\ + (29.44 \pm 1.28)\left(\frac{v_0}{v}\right)^4 + \ldots\,, \end{aligned} \tag{5.59}$$

where $v_0 = \pi a^3/6$ is the volume of a rigid sphere. When $v > 2v_0$ the series (5.59) converges, as may be demonstrated from the general theory of real gases, while when $v \gtrsim 5v_0$ extrapolation of the series gives acceptable accuracy.

Let us examine in greater detail the analysis of the rigid-sphere liquid in the superposition approximation and without the restriction to low density. We shall go over to dimensionless coordinates at once, so that the diameter of the particles may be considered to be of unit size. In addition, due to the strongly discontinuous nature of the function $\Phi(r)$ (see eq. [5.58]), it is convenient to make use of the function $u(r)$ instead of $g(r)$. From (5.58) it follows that

$$\exp\left[-\frac{\Phi(r)}{kT}\right]' = \delta(r-1), \tag{5.60}$$

where $\delta(x)$ is a one-dimensional δ function; from (5.27) we at once obtain for the pressure

$$\frac{pv}{kT} = 1 + \tfrac{1}{3}\lambda u(1) = 1 + \tfrac{2}{3}\lambda^*\,, \tag{5.61}$$

with the definition

$$\lambda^* = \tfrac{1}{2}\lambda u(1) = \frac{\pi a^3}{v} u(1) = 6\,\frac{v_0}{v}\,u(1). \qquad (5.62)$$

Furthermore, for the function $\bar{E}(x)$ defined in (5.24) we obtain with the aid of (5.60)

$$\begin{aligned} \bar{E}(x) &= -u(1) \quad \text{when} \quad x < 1, \\ \bar{E}(x) &= 0 \quad \text{when} \quad x > 1, \end{aligned} \qquad (5.63)$$

and the integral equation (5.25) for the function $u(r)$, after simple transformations, appears in the form

$$\begin{aligned} r \ln u(r) = {} & \frac{\lambda^*}{12} r^2(4 - r^2) \\ & + \lambda^* \int_1^{r+1} [(r-\rho)^2 - 1][u(\rho) - 1]\rho\, d\rho, \end{aligned} \qquad (5.64)$$

if $r \leq 2$ and

$$r \ln u(r) = \lambda^* \int_{r-1}^{r+1} [(r-\rho)^2 - 1][u(\rho) - 1]\rho\, d\rho, \qquad (5.65)$$

if $r > 2$. It is not difficult to verify that at the points $r = 1$ and $r = 2$, the function $u(r)$ is continuous and differentiable.

From (5.23) and (5.58) the radial distribution function $g(r)$ is related to the function $u(r)$ by

$$\begin{aligned} g(r) &= 0 \quad \text{when} \quad r < 1, \\ g(r) &= u(r) \quad \text{when} \quad r > 1. \end{aligned} \qquad (5.66)$$

Taking these relationships into consideration, equations (5.64) and (5.65) may be written more compactly in the form of one equation for $g(r)$ when $r > 1$:

$$r \ln g(r) = \lambda^* \int_{r-1}^{r+1} [(r-\rho)^2 - 1][g(\rho) - 1]\rho\, d\rho, \qquad (5.67)$$

and $g(r) = 0$ when $r < 1$.

For small values of the parameter λ^*, approximately up to $\lambda^* \sim 1$, equations (5.64) to (5.65) or (5.67) may be solved with comparative ease by various approximation methods. For large values of λ^*, the problem becomes considerably more complex. The paper of Kirkwood and his collaborators [6] gives the results of numerical integration of these equations with the aid of high-speed computers. By using a complex procedure of successive approximations, the functions, $g(r)$, were found for values of λ^* equal to 1.25; 2.50; 5.00; 6.85; 8.25; 8.70. The results are given in the form of tables and graphs. In Figure 7 we show curves for several functions, $g(r)$, obtained in this way. The qualitative agreement of these curves with the experimentally obtained functions, $g(r)$, is obvious. It is evident that as the density of the system increases the short-range order characteristic of liquids or dense gases becomes clearer and clearer. The sharpness of the peak at $r = 1$ is related to the discontinuous character of the potential $\Phi(r)$ (see eq. [5.58]).

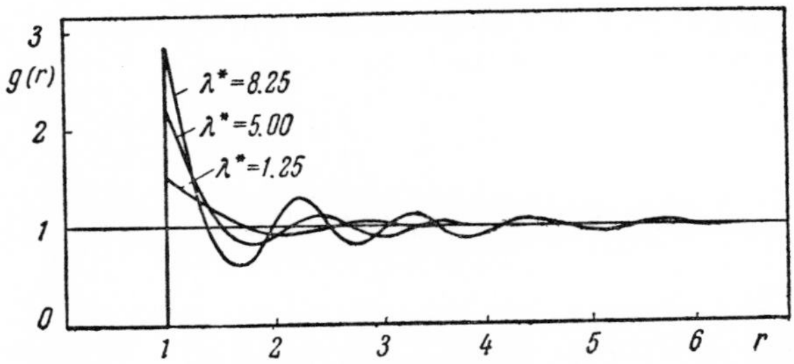

FIG. 7.—Theoretical radial distribution functions in a system of rigid spheres at three values of the density [6].

TABLE 8

λ^*	$u(1)$	v/v_0	λ^*	$u(1)$	v/v_0
0.33	1.14	20.34	2.50	1.80	4.32
0.56	1.20	12.96	5.00	2.36	2.83
0.71	1.26	10.55	6.85	2.66	2.34
0.91	1.33	8.75	8.25	2.85	2.07
1.25	1.45	6.95	8.70	2.90	2.00

It is evident from the results obtained in paper [6] that, at least qualitatively, the superposition approximation correctly reproduces the molecular structure of the condensed system.

Table 8 gives the values of λ^* and $u(1)$ corresponding to some values of the density v_0/v. The data for large values of the density are taken from paper [6]. The case $v_0/v = 0.50$ is the maximum possible density in a disordered system of spheres which still satisfies the "boundary condition" (5.56).

Knowledge of the function $u(1)$ and its dependence on v makes it possible to develop completely the thermodynamics of a system of rigid spheres; however, the thermodynamics of a one-phase liquid of rigid spheres is of little interest due to the special features of the pair potential. The potential (5.58) results in a radial distribution function that does not depend on temperature, and, therefore from (5.61), the pressure is a linear function of the temperature:

$$p = \frac{kT}{v_0} f\left(\frac{v_0}{v}\right), \tag{5.68}$$

where $f(x)$ is some function. In addition, from (2.31), the average potential energy of the system is equal to zero, so that the total energy does not depend on the volume:

$$E = \tfrac{3}{2} NkT\,. \tag{5.69}$$

Thus, we obtain

$$\left(\frac{\partial E}{\partial v}\right)_T = \left(\frac{\partial^2 p}{\partial T^2}\right)_v = 0\,. \tag{5.70}$$

For real systems this is of little interest, and we therefore shall not consider the matter in any greater detail.

6. RESULTS OF THE NUMERICAL INTEGRATION OF THE BOGOLYUBOV EQUATION FOR A SYSTEM OF INTERACTING PARTICLES

Solution of the integral equation for the radial distribution function for the more interesting case of a system of interacting particles has been carried out by Kirkwood and his co-workers [7]. Integration was carried out numerically with the aid of a high-speed computer and the results presented in tables and graphs. The solutions of equations (5.10) and (5.22) led to very similar results. The majority of the calculations were made with the Bogolyubov equation (5.10).

A system with a modified Lennard-Jones potential was selected:

$$\begin{aligned} \Phi(r) &= +\infty \qquad \text{when} \quad r < a\,, \\ \Phi(r) &= 4\epsilon\left[\left(\frac{a}{r}\right)^{12} - \left(\frac{a}{r}\right)^{6}\right] \qquad \text{when} \quad r > a\,, \end{aligned} \tag{5.71}$$

so that the particles are rigid spheres, but interact with a Lennard-Jones potential if they do not come into contact. Therefore, when, $r < a$, $g(r) = 0$. When $r > a$ the calculation was carried out using the following scheme. The function $\psi(r) = r \ln g(r)$ was introduced together with the function $g(r)$, and then $\psi(r)$ was sought from equation (5.10) in the form of a power series in ϵ/kT:

$$\psi(r) = \psi_0(r) + \frac{\epsilon}{kT}\psi_1(r) + \left(\frac{\epsilon}{kT}\right)^2 \psi_2(r) + \ldots\,. \tag{5.72}$$

In the zeroth approximation this leads to the rigid-sphere problem, and $\psi_0(r)$ may be considered to be known. For higher approximations, after transformation to dimensionless units of length, $r \to r' = r/a$, linear inhomogeneous integral equations are obtained:

$$\psi_k(r) = f_k(r) + \lambda^* \int_{r-1}^{r+1} [(r-\rho)^2 - 1]\, g_0(\rho)\psi_k(\rho)\, d\rho\,, \quad (5.73)$$

where $k = 1, 2, \ldots$ and

$$\lambda^* = 6\left(\frac{v_0}{v}\right) g_0(1+0), \quad (5.74)$$

while the inhomogeneous term $f_k(r)$ is expressed, although in a very cumbersome manner, by integrals of the functions $\psi_{k-1}, \psi_{k-2} \ldots$. The subscript zero in (5.73) and (5.74) refers to the zeroth (rigid-sphere) approximation.

By using the zeroth approximation from paper [6], the next two terms of $\psi(r)$ were calculated, leading to the final (approximate) result for the radial distribution function

$$g(r) = \exp\left\{\frac{1}{r}\left[\psi_0(r) + \frac{\epsilon}{kT}\psi_1(r) + \left(\frac{\epsilon}{kT}\right)^2 \psi_2(r)\right]\right\}. \quad (5.75)$$

In the judgment of the authors of paper [7], (5.75) gives $g(r)$ with sufficient accuracy in the temperature range from $T = \infty$ to approximately two-thirds of the critical temperature. Such solutions have been obtained for values of λ^* equal to 1.25; 2.50; 5.00; 6.85; 8.25, which cover the density range from approximately one-third to three times the density at the critical point.

As a result of the calculations, there are available a family of functions $g(r)$ for various values of T and v, tabulated in detail. In contrast to the rigid-sphere fluid, when $T \neq \infty$, the function $g(r)$ now has a rounded off first maximum at a distance somewhat exceeding $r = 1$. How well these functions correspond to the radial distribution functions of particles in a real liquid is evident from Figure 8, where the theoretical function $g(r)$ for $\lambda^* = 6.85$ and $\epsilon/kT = 1.2$ is shown by the dotted line and compared with the experimentally obtained $g(r)$ for argon (solid line). The experimental data taken from paper [8] correspond to $T = 91.8°$ K and a pressure of 1.8 atm., which is close to the values of λ^* and ϵ/kT for the theoretical curve. In this case, the unit of length a for the theoretical curve was so chosen that the abscissas of the first maxima of both curves coincided. It is evident from the chart that the qualitative agreement of the curves is very good; however, the oscillations of the theoretical curve are somewhat broader, which is possibly related to the "rigidity" of the particles (see eq. [5.71]).

Of special interest are the changes in the function $g(r; v, T)$, with changes in the thermodynamic parameters v and T. Calculations have shown that an increase in the density of the system and a decrease in the temperature result in an increase in the amplitude of the oscillations of $g(r)$ and an increase in the radius of correlation of the particles of the system. Simultaneously, there occurs some displacement of the extrema and the nodes of the function $g(r) - 1$. All these observations correspond qualitatively to what might be expected on the basis of our physical picture of the radial distribution function. These results are

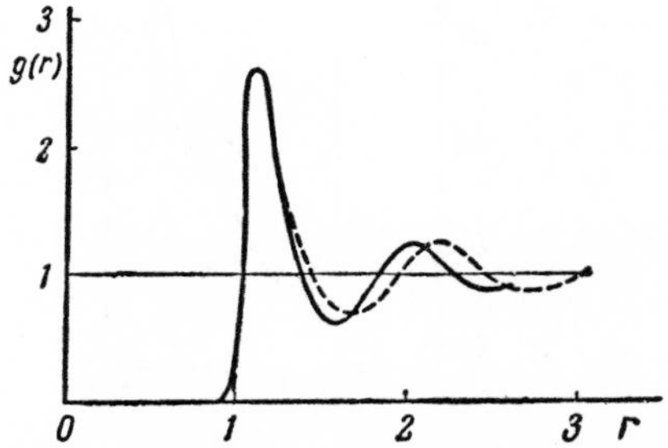

FIG. 8.—Theoretical (dashed line) and experimental (solid line) radial distribution functions of liquid argon at 92° K and a pressure of 1.8 atm.

also in qualitative agreement with experimental data for the function $g(r)$, if some effects connected with the presence of a hard "core" in the theoretical calculations (5.71) are excluded.

Consider now the results of calculations of the thermodynamic properties of the system under examination. Figure 9, taken from paper [7], gives an idea of the accuracy of this model and of the method used. It shows the isotherms of gaseous argon at 0° C. The dimensionless function pv/kT is plotted as a function of density in Amagat units: curve A is the experimental data [9]; curve B (dotted) is the theoretical prediction; and curve C is the free-volume equation of state [10]. It is evident from the figure that at not too great densities, the agreement between theory and experiment is not bad, but, nevertheless, the theoretical curve has too small a slope, and at higher densities this results in a considerable divergence from the experimental data.

At lower temperatures the $p - v$ isotherms at some average densities are of such a shape that from the higher-density side the points on the isotherm lie lower than those from the lower-density side. This indicates the presence of a (liquid-gas) phase transition in the system. From the conditions $p_L = p_G$ and $\mu_L = \mu_G$ where μ is the chemical potential (the subscripts representing liquid and gas, respectively), it is possible to find for each temperature the phase boundaries. Figure 10 shows the family of isotherms of a liquid and a gas, including the

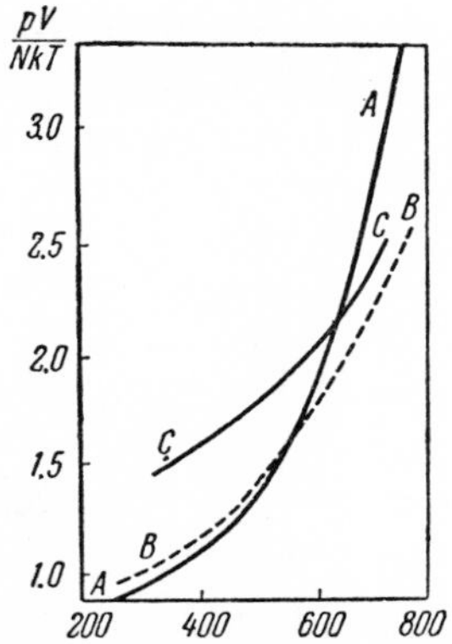

FIG. 9.—Isotherms of gaseous argon at 0° C. Curve *AA* is experimental. Curves *BB* and *CC* are theoretical with the use of superposition approximation and according to the free volume theory, respectively.

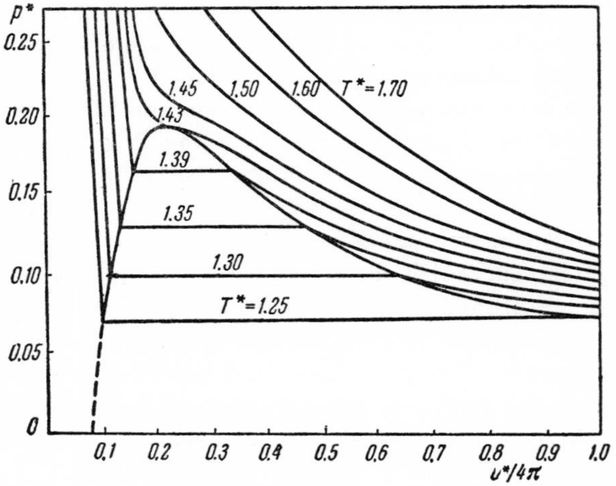

FIG. 10.—The family of theoretical isotherms for argon in the gaseous, liquid, and transition regions [7].

transition region obtained in this way. The pressure, volume, and temperature are indicated here in dimensionless units

$$p^* = \frac{a^3}{\epsilon} p, \qquad v^* = \frac{v}{a^3}, \qquad T^* = \frac{k}{\epsilon} T \tag{5.76}$$

($v^*/4\pi$ is the unit on the horizontal axis of the diagram). It is evident from the diagram that, at least qualitatively, the theory describes the properties of real liquids and gases well, including such complex phenomena as condensation and the critical point. For the critical parameters, it is found that

$$p^*_{cr} = 0.199 , \qquad v^* = 2.585 , \qquad T^* = 1.433 , \tag{5.77}$$

instead of the experimental values 0.12, 3.16, and 1.26, respectively. The value 0.358 was obtained for the dimensionless ratio pv/kT at the critical point instead of the experimental (Ar) value 0.292.

The energy, entropy, and other thermodynamic properties of the system investigated were also calculated in paper [7]. Comparison of the reduced values of these quantities with the experimentally reduced values for argon shows that, at low and moderate densities, the theory agrees well with experiment, but as the density increases the discrepancies increase. At densities of order of the critical density, the discrepancy between theory and experiment for the volume-dependent contributions to the pressure, entropy, and energy amounts to about 30 per cent and then increases even more.

Thus, we see that the theory based on the integral equation (5.10) accurately describes the presence of short-range order and the basic thermodynamic properties of liquids and gases in qualitative terms. The quantitative deductions of the theory at liquid densities are unsatisfactory.

The volume-dependent contributions to the pressure, entropy, and energy in the liquid state are noticeably less than the experimental values for liquid argon. The principal reason for these discrepancies is the use of the superposition approximation. Inasmuch as the theoretical entropy of the liquid is too small, one may conclude that superposition approximation ascribes to a liquid a larger degree of order than occurs in reality.

It is possible, however, that part of the discrepancy between theory and experiment found in paper [7] arises from other factors, for example, the assumed analytic form of the intermolecular potential. It may also be noted that recalculation of the pressure from equation (2.69) instead of (2.40) leads, within the framework of the superposition approximation, to notably better results and reduces the discrepancy with experimental data.

7. REFINEMENT OF THE SUPERPOSITION APPROXIMATION

We may deduce from the results of the preceding section that it is necessary to develop an approximate theory which will make it possible to determine the lower-order correlation functions more accurately than can be obtained from the superposition approximation. In recent years many studies have been devoted to this problem, some of which we will briefly review below.

Kirkwood has introduced a new partial cluster expansion-integral equation for the correlation functions [11]. Thus, it is possible to obtain an integro-differential equation of the type of equation (4.9) for these functions. When the range of the intermolecular potential is strictly finite, only a finite number of particles can simultaneously be within the field of one molecule. Then the (exact) system of equations for the new correlation functions is also finite. If the radius of action of the intermolecular forces only extends to the near neighbors of a molecule, there results a system of 12 integro-differential equations for 12 unknown correlation functions, corresponding to the maximum possible number of neighbors of a spherical particle. These equations are exact; however, simplification is necessary for practical solution.

Sarolea and Mayer [12] have developed a general method of constructing approximations to the exact equations (4.9). Unfortunately, approximations which exceed in accuracy the superposition approximation also result in complex and cumbersome systems of equations. Up to the present time, the methods of papers [11] and [12] have not yielded any new results in the theory of liquids.

Let us examine another approach to the problem. It is obvious that the revised superposition approximation in the case of a uniform system must have the form

$$F_3(q, q', q'') \\ = g(|q-q'|)g(|q-q''|)g(|q'-q''|)\chi(q, q', q''), \tag{5.78}$$

where χ is some correction function. In particular, there must exist one such function (of) χ which satisfies equation (5.78). Paper [13] contains a formal solution of the problem of constructing the function $\chi(q, q', q'')$ in the form of an infinite power series in the density, based on the use of the "irreducible" integrals of the theory of real gases. In practice, this solution is only applicable to gaseous systems at low density.

Paper [14] sought the "best" value of χ, starting from a variational principle related to the requirement of minimum free energy in the system. However, the "best" χ found in this paper was a function equal to some constant depending only on temperature and volume. This is clearly inadmissible in the theory of correlation functions which we use. For when χ is equal to a constant (independent of coordinates) in (5.78), the normalization conditions and the asymptotic behavior of F_3 are incorrect if this constant differs from unity.

It is possible, however, to approach the problem in a different manner and to try to construct an approximate theory of liquids, which is more precise than the theory in the superposition approximation, by determining the function χ in (5.78) by an approximation method in such a way that it satisfies the necessary conditions at infinity. We note that from chapter 2, section 5, the superposition approximation corresponds to setting equal to zero the three body correlation potential Ψ_3, determined from equation (2.84). It is possible to construct a "super-superposition" approximation by assuming that $\Psi_3 \neq 0$, but setting $\Psi_4 = 0$. In a homogeneous liquid this gives us, instead of (5.3), a new relationship

$$F_4(q,q',q'',q''') = \frac{F_3(q,q',q'')F_3(q,q',q''')F_3(q,q'',q''')F_3(q',q'',q''')}{F_2(q,q')F_2(q,q'')F_2(q,q''')F_2(q',q'')F_2(q',q''')F_2(q'',q''')}, \quad (5.79)$$

where $F_1(q) = 1$. On substitution into (4.9), the infinite chain of equations is broken one link further than in the case of (5.3). From (5.78) and (5.79), taking into consideration that $F_2(q, q') = g(|q - q'|)$, we have

$$\begin{aligned} F_4(q, q', q'', q''') = {} & g(|q-q'|)g(|q-q''|) \\ & \times g(|q-q'''|)g(|q'-q''|)g(|q'-q'''|) \\ & \times g(|q''-q'''|)\chi(q, q', q'')\chi(q, q', q''') \\ & \times \chi(q, q'', q''')\chi(q', q'', q'''). \end{aligned} \quad (5.80)$$

If we now require that

$$g(r) \to 1 \qquad \text{when} \qquad r \to \infty \quad (5.81)$$

and

$$\chi(q, q', q'') \to 1, \quad (5.82)$$

then, if any one particle of the three moves away to infinity, the normalization conditions and the asymptotic conditions are fulfilled for all three functions F_2, F_3, and F_4. In addition, the functions $\chi(q, q', q'')$, must, of course, be symmetric in the positions of the three particles.

By placing the relationships (5.78) and (5.80) into the basic equations (4.9) with $s = 2$ and $s = 3$, we obtain a closed system of equations for two unknown functions g and χ. After some simplification, these equations have the form

$$kT\nabla_q \ln g(|q-q'|) + \nabla_q\Phi(|q-q'|) + \frac{1}{v}\int \nabla_q\Phi(|q-q''|)\, g(|q-q''|)\, g(|q'-q''|) \times \chi(q, q', q'')\, dq'' = 0\,, \tag{5.83}$$

$$\begin{aligned} kT\nabla_q \ln \chi(q, q', q'') + \frac{1}{v}\int \nabla_q\Phi(|q-q'''|) &\times g(|q-q'''|)[g(|q'-q'''|)\, g(|q''-q'''|) \\ &\times \chi(q, q', q''')\chi(q', q'', q''')\chi(q, q'', q''') \\ &- g(|q'-q'''|)\chi(q, q', q''') - g(|q''-q'''|) \\ &\times \chi(q, q'', q''')]\, dq''' = 0\,. \end{aligned} \tag{5.84}$$

As conditions, equations (5.81) and (5.82) and the symmetry properties of χ must be satisfied. If in this case, we let $\chi = 1$, then we return to the equations of the superposition approximation theory.

One would expect that equations (5.83) to (5.84) are a better approximation to the exact equation (4.9) than is equation (5.10). We can convince ourselves that this is actually so from the study of the gas. If we seek solutions of equations (5.83) and (5.84) in the form of a series

$$g(r) = g_0(r) + \frac{1}{v}\, g_1(r) + \frac{1}{v^2}\, g_2(r) + \dots\,, \tag{5.85}$$

$$\chi = \chi_0 + \frac{1}{v}\, \chi_1 + \frac{1}{v^2}\, \chi_2 + \dots\,, \tag{5.86}$$

then, by using the procedure with which we are already acquainted, it is not difficult to find successively the functions g_0, χ_0, g_1, etc. It is also not difficult to verify that the solution for the function $g(r)$, written correctly up to terms of the order $1/v^2$, corresponds exactly with the first terms of the expansion (4.51) in the solution of the exact equations in (4.9). At the same time, it is known that in the superposition approximation an exact solution is obtained only up to the term of order $1/v$. In addition, one would expect that the error in the higher-order terms of the expansion (5.85) would be less than in the case of the superposition approximation.

The first terms of the expansion (5.86) for the function χ, from (5.84), have the form

$$\chi(q, q', q'') = 1 + \frac{1}{v} \int \left\{ \exp\left[-\frac{\Phi(|q - q'''|)}{kT} \right] - 1 \right\} \times \left\{ \exp\left[-\frac{\Phi(|q' - q'''|)}{kT} \right] - 1 \right\} \times \left\{ \exp\left[-\frac{\Phi(|q'' - q'''|)}{kT} \right] - 1 \right\} dq''' + \dots, \qquad (5.87)$$

which coincides with the results of paper [13].

If we are interested in the pressure of a gas, the result obtained indicates that our theory gives correct values for the second, third, and fourth virial coefficients, while the superposition approximation gives correct values only for the second and third virial coefficients. Therefore, for the case of a comparatively dense gas, the theory based on equations (5.83) to (5.84) is sufficiently accurate. One might, therefore, think that equations (5.83) to (5.84) might serve as the basis for a more precise theory of the liquid also.

REFERENCES

[1] N. N. Bogolyubov, *Problemy dinamicheskoi teorii v statisticheskoi fizike*, Gostekhizdat (Problems of Dynamical Theory in Statistical Physics), State Technical Press, 1946.
[2] M. Born and H. Green, *Proc. Roy. Soc., ser. A*, **188** (1946), 10.
[3] J. Kirkwood and E. Boggs, *J. Chem. Phys.*, **10** (1942), 394.
[4] I. Z. Fisher, *Zh. Eksperim. i. Teor. Fiz.*, **28** (1955), 171.
[5] M. Rosenbluth and A. Rosenbluth, *J. Chem. Phys.*, **22** (1954), 881.
[6] J. Kirkwood, E. Mann, and B. Alder, *J. Chem. Phys.*, **18** (1950), 1040.
[7] J. Kirkwood, V. Levinson, and B. Alder, *J. Chem. Phys.*, **20** (1952), 929.
[8] A. Eisenstein and N. Gingrich, *Phys. Rev.*, **62** (1942), 261.
[9] A. Michels and H. Wijker, *Physica*, **15** (1949), 627.
[10] R. Wentorf, R. Bueler, J. Hirschfelder, and C. Curtiss, *J. Chem. Phys.*, **18** (1950), 1484.
[11] J. Kirkwood, *Discussions Faraday Soc.*, **15** (1953), 35.
[12] L. Sarolea and J. Mayer, *Phys. Rev.*, **101** (1956), 1627.
[13] R. Abe, *Progr. Theor. Phys.*, **21** (1959), 421.
[14] A. Richardson, *J. Chem. Phys.*, **23** (1956), 2304.

CHAPTER 6

SURFACE PHENOMENA IN LIQUIDS

1. CORRELATION FUNCTIONS OF A TWO-PHASE SYSTEM

In this chapter we shall consider an extension of the method of correlation functions to an equilibrium two-phase system consisting of a liquid and its saturated vapor. The theory of the structure and physical properties of the transition layer between these two phases has as yet been very little studied, despite the great interest in and importance of this problem. The application to this field of the apparatus of correlation functions opens up great possibilities for further progress.

The specific difficulty that arises in an attempt to apply the Gibbs distribution function to surface phenomena centers on the means of obtaining from this distribution function information relating to the localization and structure of the transition layer between the phases. As a matter of fact, if we assume a molecular system under conditions such that it is stable only in the form of a mixture of two phases, this fact cannot in any way be clearly deduced from the standard Gibbs distribution function: only the subsequent evaluation of the thermodynamic properties of the system will disclose the separation into two phases. The localization and structure of the transition layer between the phases is clearly not contained in the Gibbs distribution function, precisely as it is clearly not contained in the thermodynamic functions of a two-phase system. The problem of obtaining from the general laws of statistical physics information on the structure and properties of the interphase layer is very complex.

This difficulty of necessity leads us to apply to the theory of surface phenomena the apparatus of correlation functions; it is evident that problems of the localization and structure of the transitional interphase layer may thus be easily expressed. Here again we note the flexibility of correlation functions. This method, within the framework of the general Gibbsian statistical mechanics, makes it possible to proceed much farther in many problems than is possible with the usual theory.

The possibility of extending the method of correlation functions to a two-phase liquid-vapor system, including the transition region, is based on the well-known fact that the Gibbs method, to which the method of correlation functions is equivalent, actually contains within itself the liquid-vapor phase transition. This is clearly seen, for example, in the Mayer theory of real gases and also in the superposition approximation theory discussed above. There exist two different values of the density of the system, referring to the gas and liquid, respectively, such that at a given temperature the pressures and chemical potentials of the two phases at these densities are identical, and consequently both phases may coexist in equilibrium.

We will consider a system of the same type as before, but now let the quantities N, V, and T be such that the system breaks up into gaseous and liquid phases. Due to a weak external field (or for other reasons) the phases are totally separated in space. We shall assume the boundary between the phases to be planar. Let us designate by V', N' and V'', N'' the volumes and average numbers of particles in the different phases. If these values are sufficiently large, it is possible to disregard the volume of the transition layer V''' and the average number of particles in it N''', so that

$$V = V' + V'' , \qquad N = N' + N'' . \tag{6.1}$$

Let $v' = V'/N'$ and $v'' = V''/N''$. The values v', v'', and T are interrelated by the conditions of stability in a two-phase equilibrium

$$p(v', T) = p(v'', T), \qquad \mu(v', T) = \mu(v'', T), \tag{6.2}$$

where p and μ are pressure and chemical potential, respectively.

The correlation functions of the two-phase system may be formally computed as in the case of a homogeneous fluid. It is now more convenient, however, to leave the normalization arbitrary so that, if desired, it is possible to normalize independently of the ratio of the volumes V'/V''. Thus, instead of (2.1), we now assume for our two-phase system

$$dW(\mathbf{q}_1, \ldots, \mathbf{q}_s) = a_s F_s(\mathbf{q}_1, \ldots, \mathbf{q}_s) \frac{d\mathbf{q}_1 d\mathbf{q}_2 \ldots d\mathbf{q}_s}{V^s}, \tag{6.3}$$

where the a_s are dimensionless coefficients depending on the normalization of F_s. Then, instead of (2.10),

$$a_s F_s(q_1, \ldots, q_s) = V^s \int_V \ldots \int_V D_N(q_1, \ldots, q_N)\, dq_{s+1} \ldots dq_N \quad (6.4)$$

and, instead of (2.6) and (2.7),

$$\frac{a_1}{V} \int_V F_1(q)\, dq = 1\,, \quad (6.5)$$

$$\frac{a_s}{V} \int_V F_s(q_1, \ldots, q_s)\, dq_s = a_{s-1} F_{s-1}(q_1, \ldots, q_{s-1}). \quad (6.6)$$

In equation (6.4) it is assumed that the Gibbs distribution function contains the spatial distribution of phases, for example by inclusion of the external field. Finally, as previously, all F_s should be symmetrical functions of all their arguments, and should satisfy the asymptotic conditions, which now assume the form

$$a_s F_s(q_1, \ldots, q_s)\, a_1^s \prod_{1 \leq i \leq s} F_1(q_i), \quad (6.7)$$

when all $|q_i - q_j| \to \infty$, $i, j = 1, 2, \ldots, s$.

In contrast to the discussion of the preceding chapters the system is now non-uniform even in the absence of an external field: the points within V' and V'' and even near the boundary dividing V' and V'' are not uniformly distributed. In particular, $F_1(q)$ is not now equal to a constant and $F_2(q, q') \neq g(|q - q'|)$. In the transition from V' to V'' the function $F_1(q)$, and also all remaining F_s, change drastically.

The coefficients a_s must be introduced because of the nature of the limiting process, $N \to \infty$, $V \to \infty$. In the single-phase case, after the limit $N \to \infty$ and $V \to \infty$ is taken, with $v = V/N =$ const, v remains the most important thermodynamic parameter of the system and enters into all equations which relate the correlation functions to physical situations. In the two-phase system, v is not an important physical parameter, and it depends on the volumes of both the phases, V' and V''. The limit $N \to \infty$, $V \to \infty$ should be taken in such a way that $v' = V'/N'$ and $v'' = V''/N''$ both remain unchanged. Now the parameter v is physically meaningless, and its numerical value depends on the limit of the ratio V'/V''. It is, therefore, desirable to normalize the correlation functions and the equations which relate them to various physical quantities independent of the parameter v. This may be achieved by a set of matched coefficients a_s which in other respects remain arbitrary. For different problems it may be convenient to have different sets of coefficients a_s.

2. EQUATIONS FOR THE CORRELATION FUNCTIONS OF A TWO-PHASE SYSTEM

Our most immediate problem is to obtain a system of integro-differential equations for the correlation functions F_s of a two-phase system. For this purpose, it is possible to utilize the relationships between the correlation functions and the Gibbs distribution function $D_N(q_1, \ldots, q_N)$ (6.4) and then proceed as in our previous analysis of the single-phase case in chapter 4. It is essential in this case, however, to indicate in the function $D_N(q_1, \ldots, q_N)$ (as has already been mentioned) the spatial separation of the phases and the localization of the phase boundary. In order not to complicate the theory by the introduction and calculation of external-force fields, wettability of the vessel walls, etc., we proceed as follows [1]. Let us assume that the phases have been separated from one another leaving planar bounding surfaces. Further, we imagine the phases to be separated from one another by means of an infinitely thin ideal membrane penetrable by the intermolecular forces but impermeable to particles, so that diffusion of particles between the phases is impossible. The position of the membrane is such that the pressures of the vapor and of the liquid on both sides of it are equal, and the slightest shift of the membrane would cause either condensation of the vapor and evaporation of the liquid or the appearance of differences in pressure on both sides, depending on the direction of the shift. Immediately adjacent to the membrane the surface layers differ somewhat from the natural liquid-vapor transition layer. The transition from an artificial system with a membrane to a natural two-phase system is achieved by removing the membrane.

Prior to the removal of the membrane, the system is described by the Gibbs distribution function,

$$D_{N'+N''}(q'_1, \ldots, q'_{N'}; q''_1, \ldots, q''_{N''}) = Q^{-1}_{N'+N''} \exp\left\{-\frac{U_{N'} + U_{N''} + U^*}{kT}\right\}, \tag{6.8}$$

where

$$U_{N'} = \sum_{1 \le i < j \le N'} \Phi(|q'_i - q'_j|),$$
$$U_{N''} = \sum_{1 \le i < j \le N''} \Phi(|q''_i - q''_j|), \tag{6.9}$$
$$U^* = \sum_{\substack{1 \le i \le N' \\ 1 \le j \le N''}} \Phi(|q'_i - q''_j|),$$

whereupon

$$\begin{aligned} q_i'(i=1,2,\ldots,N') &\quad \text{lies in} \quad V', \\ q_j''(j=1,2,\ldots,N'') &\quad \text{lies in} \quad V''. \end{aligned} \tag{6.10}$$

The first two terms in (6.9) correspond to the interactions within each sub-system, the last to the interactions of the sub-systems through the membrane.

Let us select any r particles from V' and t particles from V'' and construct the correlation function F_{r+t}, assuming in (6.3) that

$$a_{r+t} = \frac{(V'+V'')^{r+t}}{(V')^r(V'')^t}, \tag{6.11}$$

so that

$$F_{r+t}(q_1', \ldots, q_r'; q_1'', \ldots, q_t'') = (V')^r(V'')^t \int_{V'} \cdots \int_{V'} \int_{V''} \cdots \int_{V''} \tag{6.12}$$

$$\times D_{N'+N''}(q_1', \ldots, q_{N''}'') \, dq_{r+1}' \ldots dq_{N'}' dq_{t+1}'' \ldots dq_{N''}''.$$

Differentiate (6.12) with respect to any of the variables q_i' or q_j'', for example q_1'. Taking (6.8) into consideration, we obtain

$$\nabla_{q_1'} F_{r+t} + \frac{(V')^r(V'')^t}{kT} \int_{V'} \cdots \int_{V'} \int_{V''} \cdots \int_{V''}$$

$$\times D_{N'+N''}(q_1', \ldots, q_{N''}'') \nabla_{q_1'}(U_{N'} + U_{N''} + U^*) \tag{6.13}$$

$$\times dq_{r+1}' \ldots dq_{N'}' dq_{t+1}'' \ldots dq_{N''}'' = 0.$$

Now in the total energy of interaction, separate out the interactions of the $r+t$ selected particles:

$$U_{N'} + U_{N''} + U^* = U_{r+t} + \tilde{U}, \tag{6.14}$$

whereupon

$$U_{r+t} = \sum_{1 \leq i < j \leq r} \Phi(|q_i' - q_j'|) + \sum_{1 \leq i < j \leq t} \Phi(|q_i'' - q_j''|) + \sum_{\substack{1 \leq i \leq r \\ 1 \leq j \leq t}} \Phi(|q_i' - q_j''|), \tag{6.15}$$

$$\tilde{U} = \sum_{r+1 \leq i < j \leq N'} \Phi(|q_i' - q_j'|) + \sum_{t+1 \leq i < j \leq N''} \Phi(|q_i'' - q_j''|) + \sum_{\substack{r+1 \leq i \leq N' \\ t+1 \leq j \leq N''}} \Phi(|q_i' - q_j''|) \tag{6.16}$$

Clearly the term U_{r+t} may be removed from the integral (6.13), and for the remaining terms in (6.16) we have

$$\nabla_{q_1'}\tilde{U} = \sum_{r+1\leq i\leq N'} \nabla_{q_1'}\Phi(|q_1' - q_i'|) + \sum_{t+1\leq i\leq N''} \Phi(|q_1' - q_i''|). \tag{6.17}$$

Using the definition (6.12), after simple transformations it is found that

$$kT\nabla_{q_1'}F_{r+t} + F_{r+t}\nabla_{q_1'}U_{r+t} + \frac{N'-r}{V'}\int_{V'}\nabla_{q_1'}\Phi(|q_1' - q_{r+1}'|)F_{(r+1)+t}\,dq_{r+1}' + \frac{N''-t}{V''}\int_{V''}\nabla_{q_1'}\Phi(|q_1' - q_{t+1}''|)F_{r+(t+1)}\,dq_{t+1}'' = 0. \tag{6.18}$$

Analogous equations are obtained by differentiation with respect to q_1'' instead of q_1'.

Consider the limit $N' \to \infty$, $V' \to \infty$, $N'' \to \infty$, and $V'' \to \infty$, with $v' = V''/N''$ constant. The domains of integration in (6.18) become two semi-infinite spaces bounded by the plane of the membrane. Assuming this plane to be the xOy plane of the Cartesian system of coordinates, we obtain

$$kT\nabla_{q_1'}F_{r+t} + F_{r+t}\nabla_{q_1'}U_{r+t} + \frac{1}{v'}\int_{z_{r+1}'>0}\nabla_{q_1'}\Phi(|q_1' - q_{r+1}'|)F_{(r+1)+t}\,dq_{r+1}' + \frac{1}{v''}\int_{z_{t+1}''<0}\nabla_{q_1'}\Phi(|q_1 - q_{t+1}''|)F_{r+(t+1)}\,dq_{t+1}'' = 0. \tag{6.19}$$

These equations must be considered together with conditions (6.10); their solutions describe the asymptotic behavior of a two-phase system with the membrane unremoved.

In order to go over to a real system with a free surface between the liquid and vapor, it is necessary to remove the membrane. This simply means that it is necessary to give up the restrictions of (6.10) and the discrimination between the particles of the different phases. Introducing a continuous numbering of the particles and assuming that $r + t = s$, we obtain

$$kT\nabla_1F_s + F_s\nabla_1U_s + \frac{1}{v'}\int_{z_{s+1}>0}\nabla_1\Phi_{1,s+1}F_{s+1}\,dq_{s+1} + \frac{1}{v''}\int_{z_{s+1}<0}\nabla_1\Phi_{1,s+1}F_{s+1}\,dq_{s+1} = 0, \tag{6.20}$$

$s = 1, 2, \ldots$, while the q_i now range from $-\infty$ to $+\infty$ in all directions. The integration is carried over two semi-infinite spaces.

If we introduce the discontinuous function $\Theta(z)$:

$$\begin{aligned} \Theta(z) &= 0, \qquad \text{if } z < 0, \\ \Theta(z) &= 1, \qquad \text{if } z > 0, \end{aligned} \tag{6.21}$$

equation (6.20) may be written in the more compact form [2]

$$kT\nabla_1 F_s + F_s \nabla_1 U_s + \int \nabla_1 \Phi_{1,s+1} \left[\frac{\Theta(z_{s+1})}{v'} + \frac{1-\Theta(z_{s+1})}{v''} \right] F_{s+1} d q_{s+1} = 0, \tag{6.22}$$

where the integration is over all space.

Equations (6.20) or (6.22) are equations for the determination of the asymptotic ($N \to \infty$, $V \to \infty$) correlation functions of a two-phase system with densities $1/v'$ and $1/v''$, respectively. The transition layer is localized in the neighborhood of the plane $z = 0$. The choice of normalization coefficients a_s in the form (6.11) was chosen for convenience in the intermediate calculations. It is not difficult to verify that the final equations (6.20) or (6.22) are invariant to the choice of normalization coefficients a_s that satisfy (6.5) and (6.6).

In equations (6.20) or (6.22) it is assumed that the volumes v' and v'' satisfy (6.2), corresponding to stable equilibrium in the system. One might think that these equations, considered from a purely formal point of view, would also be soluble for other values of v' and v'' or even for any values of v' and v''. In this case only those solutions of these equations with v' and v'' related as in (6.2) will be physically realizable at equilibrium.

The procedure of introducing and then removing a hypothetical membrane permits the formulation, in terms of correlation functions, of a theory in which the spatial separation of the phases is clearly preserved. When the Gibbs distribution function is used directly, as has already been mentioned, this separation cannot be achieved. As a matter of fact, if in equation (6.8) we ignore the limitations of (6.10) (in which the removal of the membrane is included), we return to the ordinary Gibbs function in which the separation into phases and the localization of the phase boundary is not clearly shown.

3. GENERAL EXAMINATION OF THE EQUATIONS FOR THE CORRELATION FUNCTIONS OF A TWO-PHASE SYSTEM

The equations obtained for the correlation functions of a two-phase system are still more complex than the same equations for a uniform single-phase fluid, and no simple method for solving them exists. Therefore, let us consider some simple deductions that may be made from the general properties of these equations.

First of all, it is evident that equations (6.20) or (6.22) are invariant to arbitrary translations of the entire space in the xOy plane. From this it follows that the singlet correlation function $F_1(q)$ is dependent only on the coordinate z of a particle, and does not depend on the coordinates x and y:

$$F_1(\boldsymbol{q}) = F_1(z). \tag{6.23}$$

Analogously, the binary correlation function $F_2(q, q')$ is dependent only on three, and not on six arguments:

$$F_2(\boldsymbol{q}, \boldsymbol{q}') = F_2(|\boldsymbol{q} - \boldsymbol{q}'|, z, z'), \tag{6.24}$$

etc.

Now let all the coordinates z of the s particles under consideration tend either to $-\infty$ or to $+\infty$. Because of the rapid decrease in the function $\Phi(r)$ with increasing r, equations (6.20) become the usual Bogolyubov equations:

$$kT\nabla_1 F_s + F_s \nabla_1 U_s + \frac{1}{v} \int \nabla_1 \Phi_{1,s+1} F_{s+1} d\boldsymbol{q}_{s+1} = 0, \tag{6.25}$$

where v is equal to v' or v'' and the integration is over all space. Consequently, on both sides of the boundary, and far from it, equations (6.20) or (6.22) describe pure liquid or gaseous phases, as would be expected. Only near the plane $z = 0$ does the system differ essentially from the usual fluid. In the system studied, one phase goes continuously over into the other. For the usual short-range forces between particles, one would expect this transition to be complete in a distance of the order of several particle spacings.

The singlet correlation function, $F_1(z)$, which describes the microstructure of the transition layer is now of special significance. Equation (6.22), for the case $s = 1$, takes the form

$$kT \frac{\partial F_1(z)}{\partial z} + \int \frac{\partial \Phi(|\boldsymbol{q} - \boldsymbol{q}'|)}{\partial z} \left\{ \frac{1}{v'} \Theta(z') + \frac{1}{v''} [1 - \Theta(z')] \right\} F_2(\boldsymbol{q}, \boldsymbol{q}') d\boldsymbol{q}' = 0, \tag{6.26}$$

where the vector q is taken to be $q = \{0, 0, z\}$. From (6.25) and (6.26), it is seen that far from the plane $z = 0$ (on both sides) function $F_1(z)$ has a constant value, and only in a region near the plane $z = 0$ does it change from one constant value to the other. This is represented in schematic form in Figure 11 by the thick continuous line. Note that equation (6.26) assures the continuity of $F_1(z)$ at $z = 0$. The absolute values of the constants $F_1(+\infty)$ and $F_1(-\infty)$ depend on the choice of the normalization coefficients a_s in (6.3). However their ratio is determined directly from (6.3) and is equal to

$$\frac{F_1(-\infty)}{F_1(+\infty)} = \frac{v'}{v''}. \qquad (6.27)$$

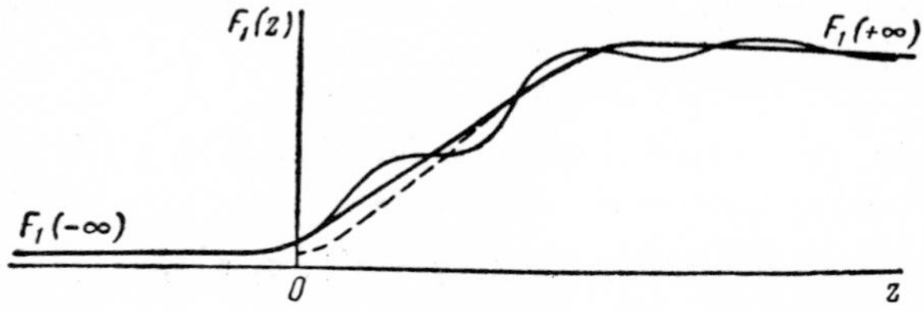

FIG. 11.—Schematic representation of the microdensity $F_1(z)$ in the liquid-vapor transition layer and in the transition layer of a liquid next to an ideal wall (dashed line). Both cases refer to a thermodynamic state far from the critical point.

The very complicated structure of equations (6.20) or (6.22) makes it extremely difficult to give a more detailed analysis of the solutions. However, under certain conditions their solution can be substantially simplified and reduced to the problem of a fluid at an ideal wall [3], a problem discussed in chapter 4.

A liquid and its saturated vapor may coexist on an interval of the temperature axis from the triple point to the critical point. At the critical point $v' = v''$, but far from the critical point the ratio v'/v'' decreases rapidly and at the triple point becomes extremely small. In the case of argon, for example, $v'/v'' = 0.005$ at the triple point, and even 20° from the critical point $v'/v'' = 0.1$. Therefore, in equations (6.20), far from the critical point, it is possible to neglect the first integral term relative to the second, and we obtain the approximate equations

$$kT\nabla_1 F_s + F_s \nabla_1 U_s + \frac{1}{v}\int_{z_{s+1}>0} \nabla_1 \Phi_{1,\,s+1} F_{s+1} d\boldsymbol{q}_{s+1} = 0, \quad (6.28)$$

where $v = v'$. The error in this case is of the order of v'/v'': the theory of the transition layer based on these equations is not applicable in the neighborhood of the critical point. But in the critical region the situation is more favorable inasmuch as the van der Waals thermodynamic theory of the transition layer is then applicable (see below). In this sense, the theory based on equations (6.28) and the van der Waals theory supplement each other.

The equations in (6.28), if we disregard the limitation $v = v'$, are identical with the equations in (4.54), which describe the behavior of a liquid system bounded by an ideal wall. In chapter 4 we saw that (4.71) is valid, and we repeat it below:

$$F_1(0) = \frac{pv}{kT}. \tag{6.29}$$

This is fulfilled if the normalization coefficients a_s are chosen in such a way that $F_1(+\infty) = 1$, as is assumed below.

Table 9 gives the values of $F_1(0)$ for argon at various temperatures

TABLE 9

T (° K)	$F_1(0) = pv/kT$	T (° K)	$F_1(0) = pv/kT$
83.7	0.0028	144.1	0.1479
84.35	.0033	149.0	.1922
91.8	.0069	150.7	0.2923
126.7	0.0645		

from the triple point to the critical point along the liquid-vapor coexistence curve, calculated from (6.29), and the experimental data from [4]. It can be seen from the table that even near the critical point $F_1(0)$ is comparatively small, and far from the critical point $F_1(0)$ assumes very small values.

From this observation we may draw the following conclusion relative to the precision of the approximate equations (6.28) and the character of their solutions. Consider equations (6.28) for $F_1(z)$, i.e., when $s = 1$. Far from the critical point $F_1(0)$ is very small, of the order of magnitude of the ratio v'/v'', which determines the magnitude of the deviation of exact equations (6.20) from the approximate equations in (6.28). As a matter of fact, far from the critical point

$$F_1(0) = \frac{pv'}{kT} = \frac{pv''}{kT} \cdot \frac{v'}{v''} \approx \frac{v'}{v''}. \tag{6.30}$$

For argon at 126.7° K, for example, the experimental value of v'/v'' is 0.077, while at 91.8° K it is 0.005, which is close to the corresponding numbers in Table 9. But with the normalization that we have taken,

$F_1(+\infty) = 1$, the value of v'/v'' corresponds, according to (6.27), to the value of $F_1(-\infty)$, i.e., to the value of $F_1(z)$ at a depth in the gas far from the boundary with the liquid, which boundary would be obtained from the exact equations (6.20). Thus, if we were interested in the gaseous region, i.e., the region where $z < 0$ in equations (6.20), it would appear that

$$F_1(-\infty) \approx F_1(0), \tag{6.31}$$

i.e., in changing from $z = -\infty$ to $z = 0$, the function $F_1(z)$ would change insignificantly in comparison with the value $F_1(+\infty) = 1$, and, consequently, the entire transition region between gas and liquid would lie practically at $z > 0$. But the region of positive values of z is described accurately enough by the equations in (6.28).

This is illustrated by the dashed line in Figure 11, which corresponds, schematically, to the solution $F_1(z)$ of the approximate equations (6.28) far from the critical point. The deviation of the dotted line from the heavy solid line, which schematically represents the exact function $F_1(z)$ in the region $z > 0$, is small everywhere.

Thus, the study of a liquid at an ideal wall may serve as a good model for the real free liquid-vapor boundary, with appropriate selection of the parameter v. Such a model seems physically entirely justified since it disregards the influence of the vapor particles on the structure of the boundary layer of the liquid. Far from the critical point, the density of the vapor is very small; the neglect of the influence of the vapor is legitimate.

4. THE STRUCTURE OF THE TRANSITION LAYER BETWEEN LIQUID AND VAPOR

One of the most interesting problems in the theory of surface phenomena is the study of the dimensions and microstructure of the layer between coexisting gas and liquid. An answer to this problem is very important for a large number of applications in molecular physics, optics, and in the physical chemistry of surfaces; it has been widely discussed in the literature. As elsewhere in this book, we shall limit ourselves to an idealized simple liquid.

A complete solution of the problem should be given by a set of correlation functions F_s in the neighborhood of $z = 0$. In this case, the function $F_1(z)$ is of the greatest importance. With the normalization $F_1(+\infty) = 1$ assumed above, which corresponds to the choice $a_1 =$

v/v' in (6.3), we obtain for the microdensity $\rho(z)$ in the transition layer

$$\rho(z) = \frac{a_1}{v} F_1(z) = \frac{1}{v'} F_1(z), \tag{6.32}$$

where v' is the volume per particle in the liquid in equilibrium with its saturated vapor.

The dimensions and structure of the transition layer depend markedly on the temperature along the liquid-vapor equilibrium line. Near the critical point the difference between v' and v'' is small, and one would expect, on the average, a smooth and extended transition layer. Then it is possible to divide the whole layer into thinner layers, each having a different density, and to consider them in mutual thermodynamic equilibrium. By using the classical theory of the behavior of thermodynamic functions in the neighborhood of the critical point, it is possible to develop a complete thermodynamic theory of the transition layer [5]. For a density smoothed over a large number of atomic layers, $\langle\rho(z)\rangle$, this leads to the expression

$$\langle\rho(z)\rangle = \frac{A}{(1+B)(\beta z+\delta)}, \tag{6.33}$$

where all the constants depend on the temperature. In particular, the constant $\beta \sim \sqrt{(T_{CR} - T)}$, and, consequently, the thickness of the transition layer in the vicinity of the critical point is of the order $\sim(T_{CR} - T)^{-1/2}$. In deriving (6.33), use was made of the assumption of the differentiability of the thermodynamic functions at the critical point and of the assumption that $(\partial^3 p/\partial v^3)_{T,\,\mathrm{crit}} \neq 0$.

Far from the critical point the thermodynamic theory is completely inapplicable and it is necessary to return to the rigorous equations (6.20) or to their simplified variant (6.28).

Detailed analysis of these equations is difficult due to their unusual complexity. However, we may use the superposition approximation applied to the problem of a liquid at an ideal wall, and it may be assumed that far from the critical point this will give a good approximation for the case of a real transition layer. The equations for the problem thus formulated have already been discussed in chapter 5, section 4. Let us once again present the necessary equations, changing the notation somewhat. We shall use the dimensionless distances $r' = r/a$, $z' = z/a$, etc., and the dimensionless intermolecular potentials $\Phi_0(r')$: $\Phi(r) = \epsilon\Phi_0(r')$. Here a and ϵ are characteristic molecular constants with dimensions of length and energy, respectively. In what follows we will drop the primes in the case of r and z. Then the behavior of the function $F_1(z)$ is determined from the closed integral equation (5.51):

$$\ln F_1(z) + \lambda f(z) = \lambda \int_0^\infty K(|z-z'|)[F_1(z')-1]\,dz', \quad z \geq 0, \tag{6.34}$$

whereupon

$$f(z) = \int_z^\infty K(x)\,dx \tag{6.35}$$

and

$$K(x) = \tfrac{1}{2}\int_{|x|}^\infty \Phi_0'(t)\,g(t)(t^2 - x^2)\,dt. \tag{6.36}$$

Here $g(r)$ is the ordinary radial distribution function of a liquid far from the boundary. The dimensionless parameter λ is now a function only of the temperature and is equal to

$$\lambda = \lambda(T) = \frac{\epsilon}{kT}\cdot\frac{2\pi a^3}{v'(T)}, \tag{6.37}$$

where $v'(T)$ is the average volume per particle in the liquid in equilibrium with its vapor.

Thus, the structure of the transition layer is wholly determined by the state and structure of the liquid far from the boundary and by the values $v'(T)$ and $g(r)$. From (6.34) it follows that

$$F_1(z) \to 1 \quad \text{when} \quad z \to \infty. \tag{6.38}$$

Equation (6.34) is of the same type as the Bogolyubov equation (5.10) and it is even simpler if we consider the function $g(r)$ to be known. It would not be difficult to solve this equation numerically using modern methods, but unfortunately this computation has not as yet been carried out.

The similarity of equations (6.34) and (5.10) leads one to expect the appearance of oscillating solutions. The oscillations should be superimposed on the smoothed $F_1(z)$, corresponding to an increase of $F_1(z)$ from $F_1(0) \approx v'/v''$ to $F_1(\infty) = 1$ in the transition layer. This is shown schematically by the continuous thin line in Figure 11. The real existence of these oscillations is evident from the solution of equation (6.34) far from the wall. In the preceding chapter we saw that when $z \gg a$, the solution of equation (6.34) has the form (5.57):

$$F_1(z) = 1 + \sum_n A_n' \exp(-|\alpha_n|z)\cos(\beta_n z + \delta_n'). \tag{6.39}$$

In this series, in fact, only the term with the smallest value of $|\alpha_n|$ is important, and if this is designated by $|\alpha_1|$ we obtain

$$F_1(z) \approx 1 + A_1' \exp(-|\alpha_1|z)\cos(\beta_1 z + \delta_1'). \tag{6.40}$$

We thus come to the conclusion that the transition layer between the liquid and its vapor must possess a specific, more or less strongly expressed, layered structure corresponding to some ordering of the particles in the layer. It is possible that this layering is essential to many phenomena of the physics of surfaces. These oscillations should also be observed in the solution of the rigorous equation (6.26) for all values of v' and v''. In particular, the thermodynamic equation (6.33) should be obtainable as the result of the flattening out of $F_1(z)$ into extremely broad oscillations in the vicinity of the critical point, as is shown schematically in Figure 12.

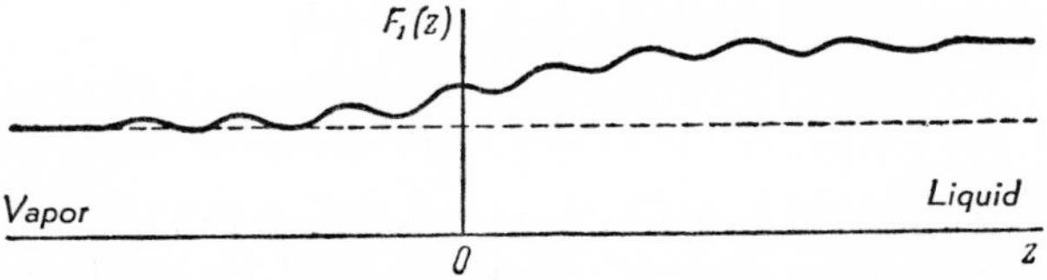

FIG. 12.—Schematic representation of the microdensity, $F_1(z)$, in the liquid-vapor transition layer near the critical point.

The constant $|\alpha_1|$ in (6.40) has an obvious significance as the reciprocal of the effective thickness of the transition layer. Since z is dimensionless in this equation, the thickness d of the surface layer is

$$d(T) \sim \frac{a}{|\alpha_1(T)|}. \tag{6.41}$$

In this case, $|\alpha_1|$ is defined as the smallest (in absolute magnitude), of the imaginary parts of the complex roots of equation (5.35). Under ordinary conditions one would expect that $|\alpha_1| \sim 1$.

In view of the complexity of the mathematical formulation of the problems discussed above it is interesting to examine the corresponding one-dimensional model where full and rigorous solution is possible [6]. In this case, a complication arises because, as we saw in chapter 1, a liquid-gas phase transition is impossible in a one-dimensional system. Therefore, the equilibrium liquid-gas transition layer also cannot exist. In this case, however, a transition layer next to a wall is entirely possible, and if the wall is chosen as ideal, we will obtain a one-dimensional model of a real transition layer.

If we consider the same one-dimensional system as in chapter 1, sections 6 and 7 and in chapter 3, section 2, but substituting an ideal infinitely high potential wall for one of the boundaries of the system, then, using reasoning similar to that of chapter 3, section 2, it is not difficult to find an exact solution for our problem in the form [6]

$$F_1(z) = \frac{pl}{kT} \exp\left(-\frac{pz}{kT}\right) \sum_{0 \leq m \leq \infty} \frac{1}{[\varphi(p, T)]^m} \int_0^z f_m(x)\,dx\,, \quad (6.42)$$

where the notation of (1.81) and (1.98) is used. In this case,

$$\int_0^z f_0 dx \equiv 1$$

and z designates the distance from the wall. Each term of this series corresponds to the probability of finding the corresponding particle next to the wall. Hence, when $z = 0$, we obtain

$$F_1(0) = \frac{pl}{kT}, \quad (6.43)$$

which is a one-dimensional analog of equation (6.29).

In order to give a graphic representation of the result (6.42), we present in Figure 13 a curve of the function $F_1(z)$ calculated from equa-

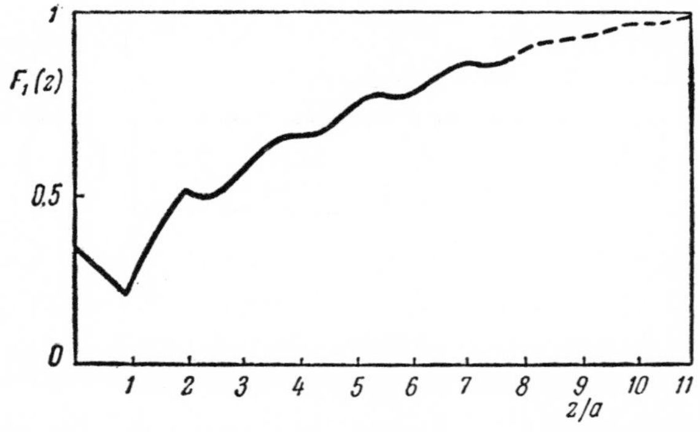

FIG. 13.—Microdensity, $F_1(z)$, in a one-dimensional model of a liquid next to an ideal wall [6].

tion (6.42) in paper [6]. A system of hard spheres was chosen with attractive forces represented by a square well. In order to simplify the calculation, the width of the well was taken equal to the diameter of the sphere. The following values of the thermodynamic parameters were chosen:

$$l = 1.55a\,, \qquad kT = 0.10\epsilon, \qquad p = 0.02\,\frac{\epsilon}{a}, \qquad (6.44)$$

corresponding to one of the most "liquid-like" states of a one-dimensional system: eight terms of the series (6.42) were calculated. The dashed line in the graph was obtained by extrapolation. As mentioned above, the microstructure of the transition layer stands out clearly in the graph in the form of oscillations of $F_1(z)$.

5. EXPRESSION OF THE SURFACE TENSION OF A LIQUID IN TERMS OF CORRELATION FUNCTIONS

The most important thermodynamic function characterizing the surface layer of a liquid is the surface tension $\sigma(T)$, which is equal to the excess free energy required to extend the surface of the system by unit area. Of course, $\sigma(T)$ is related to the surface energy of a liquid $u(T)$, i.e., to the excess energy per unit surface area, by the Gibbs-Helmholtz equation

$$u(T) = \sigma(T) - T\sigma'(T). \qquad (6.45)$$

The values $\sigma(T)$ and $u(T)$ depend on the curvature of the free surface. In all cases considered below, the surface of the liquid is considered to be planar. The goal of this section is to express $\sigma(T)$ in terms of the correlation functions for a two-phase system.

The surface tension $\sigma(T)$ may be expressed directly in terms of the stress tensor $\Pi_{\alpha\beta}(q)$ of the system [7]. Inasmuch as the liquid is non-uniform in the surface layer, $-\Pi_{xx}(z)$ in the surface layer is not equal to the equilibrium pressure $p = -\Pi_{zz}(z)$, which characterizes the entire system.

Consider a column of a substance of unit square cross-section, oriented along the axes Ox and Oy. Let the height of the column be much greater than the thickness of the surface layer, which is situated in the neighborhood of the plane $z = 0$. The ends of the column are located in the interior of the liquid and the interior of the gas at distances h' and h'' from the plane $z = 0$, respectively. Now consider the reversible isothermal process consisting of: (1) extension of the system along the axis Ox, a distance δx; and (2) subsequent compression of the system along the axis Oz, by distances $\delta h'$ and $\delta h''$. Both processes are shown in Figure 14 by numbered arrows. The compression is to take place in such a way that at the end of the process the volumes of both phases are equal to the original volumes, so that

$$\delta h' = -h'\delta x, \qquad \delta h'' = -h''\delta x. \qquad (6.46)$$

Because of the equality of volumes and the constant temperature, the pressure in the system at the end of the process is equal to the original pressure, and the only change in the system is an increase in the surface between the phases. If we designate the entire work done by the system in the course of the process by δA, we obtain

$$\sigma(T)\,\delta x = -\,\delta A\,. \tag{6.47}$$

The work δA consists of the work δA_1 and δA_2 in each of the two processes mentioned above. To the same accuracy as (6.46), we have

$$\begin{aligned} \delta A_1 &= \delta x \int_{-h''}^{h'} [\,-\Pi_{xx}(z)\,]\,dz\,, \\ \delta A_2 &= -\,p\,(h' + h'')\,\delta x = -\,\delta x \int_{-h''}^{h'} p\,dz\,. \end{aligned} \tag{6.48}$$

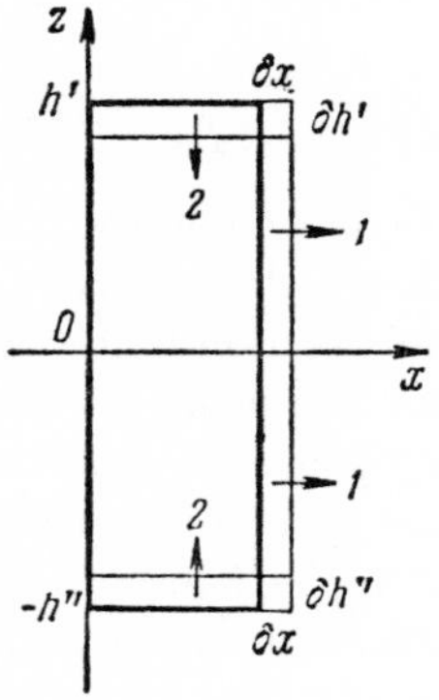

FIG. 14.—Diagram for deriving an equation for the surface tension

Substitution in (6.47) then leads to the final expression for the surface tension

$$\sigma = \int_{-\infty}^{\infty} [\Pi_{xx}(z) + p]\,dz\,. \tag{6.49}$$

In (6.49) we have changed the limits of integration in (6.48) to infinity, since in the interior of the gas or liquid $\Pi_{xx}(z)$ rapidly approaches a constant value p, and the integral vanishes. For the same reason, equation (6.49) may be written, after partial integration, in the form

$$\sigma = -\int_{-\infty}^{\infty} \frac{d\Pi_{xx}}{dz}\,z\,dz\,. \tag{6.50}$$

If now we use an explicit expression for $\Pi_{\alpha\beta}$, say (2.56), and the well-known expression for pressure, then, with the aid of (6.49), we obtain an expression for the surface tension expressed directly in terms of the correlation functions F_1 and F_2 of a two-phase system. Depending on the normalization of the correlation functions and on the choice of the explicit expression for pressure, the result may be presented in several equivalent forms.

In the case of arbitrary normalization of the correlation functions as in (6.3), equation (2.56) for the stress tensor may be written in the form

$$\Pi_{\alpha\beta}(z) = -kT\frac{a_1}{v}F_1(z)\,\delta_{\alpha\beta} + \frac{a_2}{2v^2}\int\Phi'(\rho)F_2^*(\rho, z)\frac{(\boldsymbol{\varrho})_\alpha(\boldsymbol{\varrho})_\beta}{\rho}\,d\boldsymbol{\varrho}\,. \tag{6.51}$$

We select, as in the preceding sections, a normalization of the functions F_s, such that when $z_1, \ldots, z_s \to +\infty$ the correlation functions go over into the ordinary correlation functions of a pure liquid:

$$F_1(z) \to 1\,, \qquad F_2^*(\rho, z) \to g_L(\rho), \text{ etc.} \tag{6.52}$$

For this purpose it is obviously necessary to set

$$a_1 = \frac{v}{v'}, \qquad a_2 = \left(\frac{v}{v'}\right)^2, \text{ etc.} \tag{6.53}$$

Then, in the limit $z_1, \ldots, z_s \to -\infty$, it appears that

$$F_1(z) \to \frac{v'}{v''}, \qquad F_2^*(\rho, z) \to \left(\frac{v'}{v''}\right)^2 g_G(\rho), \text{ etc.} \tag{6.54}$$

If we designate the components of the vector $\boldsymbol{\varrho}$ by $\{\xi, \eta, \zeta\}$ and use the normalization of (6.51), we obtain

$$\Pi_{xx}(z) = -\frac{kT}{v'}F_1(z) + \frac{1}{2v'^2}\int\Phi'(\rho)F_2^*(\rho, z)\frac{\xi^2}{\rho}\,d\boldsymbol{\varrho}\,. \tag{6.55}$$

The most convenient expression for the pressure is $p = -\Pi_{zz}(z) =$ const, so that

$$p = \frac{kT}{v'}F_1(z) - \frac{1}{2v'^2}\int\Phi'(\rho)F_2^*(\rho, z)\frac{\zeta^2}{\rho}\,d\boldsymbol{\varrho}\,. \tag{6.56}$$

Then we obtain

$$\Pi_{xx}(z) + p = \frac{1}{2v'^2}\int\Phi'(\rho)F_2^*(\rho, z)\frac{\xi^2 - \zeta^2}{\rho}\,d\boldsymbol{\varrho}\,. \tag{6.57}$$

Placing this in equation (6.49), we finally find that

$$\sigma(T) = \frac{1}{2v'^2}\int_{-\infty}^{\infty}dz\int\Phi'(\rho)F_2^*(\rho, z)\frac{\xi^2 - \zeta^2}{\rho}\,d\boldsymbol{\varrho}\,. \tag{6.58}$$

This expression does not depend on the location of the plane $z = 0$ relative to the transition layer, since translations along the axis Oz do not change (6.58).

In equation (6.58) alteration of the order of integration is impossible, since when $z \to \pm\infty$, F_2^* tends toward constant limits relative to z. Therefore, let us consider the function

$$X(\rho, z) = F_2^*(\rho, z) - \left(\frac{v'}{v''}\right)^2 [1 - \theta(z)]\, g_G(\rho) - \theta(z)\, g_L(\rho), \tag{6.59}$$

where $\theta(z)$ is defined by (6.21). When $z \to \pm\infty$, we have $X(\rho, z) \to 0$. On the other hand, it is clear from considerations of symmetry that

$$\int \Phi'(\rho) X(\rho, z) \frac{\xi^2 - \zeta^2}{\rho} d\varrho = \int \Phi'(\rho) F_2^*(\rho, z) \frac{\xi^2 - \zeta^2}{\rho} d\varrho. \tag{6.60}$$

Therefore, in the internal integral in (6.58), it is possible to replace $F_2^*(\rho, z)$ by $X(\rho, z)$, and then to change the order of integration. Designating

$$\Gamma(\rho) = \int_{-\infty}^{\infty} \Big\{ F_2^*(\rho, z) - \left(\frac{v'}{v''}\right)^2 [1 - \theta(z)]\, g_G(\rho) - \theta(z)\, g_L(\rho) \Big\} dz, \tag{6.61}$$

instead of (6.58), we obtain an equation which is equivalent to it:

$$\sigma(T) = \frac{1}{2v'^2} \int \Phi'(\rho) \Gamma(\rho) \frac{\xi^2 - \zeta^2}{\rho} d\varrho. \tag{6.62}$$

Equations (6.58) or (6.62) give expressions for the surface tension of a liquid in terms of the intermolecular forces and correlation functions. In these equations it is understood, of course, that $v' = v'(T)$.

Other equivalent expressions for $\sigma(T)$ are also possible using the correlation functions, and some of these are given in paper [2]. They involve the use (instead of the equations in [6.56] for the pressure p) of one of the two equations

$$p = \frac{kT}{v'} - \frac{1}{6v'^2} \int \Phi'(\rho)\, g_L(\rho)\, \rho\, d\varrho = \frac{kT}{v'} - \frac{2\pi}{3v'^2} \int_0^\infty \Phi'(\rho)\, g_L(\rho)\, \rho^3 d\rho \tag{6.63}$$

or

$$p = \frac{kT}{v''} - \frac{1}{6v''^2} \int \Phi'(\rho)\, g_G(\rho)\, \rho\, d\varrho = \frac{kT}{v''} - \frac{2\pi}{3v''^2} \int_0^\infty \Phi'(\rho)\, g_G(\rho)\, \rho^3 d\rho \tag{6.64}$$

or combinations of them. Finally we note that it is also possible to express the surface energy $u(T)$ directly in terms of the correlation functions, thereby avoiding the use of equation (6.45). In this case, however, a very cumbersome result is obtained and we will not cite it here.

6. APPROXIMATE THEORIES OF THE SURFACE TENSION

In order that the rigorous equations of the preceding section may be applied to the calculation of the surface tension and the surface energy of a liquid, it is necessary to know the correlation functions F_1 and F_2 in the transition layer. At the present time we do not have this information. Therefore, in what follows we shall limit ourselves to some very approximate calculations.

Far from the critical point the very simplest model of the transition layer between liquid and gas is, as we have seen, a model of the boundary layer of a liquid bounded by an ideal wall. Let us make a further rough approximation, assuming that in this model the liquid is uniform right up to the wall itself, so that

$$\begin{aligned} F_1(z) &= 1 \quad \text{when} \quad z > 0\,, \\ F_1(z) &= 0 \quad \text{when} \quad z < 0 \end{aligned} \tag{6.65}$$

and

$$\begin{aligned} &F_2^*(\rho, z) = g_L(\rho) \quad \text{when} \quad z > 0 \quad \text{and} \quad \zeta \geq -z\,, \\ &F_2^*(\rho, z) = 0 \quad \text{when} \quad z < 0 \quad \text{or} \quad \zeta < -z\,. \end{aligned} \tag{6.66}$$

In this case we completely disregard the structure of the transition layer. For calculations it is simplest if we use equation (6.58) directly. Going over to spherical coordinates and taking into consideration (6.66), we obtain

$$\begin{aligned} &\int\int(\xi^2 - \zeta^2)\sin\vartheta d\vartheta d\varphi = 0\,, && \text{if } \rho < z\,, \\ &\int\int(\xi^2 - \zeta^2)\sin\vartheta d\vartheta d\varphi = \pi\,\frac{z(\rho^2 - z^2)}{\rho}\,, && \text{if } \rho > z\,. \end{aligned} \tag{6.67}$$

Therefore,

$$\begin{aligned} &\int\Phi'(\rho)F_2^*(\rho, z)\frac{\xi^2 - \zeta^2}{\rho}\,d\varrho \\ &\quad = \pi z\int_z^\infty \Phi'(\rho)\,g_L(\rho)(\rho^2 - z^2)\,\rho - d\varrho\,. \end{aligned} \tag{6.68}$$

Placing this in equation (6.58), after two partial integrations we find that

$$\sigma(T) = \frac{\pi}{8v'^2}\int_0^\infty \Phi'(r)\,g_L(r)\,r^4 dr\,. \tag{6.69}$$

Here $v' = v'(T)$ and $g_L(r) = g_L[r; v'(T), T]$ and both refer to the liquid at the saturated vapor pressure. In the same approximation, using the model defined by (6.65) and (6.66), it is also easy to calculate the surface energy of the liquid $u(T)$. For the total energy of the system, according to the general theory developed in chapter 2, we have

$$E = \tfrac{3}{2}NkT + \frac{1}{2v'^2}\int_V\int_V \Phi(|q-q'|)F_2(q, q')\,dq\,dq'\,. \tag{6.70}$$

For our model, using (6.66), we may write

$$E = \tfrac{3}{2}NkT + \frac{1}{2v'^2}\int_V dq \int_V \Phi(|q'-q|)\,g_L(|q'-q|)\,dq'\,. \tag{6.71}$$

The internal integral is easily calculated; it is equal to

$$4\pi\int_0^\infty \Phi(r)\,g_L(r)\,r^2 dr + 2\pi\int_z^\infty \Phi(r)\,g_L(r)(rz - r^2)\,dr\,, \tag{6.72}$$

where $q = \{0, 0, z\}$. Placing this in (6.71) and comparing the result with equation (2.31) of the general theory, we obtain

$$E = E_V + \frac{\pi}{v'^2}\int_V dq \int_z^\infty \Phi(r)\,g_L(r)(rz - r^2)\,dr\,, \tag{6.73}$$

where E_V is the usual volume part of the energy of the system (2.31). Consequently the second term in equation (6.73) represents the surface part of the energy, E_S:

$$E = E_V + E_S\,. \tag{6.74}$$

As a matter of fact, writing $dq = dxdydz$, and integrating in (6.73) over $dxdy$, we obtain a surface area S, while the remaining integral along dz is easy to evaluate using two integrations by parts: we obtain

$$E_S = -\frac{\pi S}{2v'^2}\int_0^\infty \Phi(r)\,g_L(r)\,r^2 dr\,. \tag{6.75}$$

Therefore, for the surface energy $u(T)$ per unit of surface area $E_S = Su$, we have

$$u(T) = -\frac{\pi}{2v'^2}\int_0^\infty \Phi(r)\,g_L(r)\,r^3 dr\,. \tag{6.76}$$

As in the case of equation (6.69), v' and $g_L(r)$ depend on the temperature along the liquid-vapor coexistence line.

Despite the great crudeness of the assumed model for the transition layer of the liquid at the vapor boundary, (6.65) and (6.66), it is possible that far from the critical point the theory discussed would be at least qualitatively acceptable. Numerical calculations have been made in paper [2] for the case of liquid argon, in which experimentally obtained radial distribution functions $g_L(r)$ for argon were used, and the intermolecular potential $\Phi(r)$ was taken in the form of a slightly modified Lennard-Jones potential, the constants of which were determined from studies of the properties of gaseous argon. As a result of calculations for $T = 90°$ K, the following were obtained

$$\sigma = 14.9 \text{ dynes/cm}, \qquad u = 27.2 \text{ dynes/cm} \tag{6.77}$$

instead of the experimental values

$$\sigma = 11.9 \text{ dynes/cm}, \qquad u = 35 \text{ dynes/cm}, \tag{6.78}$$

respectively. Considering the crudeness of the model, the results should be considered extremely good.

In connection with the method of derivation of equation (6.74) for the surface energy, we note that if we give up the crude approximation (6.65) and (6.66), but retain as the model of the surface layer the boundary layer of a liquid at an ideal wall, the result (6.75) may be somewhat improved. If in equation (6.70) we use the identity

$$F_2(\mathbf{q}, \mathbf{q}') = g_L(|\mathbf{q}-\mathbf{q}'|) + [F_2(\mathbf{q}, \mathbf{q}') - g_L(|\mathbf{q}-\mathbf{q}'|)], \tag{6.79}$$

then, instead of (6.75), we obtain

$$\begin{aligned} E_S = &-\frac{\pi S}{2v'^2}\int_0^\infty \Phi(r)\, g_L(r)\, r^3 dr \\ &+\frac{1}{2v'^2}\int_V\int_V \Phi(|\mathbf{q}-\mathbf{q}'|)[F_2(\mathbf{q}, \mathbf{q}') - g_L(|\mathbf{q}-\mathbf{q}'|)]\, d\mathbf{q}\,. \end{aligned} \tag{6.80}$$

Because of the short range of the potential $\Phi(r)$ and due to the rapid decrease toward zero of $(F_2 - g_L)$ when $z, z' \to \infty$, it is clear that the double integral is proportional to the area of surface S, so that

$$\begin{aligned} u(T) = &-\frac{\pi}{2v'^2}\int_0^\infty \Phi(r)\, g_L(r)\, r^3 dr + \frac{1}{2v'^2}\int_0^\infty dz \\ &\times \int_{z'>0} \Phi(|\mathbf{q}-\mathbf{q}'|)[F_2(\mathbf{q}, \mathbf{q}') - g_L(|\mathbf{q}-\mathbf{q}'|)]\, d\mathbf{q}'\,, \end{aligned} \tag{6.81}$$

where again $\mathbf{q} = \{0, 0, z\}$. This result is correct within the framework of the assumed model of a liquid at an ideal wall. It may be still further simplified if we make use of the superposition approximation (5.45). Then we obtain

$$u(T) = -\frac{\pi}{2v'^2}\int_0^\infty \Phi(r)\, g_L(r)\, r^3 dr + \frac{1}{2v'^2}\int_0^\infty dz \int_{z'>0} \times \Phi(|q-q'|)\, g_L(|q-q'|)[F_1(z)F_1(z') - 1]\, dq' . \tag{6.82}$$

In contrast to equation (6.76), expressions (6.81) and (6.82) take into consideration the structure of the transition layer. In equation (6.82), $F_1(z)$ is the solution of equation (6.34). From the results in (6.77) it follows that far from the critical point the contribution to the surface energy from the specific structure of the transition layer is comparatively small.

It should be noted that in the same way it is also possible to obtain somewhat more precise expressions for the surface tension $\sigma(T)$, instead of the simple expression (6.69).

Up until now we have not taken into consideration the interactions of particles of the liquid with particles of vapor, which may be significant when v' and v'' are comparable, for example near the critical point. For a very crude evaluation of the effect we carry out the calculation, neglecting completely the correlation of the particles of the system, i.e., assuming that

$$F_2(q, q') \approx F_1(z)F_1(z'). \tag{6.83}$$

Furthermore, we assume that

$$\begin{aligned} F_1(z) &= 1 , && \text{if } z > 0 , \\ F_1(z) &= \frac{v'}{v''}, && \text{if } z < 0 . \end{aligned} \tag{6.84}$$

Fowler's theory [8] is based on this scheme. Simple calculations, analogous to those above, lead to the following expression instead of (6.76):

$$u(T) = -\frac{\pi}{2}\left(\frac{1}{v'} - \frac{1}{v''}\right)^2 \int_0^\infty \Phi(r)\, r^3 dr , \tag{6.85}$$

where this integral must be considered to be convergent, although for the potentials ordinarily used this is not so. Thus, in this theory we obtain

$$u(T) \sim [\, v'(T) - v''(T)\,]^2 . \tag{6.86}$$

On approaching the critical point we obtain from (6.86) $u(T) \to 0$, just as expected. As a matter of fact, this result is extremely rough and apparently inaccurate, since by the same method and from the same model (6.83) to (6.84) it follows from (6.58) that

$$\sigma(T) = \frac{\pi}{8}\left(\frac{1}{v'} - \frac{1}{v''}\right)^2 \int_0^\infty \Phi'(r)\, r^4 dr. \qquad (6.87)$$

Equations (6.85) and (6.87) are incompatible with each other because of (6.45) if $v'(T)$ and $v''(T)$ are temperature dependent, although they both correspond crudely to the experimental facts.

REFERENCES

[1] I. Z. FISHER and B. V. BOKUT, *Zh. Fiz. Khim.*, **30** (1956), 2547.
[2] J. KIRKWOOD and F. BUFF, *J. Chem. Phys.*, **17** (1949), 338.
[3] I. Z. FISHER and B. V. BOKUT, *Zh. Fiz. Khim.*, **30** (1956), 2747.
[4] A. EISENSTEIN and N. GINGRICH, *Phys. Rev.*, **62** (1942), 261.
[5] L. D. LANDAU and E. M. LIFSHITS, *Mekhanika sploshnykh sred*, izd. 1-oe, Gostekhizdat (The Mechanics of Complex Media), 1st ed., State Technical Press, 1944.
[6] I. Z. FISHER and B. V. BOKUT, *Zh. Fiz. Khim.*, **31** (1957), 200.
[7] R. C. TOLMAN, *J. Chem. Phys.*, **16** (1948), 758.
[8] R. FOWLER and E. GUGGENHEIM, *Statistical Thermodynamics*, Cambridge University Press, 1949.

CHAPTER 7

BOUNDARIES OF STABILITY OF LIQUIDS AND GASES

1. THE PROBLEM OF THE STABILITY OF PHASES AND PHASE TRANSFORMATIONS

In the thermodynamic space of states of a single component system, the liquid state occupies an extended region: at all temperatures this region is separated from the crystalline region, while at temperatures below the critical temperature it is also separated from the gaseous region. At high temperatures the liquid state continuously goes over into the gaseous state, so that both phases occupy the same region in the thermodynamic space of states, and distinction between the liquid and gaseous phases is not possible. We shall call the entire region occupied by states of gas and liquid (in contrast to the crystal) a fluid phase.

One of the most important problems in the theory of the liquid state is the determination of the boundaries of stability of the fluid phase, both in relation to the crystalline phase, and in relation to the two phases of which it is composed—the liquid and gaseous—at low temperatures.

A typical phase diagram for a single component system such as argon is displayed schematically in Figure 15. As basic thermodynamic parameters we have chosen the temperature T and the volume per particle v since just these parameters enter naturally into a description of the properties of the phases when using the Gibbs method and also the method of correlation functions. The cross-hatched parts of the diagram correspond to the possible phases of the system (stable and metastable); the non–cross-hatched parts correspond to the unstable states which are not realized in nature. The boundaries between them are the limits of stability of the phases. The limits of metastability, shown in the diagram by dashed lines, must also be considered. The states of the fluid phase located below the dashed lines in the diagram are themselves possible and stable, but are relatively less stable than the states of the competing phase at the same temperature and pressure. These are metastable states such as supercooled vapor, superheated liquid, etc. An analogous region of metastable states also exists in the crystalline phase.

In the phase diagram there exist three characteristic points: the critical point K, the triple point N, and its analogous point on the boundary of absolute stability M. At the critical point the stable and

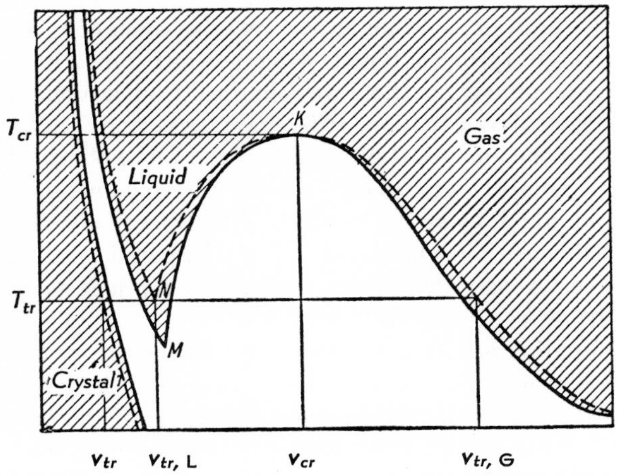

FIG. 15.—Schematic $v - T$ diagram of the states of a simple substance. The region of stable and metastable states is cross-hatched.

metastable limits coincide. Above it the liquid and gaseous phases are not distinguishable. At the triple point the temperature and pressure are such that the crystalline, liquid, and gaseous states are simultaneously in equilibrium. At only this one point may three phases coexist. The point M determines the absolute lower boundary of the temperatures at which existence of the liquid is still possible.

The boundaries of relative stability of the phases determine in the $T - v$ plane a system of coexistence lines. Their investigation, and also the investigation of the thermodynamic properties of the system near these coexistence lines is the most important problem of statistical thermodynamics. The coexistence lines are determined from the conditions of equality of pressure and chemical potential of the competing phases:

$$\mu'(v', T) = \mu''(v'', T), \qquad p'(v', T) = p''(v'', T). \quad (7.1)$$

Therefore, the theory of equilibrium between liquid (or gas) and crystal goes beyond the confines of the theory of liquids and requires the theory of the crystalline state. In contrast to this, the theory of equilibrium between liquid and gas refers entirely to the theory of fluids and in principle might be studied by the methods considered above. This, however, requires accurate knowledge of the low-order correlation functions, especially of the nature of their dependence on the thermodynamic parameters T and v, and at the present time this problem is insoluble. An example of an approximate solution of this problem by the methods of theory of liquids was given in Figure 10; the liquid-gas equilibrium curve given there was obtained from a numerical solution of the Bogolyubov equation. It is, however very difficult to say anything about the analytical properties of the curve obtained.

A large number of papers have been written about the equilibrium of gas and liquid, using the methods of the theory of real gases which were briefly mentioned in chapter 1 (see [1] especially). The complexity and the very generality of these methods as yet does not permit us to obtain definitive results.

The situation is different with respect to the theory of the limit of stability of a uniform phase. This is a subject entirely within the domain of the theory of liquids, since knowledge of the properties of a crystal is not required. The theory of crystals is also not required in the comparative evaluation of the thermodynamic properties of the two different phases, and therefore it appears that the theory developed above will be sufficient.

In this chapter we shall consider the theory of the absolute limit of stability of a uniform phase, based on the method of correlation functions. In simple liquids of the type with which we are concerned, it may be expected that the boundaries of relative and absolute stability are near to one another in the space of thermodynamic variables. Thus, the results of the theory developed below also give an approximate theory of the equilibrium coexistence line. The material of this chapter is based principally on papers [2, 3, 4].

Lack of knowledge of the exact form of the low-order correlation functions, especially of the radial distribution function, at first appears to be a serious obstacle to the construction of a theory. However, many results may be obtained even without knowledge of the explicit form of the radial distribution function, being based only on a study of the asymptotic behavior of this function at large distances. These problems were partially considered in chapter 5, sections 3 and 4; below we shall make use of the results obtained there. Although the theory thus obtained corresponds to the superposition approximation, its major results are apparently more general. As a matter of fact, the major result of chapter 5, section 3, according to which $g(r)$ at large distances is determined by equation (5.39), may with equal success be obtained from the refined equations (5.83) to (5.84), as well as from the Bogolyubov equations (5.10). In this case, the α_n and β_n are determined, as before, from equation (5.35) with the aid of the kernel of (5.32). The entire difference lies in a refinement of the form of the function $u(t)$ in (5.32). In the majority of cases the radial distribution function at small distances is not known, and the difference between the two theories is not significant. If, therefore, we assume that in the theory studied in this chapter, the functions $u(r)$ or $g(r)$ (see eqs. [5.32] and [5.36]) are the exact functions for small r, then the theory presented goes beyond the bounds of the superposition approximation.

2. THE STABILITY AND INSTABILITY OF THE SOLUTIONS OF THE BOGOLYUBOV EQUATION

Let us consider in greater detail expression (5.39) for the radial distribution function of a liquid or a gas at large distances [2, 3]. From the results of chapter 2, section 4, the function $\nu(r) = g(r) - 1$ is a "correlation function" which determines the fluctuations of density and also the correlation of the fluctuations of density in different volumes within the system. Consequently, for large r, we have

$$\nu(r) = \frac{1}{r}\sum_n A_n \exp(-|\alpha_n| r)\cos(\beta_n r + \delta_n). \qquad (7.2)$$

As is clear from equations (2.73) and (2.75), to achieve the absence of correlation in the density fluctuations in adjacent volume elements requires a very rapid decrease in the function $\nu(r)$ with increasing r. According to (7.2) this will occur if all the $|\alpha_n|$ are not equal to zero and are not too small. On the other hand, the absence of correlation in density fluctuations in adjacent small *macroscopic* volumes of the system located far from the boundaries follows from the Boltzmann principle [5] and is also confirmed by experiments on the scattering of light in liquids and gases. Therefore, for stable thermodynamic states, all values of $|\alpha_n|$ in (7.2) are different from zero, and we may number the roots γ_n of equation (5.35) in the increasing order of the magnitudes of their imaginary parts:

$$0 < |\alpha_1(\lambda)| \leq |\alpha_2(\lambda)| < \dots . \tag{7.3}$$

This numbering may also be maintained in the case of extremely small values of $|\alpha_n|$, and we will adhere to it below.

If now the density λ and the temperature T are varied within wide limits, the roots $|\alpha_n|$ will also change, and some of them may become zero. According to (7.3) the root $|\alpha_1|$ is the first to become zero. Consider now, in greater detail, the conditions such that $|\alpha_1| \to 0$ or that $\alpha_1 = 0$ already. If in this case the root α_1 is not multiple and α_2 is still not equal to zero, then in (7.2), it is possible to disregard the exponentially small terms, and for large values of r we have

$$\nu(r) = \frac{A_1}{r} \cos(\beta_1 r + \delta_1). \tag{7.4}$$

Let us study in greater detail the properties of these states. The slow decrease in $\nu(r)$ with increase in distance results, according to equations (2.66) and (2.73), in a very high level of density fluctuations in the system; moreover, correlations between the fluctuations in various volume elements will be strong. It was shown in chapter 5, section 4, that solutions of the Bogolyubov equation $g(r) = g(|q - q'|)$ give the correct correlation functions $F_2(q, q')$ only if $\nu(r)$ decreases sufficiently rapidly with increasing distance, i.e., for $|\alpha_1| \neq 0$. In the case with which we are presently concerned, this condition is not satisfied. Of course, the correlation function obtained from (2.74) by substituting (5.45) still maintains a high level of fluctuations and a strong correlation between fluctuations of density in different volumes.

In an earlier paper [6] and in other work, it was proposed that the transition from functions $\nu(r)$ that rapidly decrease with increasing distance, to functions $\nu(r)$ of the type of (7.4) that oscillate and decrease slowly, corresponds to the transition from a uniform phase (gas or liquid) to a crystalline phase, and an effort was made to connect the oscillations of $\nu(r)$ with crystalline order. Actually, this is not so. We shall show that if we continue to make use of equation (7.4) as a true correlation function, it does not, in general, correspond to any stable phase, and the state of the system described by it is thermodynamically absolutely unstable.

Indeed, let us assume that the state of the system with the correlation function (7.4) (at large distances) is thermodynamically stable.

Then there exists an equilibrium free-energy density $f_0(\lambda, T)$ such that the free energy itself is equal to

$$F = \int_V f_0(\lambda, T)\, dV\,. \qquad (7.5)$$

Furthermore, let $f - f_0$ be the deviation of the free-energy density from its equilibrium value due to a fluctuation of the density in a given volume element. Since in our case there is a noticeable correlation of the fluctuations of density in the various volume elements, then, as is well known from the thermodynamic theory of fluctuations [5, 7], the value of $f - f_0$ will depend not only on the local density but also on the density gradient. If φ is the relative density of a point, then $f - f_0$ is some differential form in φ, and for small fluctuations this form will be quadratic:

$$f - f_0 = K(\varphi, \varphi). \qquad (7.6)$$

We now use the fundamental theorem of Leontovich from statistical physics [5], according to which the correlation function $\nu(r)$ is Green's function for an Euler-Lagrange infinite space operator $L(\varphi)$ connected with the differential form $K(\varphi, \varphi)$:

$$2\int_V K(\varphi, \varphi)\, dV = -\int_V \varphi L(\varphi)\, dV + \oint_S (\ldots)\, dS\,. \qquad (7.7)$$

We will not pause at this point for a proof of this theorem since it would take us too far afield. Let us note only that in it the correlation function $\nu(r)$ is used in a "thermodynamic sense," i.e., disregarding the behavior of the system at distances of the order of atomic dimensions. Therefore, we may use the correlation function $\nu(r)$ from (7.4), rejecting lack of knowledge of its precise form at small distances, since from the thermodynamic point of view this is not significant.

In such a case we see, first of all, that the function $\nu(r)$ is Green's function in the infinite space of the linear differential operator

$$L(\varphi) = \Delta\varphi + \beta_1^2\varphi\,, \qquad (7.8)$$

where Δ is the Laplace operator. Then it is possible without difficulty to establish the differential form of $K(\varphi, \varphi)$, the combined operator (7.8), and also the deviation of the free-energy density from its equilibrium value. For the latter we obviously obtain

$$f - f_0 = B[(\nabla\varphi)^2 - \beta_1^2\varphi^2]\,, \qquad (7.9)$$

where B is some constant (relative to φ).

The expression for $f - f_0$ thus determined corresponds to the correlation function (7.4), and therefore f_0 cannot be the minimum free-energy density while expression (7.5) gives the minimum free energy. Consequently, the state of the system with $|\alpha_1| = 0$ is absolutely unstable, and the assumption regarding equilibrium is untrue.

To sum up we can say that when in the solution of the Bogolyubov equation for $g(r)$, $|\alpha_1| \to 0$, the thermodynamic state of the system becomes absolutely unstable, and simultaneously $g(r)$ ceases to be a correct binary correlation function F_2.

It should be mentioned that when $|\alpha_1(\lambda)|$ is zero another peculiarity occurs in the system. Recall that the $|\alpha_n|$ also entered into expression (5.57) for the one-particle correlation function $F_1(z)$, far from the wall bounding the system. From this expression for $F_1(z)$ it is clear that $|\alpha_1(\lambda)|$ is the effective thickness of the surface layer next to the wall of the system. Since equation (5.57) is written in dimensionless units of length, for the thickness of the surface layer of the system d we have

$$d \sim \frac{a}{|\alpha_1(\lambda, T)|}. \tag{7.10}$$

It therefore appears that when $|\alpha_1| \to 0$, i.e., when the system approaches thermodynamically unstable states, the thickness of the surface layer of the system increases without limit.

In conclusion let us note that if we use equation (2.69), then, simultaneously with $|\alpha_1| \to 0$, we also find that

$$\left(-\frac{\partial p}{\partial v}\right)_T \to 0. \tag{7.11}$$

Thus the approach of the system to unstable states in the sense indicated above coincides with the usual thermodynamic criterion of the loss of stability. In fact, however, the situation is more complex inasmuch as when there is a slow approach of $F_2(q, q')$ toward $F_1(q)F_1(q')$ for $q - q' \to \infty$, as occurs when $|\alpha_1| \to 0$, the replacement of the exact equation (2.65) by equation (2.67) is incorrect, and consequently there is no assurance that equation (2.69) is correct either. Therefore, we cannot assume that property (7.11) follows strictly from the given analysis of the asymptotic behavior of $g(r)$ at large distances and at the limit of stability, although it appears to be very probable.

3. CRITERIA FOR THE LIMIT OF STABILITY OF A ONE-DIMENSIONAL PHASE

The preceding results make it possible to formulate an analytical criterion for the absolute limit of stability of a uniform phase.

We shall assume, in the Bogolyubov equation (5.25), an intermolecular potential $\Phi(r)$ and a temperature T to be given, and we will consider the parameter λ (density) as a "parameter of an integral equation." Then the determination of the boundaries of the region of coexistence of thermodynamically stable states of the system may be formulated in terms of the determination of the spectrum of values of the parameter λ for which the solution of equation (5.25), $g(r)$, satisfies the "boundary condition" (5.56). As we have seen, this is equivalent to the determination of the domain of the parameter λ for which $|\alpha_1| > 0$, where $|\alpha_1|$ is the imaginary part of the smallest root of equation (5.35). The region where $|\alpha_1| = 0$ corresponds to absolute instability. The values $\lambda = \lambda_0$ lying on the boundary between these regions, i.e., on the boundary between the stable and unstable states, are the limiting points of stability of the uniform phase. This leads us to the following criterion for the limit of stability.

The limiting point of stability of a uniform phase at a given temperature T is determined by that value λ_0 (of the parameter λ) at which the root of the equation which is least in absolute magnitude satisfying

$$\lambda L(\gamma) = 1\,, \qquad \lambda > 0\,, \tag{7.12}$$

is real,

$$\mathrm{Im}[\gamma_1(\lambda_0)] = 0\,, \tag{7.13}$$

and there exists a neighborhood $\delta\lambda$ of the point λ_0 such that

$$|\mathrm{Im}[\gamma_1(\lambda_0 + \delta\lambda)]| > 0\,. \tag{7.14}$$

In the neighborhood $\delta\lambda$ where (7.14) is fulfilled, the phase is still stable. At the point λ_0 the system is unstable.

Let $L(\gamma)$ be the Fourier transform of the kernel $K(x)$ of the Bogolyubov equation:

$$L(\gamma) = \int_{-\infty}^{\infty} K(x)\, e^{i\gamma x} dx\,, \tag{7.15}$$

$$K(x) = \frac{1}{2}\int_{|x|}^{\infty} \left\{\exp\left[-\frac{\Phi(t)}{kT}\right]\right\}' u(t)(x^2 - t^2)\, dt\,. \tag{7.16}$$

The function $L(\gamma)$ depends on the temperature of the system, T, and the conditions (7.12) to (7.14) determine $\lambda = \lambda_0(T)$, i.e., they determine the limiting line of stability of the system in the $\lambda - T$ plane. Since, from (5.26), $\lambda \sim 1/v$, the limiting line of stability $v = v_{\mathrm{lim}}(T)$ in the $v - T$ plane of the system is thereby determined. Finally, with the aid of the equation of state (5.27) we can also find the limiting line of stability $p = p_{\mathrm{lim}}(T)$ in the $p - T$ plane:

$$p_{\mathrm{lim}} = \frac{kT}{v_{\mathrm{lim}}}\left[\!\left[1 + \frac{\lambda_0}{3}\int_0^{\infty}\left\{\exp\left[-\frac{\Phi(r)}{kT}\right]\right\}' u(r)\, r^3 dr \right]\!\right]. \tag{7.17}$$

Both lines $v = v_{\lim}(T)$ and $p = p_{\lim}(T)$ completely describe the boundaries of stability of the uniform phase of the system in the space of thermodynamic states. We wish to emphasize once again that in accordance with the theory being studied, the system is already unstable along these lines.

A classification of the limiting points of stability dependent upon their isolation or non-isolation is also possible.

1. Condition (7.14) is fulfilled only on one side of λ_0, i.e., it is possible only when $\lambda > \lambda_0$ or when $\lambda < \lambda_0$. Then we have a "normal" limiting point characteristic of crystallization, evaporation, or gaseous condensation for which the uniform phase may exist stably only at smaller (or larger) densities and is impossible at larger (smaller) densities.

2. Condition (7.14) is fulfilled on both sides of λ_0. The point $\lambda = \lambda_0$ is then an isolated point of instability on the isotherm. This instability is characteristic of the critical point.

Another classification of limiting points is possible, depending on whether $\mathrm{Re}\{\gamma_1(\lambda_0)\} = 0$ occurs simultaneously with $\mathrm{Im}\{\gamma_1(\lambda_0)\} = 0$ (see [7.13]) or whether $\mathrm{Re}\{\gamma_1(\lambda_0)\} \neq 0$. We shall call these cases limiting points of the first and second types, respectively: these cases differ significantly in their properties. Moreover, further refinement of the criterion of stability (7.12) to (7.14) is also different for both cases.

The limiting points of the first type may occur if the function $L(\gamma)$ is such that $L(0) > 0$. Then $\gamma_1(\lambda_0) = 0$, and instead of (7.12) we obtain

$$\lambda_0 L(0) = 1 . \tag{7.18}$$

This determines $\lambda = \lambda_0(T)$ or $v = v_{\lim}(T)$. By integrating by parts with the aid of (7.15) and (7.16) we find that

$$L(0) = -\frac{2}{3}\int_0^\infty \left\{\exp\left[-\frac{\Phi(r)}{kT}\right]\right\}' u(r)\, r^3 dr . \tag{7.19}$$

Comparing this with expression (7.17) we find that

$$\frac{pv}{kT} = 1 - \tfrac{1}{2}\lambda L(0) \tag{7.20}$$

or, taking (7.18) into consideration,

$$(pv)_{\lim} = \tfrac{1}{2}kT . \tag{7.21}$$

This is the general expression for the line of limiting points of stability of the first type in the $p - v$ plane. Since the equation $v = v_{\lim}(T)$ is already known from (7.18), this also determines the limiting line $p = p_{\lim}(T)$ in the $p - T$ plane.

With the aid of equations (7.18) and (7.19), the conditions for the limiting points of the first type may finally be written in the form

$$\frac{4\pi}{3\,v\,kT}\int_0^\infty \Phi'(r)\,g(r)\,r^3 dr = 1\,, \tag{7.22}$$

where we have reverted to ordinary units of length and volume and have introduced the function $g(r)$ instead of $u(r)$.

The limiting points of stability of the first type are possible, apparently, only for very special systems. The case of the limiting points of the second type is more interesting and important. Let us consider the criterion of the limit of stability (7.12) to (7.14) in greater detail.

Select some value of λ which is close to λ_0 and which satisfies condition (7.14). In (7.13) and (7.14) put $\gamma_1 = \beta + i\alpha$, where the index 1 is omitted for the sake of brevity. Now by definition β is not equal to zero at the limiting point. When λ is near to λ_0, α is small, and expanding $L(\gamma)$ in a series in powers of $i\alpha$, we can write

$$\begin{aligned} L(\gamma) = \Big[L(\beta) - \frac{\alpha^2}{2}L''(\beta) + \dots\Big] \\ + i\alpha\Big[L'(\beta) - \frac{\alpha^2}{6}L'''(\beta) + \dots\Big]. \end{aligned} \tag{7.23}$$

Because of the parity of the function $K(x)$ (see eq. [7.16]), $L(\beta)$, $L'(\beta)$, etc., are real. Placing (7.23) in equation (7.12) and separating the real and imaginary parts, instead of one complex equation we obtain two real equations of the form

$$\begin{aligned} \lambda\Big[L(\beta) - \frac{\alpha^2}{2}L''(\beta) + \dots\Big] = 1\,, \\ L'(\beta) - \frac{\alpha^2}{6}L'''(\beta) + \dots = 0\,. \end{aligned} \tag{7.24}$$

At the same limiting point $\alpha = 0$. Then

$$\lambda_0 L(\beta_0) = 1\,, \tag{7.25}$$

$$L'(\beta_0) = 0\,. \tag{7.26}$$

This system of equations is a refinement of the condition defining the limit of stability of the uniform phase for the case of limiting points of the second type. These equations in parametric form (through the parameter β_0) determine the limiting line of stability of the system in the $\lambda - T$ or $v - T$ planes: $\lambda = \lambda_0(T)$ or $v = v_{\rm lim}(T)$. With the aid of equation (7.17) we can then also find the limiting line of stability $p = p_{\rm lim}(T)$ in the $p - T$ plane of the system.

Finally, analogously to equation (7.22), we can write conditions (7.25) and (7.26) in terms of the intermolecular potential and the radial distribution function. After simple transformations we obtain

$$-\frac{4\pi}{vkT}\int_0^\infty \frac{\sin \beta r}{\beta r}\left[\int_\infty^r \Phi'(t)\,g(t)\,dt\right] r^2 dr = 1\,, \quad (7.27)$$

$$\int_0^\infty \frac{\sin \beta r - \beta r \cos \beta r}{\beta r}\left[\int_\infty^r \Phi'(t)\,g(t)\,dt\right] r^2 dr = 0\,. \quad (7.28)$$

The first of these equations was obtained for the first time by Tyablikov [8] starting from a different "criterion of crystallization" for a liquid.

Below we shall go into greater detail with regard to the properties of the limiting points of stability of each type individually.

4. LIMITING POINTS OF STABILITY OF THE FIRST TYPE

Let us consider a small neighborhood $\delta\lambda$ around the point λ_0, determined by the condition (7.18). Because of the parity of the function $K(x)$, from (7.15) it follows that $L'(0) = 0$. Therefore, equation (7.12) may be written

$$(\lambda_0 + \delta\lambda)\left[L(0) + \left(\frac{\partial L}{\partial \lambda}\right)_0 \delta\lambda + \tfrac{1}{2}L''(0)\gamma_1^2 + \ldots\right] = 1\,. \quad (7.29)$$

Let $L''(0) \neq 0$. Taking (7.18) into consideration, we find from this for small values of $\delta\lambda$ and γ_1:

$$\gamma_1(\lambda) = \frac{1}{\lambda_0}\sqrt{\left\{\frac{2\left[1 + \lambda_0^2\left(\frac{\partial L}{\partial \lambda}\right)_0\right]}{L''(0)}(\lambda_0 - \lambda)\right\}}\,. \quad (7.30)$$

Again put $\gamma_1 = \beta + i\alpha$. Then two cases are possible.

1. $L''(0) < 0$. From (7.30) it follows that

$$\beta \equiv 0\,, \qquad \alpha = \text{const}\sqrt{(\lambda_0 - \lambda)}\,, \qquad \text{if} \qquad \lambda < \lambda_0\,, \quad (7.31)$$

$$\alpha \equiv 0\,, \qquad \beta = \text{const}\sqrt{(\lambda - \lambda_0)}\,, \qquad \text{if} \qquad \lambda > \lambda_0\,. \quad (7.32)$$

The general theory shows that we have here a limiting point of the type corresponding to the boundary between supercooled vapor and liquid: the phase exists when $\lambda < \lambda_0$, and it is impossible when $\lambda > \lambda_0$.

2. $L''(0) > 0$. Then α and β in equations (7.31) and (7.32) exchange roles, and in this case we have a limiting point corresponding to the boundary between a superheated liquid and vapor: the phase exists when $\lambda > \lambda_0$ and is impossible when $\lambda < \lambda_0$.

Thus the limiting points of the type under consideration are such that on one side of them—from the side of the stable states—

$$\nu(r) = \frac{A_1}{r} e^{-|\alpha_1| r}, \tag{7.33}$$

while on the other side—from the side of the unstable states—

$$\nu(r) = \frac{A_1}{r} \cos(\beta_1 r + \delta_1), \tag{7.34}$$

and r is assumed to be large.

A function $\nu(r)$ in the same form as (7.33) has been postulated in the theory of critical opalescence [5, 6]. The deviation of the free-energy density from its equilibrium value due to fluctuations in density corresponding to (7.33) is (cf. eq. [7.9])

$$f - f_0 = B[(\nabla\varphi)^2 + \alpha_1^2\varphi^2], \tag{7.35}$$

whereupon $\alpha_1^2 B$ is proportional to $-(\partial p/\partial v)_T$ [7]. Since when $\lambda \to \lambda_0$ we have $\alpha_1 \to 0$, then at the same limiting point we obtain

$$\left(-\frac{\partial p}{\partial v}\right)_T = 0. \tag{7.36}$$

Thus, in the case of limiting points of the first type, the condition (7.11) follows rigorously from the statistical theory.

In paper [3] it was shown, moreover, that at the point $\lambda = \lambda_0$, $(\partial L/\partial\lambda)_0 = 0$ so that equations (7.31) and (7.32) are substantially simplified. It was also shown that the derivation of (7.33) to (7.34) remains correct in the case where $L''(0) = 0$. It therefore appears that the limiting points of stability of the first type always form the boundaries between the regions of stable and unstable states, and that isolated limiting points of the critical type cannot appear in this case.

As an illustration of the theory, let us consider a system of localized particles, which have an attractive potential (and no repulsion), following paper [3]. We select the intermolecular potential $\Phi(r)$ to be a square well of depth ϵ and unit width (in dimensionless units of length):

$$\begin{aligned} \Phi(r) &= -\epsilon, \quad \text{if} \quad r < 1, \\ \Phi(r) &= 0, \quad \text{if} \quad r > 1. \end{aligned} \tag{7.37}$$

Then

$$\left\{\exp\left[-\frac{\Phi(r)}{kT}\right]\right\}' = -\exp\left(\frac{\epsilon}{kT}\right)H(1-r) + H(r-1), \tag{7.38}$$

and, for the well, $K(x)$ and its Fourier transform $L(\gamma)$ become (see eqs. [7.15]–[7.16])

$$K(x) = \tfrac{1}{2}Eu(1)(1 - x^2), \tag{7.39}$$

$$L(\gamma) = 2Eu(1)(\sin\gamma - \gamma\cos\gamma)\gamma^{-3} \tag{7.40}$$

where for the sake of brevity we have set

$$E = \exp\left(\frac{\epsilon}{kT}\right) - 1 > 0\,. \tag{7.41}$$

From this we have

$$L(0) = \tfrac{2}{3}Eu(1) > 0\,, \qquad L''(0) = -\tfrac{2}{15}Eu(1) < 0\,. \tag{7.42}$$

It is therefore clear that equation (7.12) has a solution $\gamma = 0$ of the type corresponding to gaseous condensation when

$$\tfrac{2}{3}E\lambda_0 u(1) = 1\,. \tag{7.43}$$

From this we find $\lambda_0(T)$ and also $v_{\lim}(T)$ according to (5.26):

$$v_{\lim}(T) = \frac{4\pi a^3}{3}\left[\exp\left(\frac{\epsilon}{kT}\right) - 1\right]u(1)\,. \tag{7.44}$$

Consequently for $p_{\lim}(T)$ we find from (7.21) that

$$p_{\lim}(T) = \frac{3kT}{8\pi a^3 u(1)\left[\exp\left(\frac{\epsilon}{kT}\right) - 1\right]}\,. \tag{7.45}$$

In order to find the precise forms of the functions $v_{\lim}(T)$ and $p_{\lim}(T)$ it is still necessary to know the dependence of $u(1)$ on λ and T, i.e., to know the exact solution of the non-linear Bogolyubov equation (5.25) when $r = 1$; this solution is not available. In general, as an approximation it is possible to discard $u(1)$ in these expressions, since $u(r) \sim 1$. This is a good approximation at low temperatures, where $\epsilon/kT \gg 1$. Then $v_{\lim}(T)$ is large (highly rarefied gas) and the equality $u(1) \approx 1$ is fulfilled with great precision, since for an extremely rarefied gas $u(r) \equiv 1$. Thus for low temperatures we have

$$v_{\lim}(T) = \frac{4\pi a^3}{3}\exp\left(\frac{\epsilon}{kT}\right), \qquad p_{\lim}(T) = \frac{3kT}{8\pi a^3}\exp\left(-\frac{\epsilon}{kT}\right). \tag{7.46}$$

The model system under consideration, despite the fact that it is extremely simple, may serve as a plausible representation of a real molecular system if the density is sufficiently low. As a matter of fact, neglecting the repulsive forces which act between particles at very small distances is permissible if the average distance between the particles is large. The forces of attraction between the particles act over greater distances, and they must be taken into consideration. Since at the limit of stability, according to (7.46), low temperatures correspond to the case of low densities, it may be assumed that the result (7.46) describes with sufficient accuracy the limiting line of stability of the real gas phase at low temperatures, i.e., in the region of the triple point or below. Then $p_{\lim}(T)$ is the sublimation pressure or, more precisely, the pressure of the gas along the coexistence line which corresponds to sublimation. The result obtained corresponds well with the results of a calculation of the equilibrium sublimation pressure [9].

5. LIMITING POINTS OF STABILITY OF THE SECOND TYPE

Now let us consider a small neighborhood $\delta\lambda$ around a limiting point of the second type, λ_0, determined by equations (7.25) and (7.26). Assuming that $\lambda = \lambda_0 + \delta\lambda$ and $\beta = \beta_0 + \delta\beta$ and placing this in (7.24) we obtain

$$\lambda_0 + \delta\lambda\Big[L(\beta_0) + \left(\frac{\partial L}{\partial\lambda}\right)_0 \delta\lambda + \tfrac{1}{2}L''(\beta_0)(\delta\beta^2 - \alpha^2) + \ldots\Big] = 1, \quad (7.47)$$

$$\left(\frac{\partial L}{\partial\lambda}\right)_0 \delta\lambda + L''(\beta_0)\,\delta\beta - \frac{\alpha^2}{6}L'''(\beta_0) + \ldots = 0.$$

We will assume that $L''(\beta_0) \neq 0$. Then solving the system of equations obtained for α and $\delta\beta$ for small values of $\delta\lambda$, $\alpha(\lambda)$ is found to be

$$\alpha(\lambda) = \sqrt{\left\{\frac{2\left[1+\lambda_0^2\left(\frac{\partial L}{\partial\lambda}\right)_0\right]}{\lambda_0^2 L''(\beta_0)}(\lambda-\lambda_0)\right\}}. \quad (7.48)$$

For $\beta(\lambda)$ we obtain a linear function of $\delta\lambda$, which we will not write out because of its awkwardness. Now two cases are possible.

1. $L''(\beta_0)$ and $1 + \lambda_0^2(\partial L/\partial\lambda)_0$ are of opposite sign. Then the uniform phase is stable when $\lambda < \lambda_0$, and it is absolutely unstable when $\lambda > \lambda_0$ (since in this case $\alpha \equiv 0$). We have a limiting point of the type corresponding to gaseous condensation or crystallization.

2. $L''(\beta_0)$ and $1 + \lambda_0^2(\partial L/\partial\lambda)_0$ are of identical sign. Then the uniform phase is stable when $\lambda > \lambda_0$ and absolutely unstable when $\lambda < \lambda_0$. We have a limiting point of the type corresponding to liquid evaporation.

Special cases are possible when $L''(\beta_0) = 0$ or $1 + \lambda_0^2(\partial L/\partial\lambda)_0 = 0$, and they require detailed consideration. It is possible to show that the case $L''(\beta_0) = 0$ is not realized [10], while the case $1 + \lambda_0^2(\partial L/\partial\lambda)_0 = 0$ leads to a critical point and will be discussed in greater detail below.

Thus if we exclude the critical point, the limiting points of the second type are such that, for large r, on the side of the coexistence line corresponding to stable states

$$\nu(r) = \frac{A_1}{r} e^{-|\alpha_1| r} \cos(\beta_1 r + \delta_1), \tag{7.49}$$

while on the side corresponding to unstable states

$$\nu(r) = \frac{A_1}{r} \cos(\beta_1 r + \delta_1). \tag{7.50}$$

At the limiting point $\alpha_1(\lambda_0) = 0$, but $\beta_1(\lambda_0) \neq 0$. From (7.48) and (7.10) it follows that on approaching the limiting point along the isotherm, the thickness of the surface or boundary layer of the system increases without limit according to the law

$$d = \frac{\text{const}}{\sqrt{(|v - v_{\text{lim}}|)}}. \tag{7.51}$$

From (7.30) it follows that the same is also true for limiting points of the first type.

If we assume that the function $L(\gamma)$ at the limiting point also has derivatives with respect to temperature, then it is possible to carry out an analysis of α and β on T analogous to the analysis of the dependence of α and β on λ. It is not difficult to show that in this case we obtain

$$\alpha(T) = \text{const}\sqrt{(|T - T_{\text{lim}}|)}. \tag{7.52}$$

Instead of (7.51) it then follows that

$$d = \frac{\text{const}}{\sqrt{(|T - T_{\text{lim}}|)}}, \tag{7.53}$$

if the limiting point is approached along the isochore.

A more detailed analysis of limiting points of the second type, especially of the "triple" point (point M in Fig. 15) is given in papers [3, 10], and we will not discuss the matter further here.

As an illustration of the theory let us consider the limit of stability of a system of hard non-interacting spheres. More precisely, what is the minimum volume for which a system of a very large (but given) number of hard spheres of diameter a in "thermal motion" can exist in a homogeneous phase?

In dimensionless units of length we now have

$$\begin{aligned} \Phi(r) &= +\infty, \quad \text{if} \quad r<1, \\ \Phi(r) &= 0, \quad \text{if} \quad r>1, \end{aligned} \tag{7.54}$$

so that

$$\left\{\exp\left[-\frac{\Phi(r)}{kT}\right]\right\}' = \delta(r-1). \tag{7.55}$$

Then, according to (7.15) and (7.16) we find that

$$K(x) = \tfrac{1}{2}u(1)(x^2-1), \tag{7.56}$$

$$L(\gamma) = 2u(1)(\gamma\cos\gamma - \sin\gamma)\gamma^{-3}. \tag{7.57}$$

Since $L(0) = -\frac{2}{3}u(1) < 0$, there are no limiting points of the first type in our system and $\gamma \neq 0$. The basic equations (7.25) and (7.26) for λ_0 now take the form

$$\begin{aligned} 2\lambda_0 u(1)(\beta\cos\beta - \sin\beta)\beta^{-3} &= 1, \\ [(3-\beta^2)\sin\beta - 3\beta\cos\beta]\beta^{-4} &= 0. \end{aligned} \tag{7.58}$$

The second of these equations determines β at the limit of stability. The problem amounts to the solution of the transcendental equation

$$\tan\beta = \frac{3\beta}{3-\beta^2}. \tag{7.59}$$

Its solution, as may easily be seen, is equal to

$$\beta_n = \pi n\left[1 - \frac{3}{(\pi n)^2} - \frac{9}{(\pi n)^4} - \frac{81}{(\pi n)^6} - \frac{170}{(\pi n)^8} - \cdots\right], \tag{7.60}$$

where $n = 2, 3, \ldots$. This leads, according to the first of the equations in (7.58), to the result

$$[2\lambda_0 u(1)]_n = (-1)^n\left[(\pi n)^2 - \frac{9}{2} - \frac{43}{8(\pi n)^2} - \frac{4991}{112(\pi n)^4} - \cdots\right]. \tag{7.61}$$

In order to determine the necessary value of n, we note that odd values of n fall out since they lead to negative densities. Among the even values of n it is necessary to select one which will give the least value of λ_0. This leads to $n = 2$, since after simple calculation using (7.61) we obtain

$$[2\lambda_0 u(1)]_{\text{lim}} = 34.812 \tag{7.62}$$

and, from (7.60),

$$\beta_{\lim} = 5.761 \,. \tag{7.63}$$

To determine λ_0 it is necessary to know $u(1)$. If we turn to the results of the direct numerical integration of the Bogolyubov equation for the problem under consideration and use the superposition approximation, then from Table 8 we find that when $2\lambda u(1) = 34.8$, the value of $u(1)$ is equal to 2.90. Thus $\lambda_0 = 6$, and finally we have

$$v_{\lim} = \frac{\pi a^3}{3} = 2\,v_0\,, \tag{7.64}$$

where v_0 is the volume of a single hard sphere. Due to the nature of the hard-sphere potential the minimum volume does not depend on temperature.

Thus, in the superposition approximation, the limiting volume per particle for which a uniform system of hard spheres is still stable, is equal to twice the volume of a single particle. Since $\pi a^3/3 \approx a^3$, this corresponds to the fact that the limit of stability occurs almost exactly at the density, which is equal to the density of the loosest ordered structure—a simple cubic lattice with an edge equal to the diameter of a hard sphere. Actually the result (7.64) is somewhat too high, inasmuch as it is known that the superposition approximation gives values too low for the pressure and, consequently, also for $u(1)$.

Finally, with the aid of equations (7.64) and (5.61) we obtain for the pressure at the limit of stability of the system under consideration

$$p_{\lim}(T) = \frac{3.4}{v_0}\,kT\,, \tag{7.65}$$

which represents the "melting curve" of a system of non-interacting hard spheres.

6. THE LIMIT OF STABILITY OF A SYSTEM WITH AN EXPONENTIAL REPULSION BETWEEN PAIRS OF PARTICLES

Now let us consider the problem of the limit of stability of a uniform phase in a somewhat more complex system (which we will need for other purposes later on). Let the potential of the intermolecular forces be given in the form

$$\Phi(r) = 4\epsilon\left(\frac{a_0}{r}\right)^n, \tag{7.66}$$

where ϵ, a_0, and n are constants; we will assume n to be sufficiently large, say $n \sim 10$. Note that the particles of our system everywhere repel each other according to an inverse exponential law. Such an "inverse model" has often been used in statistical physics, for example, in the theory of thermal diffusion [11].

Again we transform to dimensionless units of length, having chosen for the unit of length a,

$$a = a_0\left(\frac{4\epsilon}{kT}\right)^{1/n}, \tag{7.67}$$

so that

$$r \to r' = \frac{r}{a_0}\left(\frac{kT}{4\epsilon}\right)^{1/n}. \tag{7.68}$$

Below, for the sake of simplicity, we shall not write primes on r. In the new units of length we have

$$\exp\left[-\frac{\Phi(r)}{kT}\right] \to \exp\left(-\frac{1}{r^n}\right), \tag{7.69}$$

and, according to (5.26), the parameter λ is equal to

$$\lambda = \frac{2\pi a^3}{v} = \frac{2\pi a_0^3}{v}\left(\frac{4\epsilon}{kT}\right)^{3/n}. \tag{7.70}$$

Now let us consider the kernel $K(x)$ of the Bogolyubov equation

$$K(x) = \frac{1}{2}\int_{|x|}^{\infty}\left[\exp\left(-\frac{1}{t^n}\right)\right]' u(t)(x^2 - t^2)\,dt. \tag{7.71}$$

The function $[\exp(-1/t^n)]'$ at large values of n has one sharp maximum close to the point $t = 1$, and it rapidly disappears for all remaining values of t. The height of the maximum in this case is of the order $\sim(n/e)$. Moreover, since

$$\int_0^{\infty}\left[\exp\left(-\frac{1}{t^n}\right)\right]' dt = 1, \tag{7.72}$$

it is clear that the function $[\exp(-1/t^n)]'$ behaves like a δ function:

$$\left[\exp\left(-\frac{1}{t^n}\right)\right]' \to \delta(t-1) \quad \text{when} \quad n \to \infty. \tag{7.73}$$

If, therefore, as has already been mentioned, the number n is not small, then in the first approximation it is possible to substitute for the function $[\exp(-1/t^n)]'$ in (7.71) a simple δ function (increasingly accurate the larger the value of n), and then we will have

$$\begin{aligned} K(x) &= \tfrac{1}{2}u(1)(x^2 - 1) \quad &&\text{when} \quad |x| < 1, \\ K(x) &= 0 \quad &&\text{when} \quad |x| > 1. \end{aligned} \tag{7.74}$$

It is not difficult to verify that a correction for the fact that n is finite, which should be taken into consideration here, is of the order of $1/n^2$.

But the kernel $K(x)$ in (7.74) is the same as the kernel $K(x)$ for the case of hard spheres (7.56). Therefore, we may make further use of the solution of this problem. According to (7.64) for the limiting volume we had $v_{\lim} = \pi a^3/3$, which now according to (7.67) leads to the result

$$v_{\lim}(T) = \frac{\pi a_0^3}{3}\left(\frac{4\epsilon}{kT}\right)^{3/n}. \qquad (7.75)$$

According to (7.65) for the limiting pressure, we have

$$p_{\lim}(T) = \frac{3.4}{v_0}kT = \frac{20.4}{\pi a^3}kT, \qquad (7.76)$$

so that we now obtain

$$p_{\lim}(T) = \frac{20.4}{\pi a_0^3}\frac{(kT)^{1+(3/n)}}{(4\epsilon)^{3/n}}. \qquad (7.77)$$

These equations in the approximation under consideration completely describe the locus limit of stability of the uniform phase for large values of n. In the limit $n \rightarrow \infty$, we return to the hard-sphere system as expected.

The results obtained here admit of a very simple physical interpretation. If the particles of the system are not absolutely hard, then their effective diameter depends on the energy of the colliding particles, and for the entire system as a whole, the average effective diameter of a particle is dependent on temperature $a_{\text{eff}} = a(T)$. If $\Phi(r)$ is the potential of the forces of repulsion, then it must be obvious that $\Phi(a_{\text{eff}}) \sim kT$, and, from the exponential law for $\Phi(r)$ (7.66), we obtain

$$a_{\text{eff}} \sim a_0\left(\frac{4\epsilon}{kT}\right)^{1/n}, \qquad (v_0)_{\text{eff}} \sim v_0\left(\frac{4\epsilon}{kT}\right)^{3/n}. \qquad (7.78)$$

Now considering the system as a set of spheres each with a diameter a_{eff}, from (7.64) we obtain

$$v_{\lim} \sim 2(v_0)_{\text{eff}} \sim 2v_0\left(\frac{4\epsilon}{kT}\right)^{3/n} \qquad (7.79)$$

and, analogously for $p_{\lim}$, in full correspondence with the results of the more rigorous theory.

7. APPROXIMATE THEORY OF THE MELTING CURVE

An important and physically interesting problem in the theory of the stability of liquids is the study of crystallization. For simple substances such as argon, the empirical Simon equation exists to provide the equation for the melting curve in the $p - T$ plane of the system in the form [12]

$$p_{\text{melt}}(T) = -A + BT^m ; \tag{7.80}$$

it is extremely accurate. In this case, A, B, and m are constants. For argon

$$A = 300 \frac{\text{kg}}{\text{cm}^2}, \quad B = 2.73 \frac{\text{kg}}{\text{cm}^2(\text{degree})^m}, \quad m = 1.288. \tag{7.81}$$

Later experimental studies have confirmed the accuracy of the Simon equation [13].

The Simon equation describes the line of the liquid-crystal equilibrium phase transition. We shall try below to obtain an approximate equation for the corresponding line of the absolute limit of stability of a liquid [4]. It may be assumed that for the simple liquids in which we are interested, the actual paths of the two lines should be fairly close.

Let us assume that a real liquid is described with sufficient accuracy by the intermolecular potential

$$\Phi(r) = 4\epsilon\left[\left(\frac{a_0}{r}\right)^n - \left(\frac{a_0}{r}\right)^6\right], \tag{7.82}$$

where $n > 6$. It is well known that this potential agrees best with experimental data for compressed gases when $n \sim 10$ [14]. For the constants that enter here a study of the second virial coefficient leads to the following values in the case of argon [14]:

$$\begin{aligned} &\text{when } n = 10: \ a_0 = 3.50 \cdot 10^{-8} \text{ cm}, \ \epsilon = 13.9 \cdot 10^{-15} \text{ erg}; \\ &\text{when } n = 12: \ a_0 = 3.41 \cdot 10^{-8} \text{ cm}, \ \epsilon = 16.5 \cdot 10^{-15} \text{ erg}. \end{aligned} \tag{7.83}$$

A rigorous solution of the limited stability problem of a system with a potential of the form (7.82), without knowledge of the solutions of the Bogolyubov equation for this problem, is impossible. We can, however, get an approximate solution to this problem if in (7.82) we only take repulsion into consideration as the main term, and then introduce a correction for the attractive force. This is justified at high temperatures when crystallization (and, even more, absolute loss of stability of the liquid) takes place at very high pressures so that the particle density is also very large. Under such conditions the forces of repulsion between the particles, which are highly compressed by the external pressure, play the chief role and the attractive forces play only a secondary role.

In such a case, we return in the zeroth approximation to the problem of a system interacting with the inverse potential (7.66) and the pressure at the limit of stability is determined by equation (7.77). To this should then be added a correction for the forces of attraction between the particles. This correction arises from the "internal pressure" of the liquid, which is negative in sign, so that

$$p_{\text{lim}}(T) = -|p^{\text{int}}| + \frac{20.4}{\pi a_0^3} \frac{(kT)^{1+(3/n)}}{(4\epsilon)^{3/n}}. \qquad (7.84)$$

The internal pressure at the high densities, which correspond to the crystallization of simple liquids (and even more at the limit of stability), is weakly dependent on temperature. In a first approximation the internal pressure may be assumed to be equal to a constant, and then from considerations of dimensionality it follows that

$$|p^{\text{int}}| = -\gamma \frac{\epsilon}{a_0^3}, \qquad (7.85)$$

where γ is a dimensionless coefficient. Summing up we obtain an equation for the limiting pressure in the form

$$p_{\text{lim}}(T) = -\frac{\gamma\epsilon}{a_0^3} + \frac{20.4}{\pi a_0^3} \frac{(kT)^{1+(3/n)}}{(4\epsilon)^{3/n}}. \qquad (7.86)$$

If, as has already been mentioned, we identify the limiting line of stability of a liquid with the melting curve, then it is obvious that we have obtained an equation of exactly the same type as the empirical equation (7.80), so that the general form of the temperature dependence p_{lim} agrees well with experiment. There also exists satisfactory agreement with respect to details. Let us examine this. For the constant m in (7.80), we obtain from (7.86)

$$m = 1 + \frac{3}{n} = \begin{cases} 1.30, & \text{if} \quad n = 10, \\ 1.25, & \text{if} \quad n = 12, \end{cases} \qquad (7.87)$$

which agrees very well with experimental data (7.81). For the coefficients A and B in (7.80), we have

$$A = \frac{\gamma\epsilon}{a_0^3}, \qquad B = \frac{20.4 k^{1+(3/n)}}{\pi a_0^3 (4\epsilon)^{3/n}}. \qquad (7.88)$$

Placing in the expression for A the values of (7.83) results, after comparison with (7.81), in the estimate $\gamma \sim 7$ to 9 which is entirely satisfactory. Finally, the numerical evaluation of B from (7.88) gives

$$B = \begin{cases} 3.47 \dfrac{\text{kg}}{\text{cm}^2(\text{degree})^{1.3}}, & \text{if} \quad n = 10, \\ 4.54 \dfrac{\text{kg}}{\text{cm}^2(\text{degree})^{1.25}}, & \text{if} \quad n = 12. \end{cases} \tag{7.89}$$

Comparison with the experimental data of (7.81) shows that the order of magnitude is correct, although the theoretical values are somewhat high. This may be partially explained as arising from the difference between the coexistence line of the equilibrium phase transition and locus of the absolute limit of stability.

TABLE 10

T (° K)	$(v_L)_{melt} \cdot 10^{23}$ cm³		
	Experiment	Theory	
		$n=10$	$n=12$
83.9......	4.63	7.20	6.41
126.3......	4.33	6.39	5.82
162.0......	4.20	5.94	5.49
193.1......	4.14	5.53	5.24

Now let us compare the theoretical and experimental data for the limiting volume. The theoretical result is expressed in equation (7.75). Table 10 gives the experimental data for the volume of liquid argon along the melting curve from [12] and the results of calculations from (7.75) for several temperatures. From the table it can be seen that the theory correctly describes the general properties of the limiting volume of the liquid and gives a numerical evaluation of it which is correct in order of magnitude, although somewhat high. It may also be noted that the agreement of theory with experiment improves as the temperature increases. This corresponds to the previous observation that the inverse model is unsuitable at low temperatures. Finally we should take into consideration that, along with a correction for the internal pressure on $p_{\lim}(T)$, it would be necessary to introduce an analogous correction on $v_{\lim}(T)$. It is obvious physically that this would decrease the numerical values for $v_{\lim}(T)$ and would thereby improve the agreement with the experimental data.

8. THE CRITICAL POINT

The critical point is an isolated limiting point on the isotherm which separates it from the remaining limiting points of stability in such a way that it is accessible for direct experimental study.

In the theory of critical opalescence, which has a semi-thermodynamic character, a correlation function of the type (5.7) is postulated for the neighborhood of the critical point:

$$\nu(r) = \frac{A}{r} e^{-ar}. \tag{7.90}$$

At the same critical point $a = 0$. In such a case the critical point should be a limiting point of the first type. But we have seen above that among the limiting points of the first type, isolated limiting points do not exist which would have stable states on both sides of them. Consequently the function (7.90) cannot be a true, "microscopic" correlation function in the neighborhood of the critical point.

In favor of this deduction there is also the fact that, according to (7.21), at a limiting point of the first type $(pv/kT)_{\lim} = \frac{1}{2}$. This agrees poorly with the experimental value $(pv/kT)_{\text{crit}} = 0.292$, found for all noble gases at the critical point.

Consequently the critical point must be an isolated limiting point of the second type, and in its vicinity there should be

$$\nu(r) = \frac{A_1}{r} e^{-|a_1|r} \cos(\beta_1 r + \delta_1), \tag{7.91}$$

while at the same critical point $a_1 = 0$. The correlation function (7.90) used in the semi-thermodynamic theory of fluctuations should be considered as the result of the "smoothing" of the more precise function (7.91).

In discussing equation (7.48) we saw that, when $1 + \lambda_0^2(\partial L/\partial\lambda)_0 \neq 0$ and $L''(\beta) \neq 0$, a limiting point of the second type is always the normal one and not the isolated one. Inasmuch as the case where $L''(\beta_0) = 0$ is unrealizable [10], there remains for study the case where

$$\lambda_0^2\left[\frac{\partial L(\beta)}{\partial\lambda}\right]_0 + 1 = 0. \tag{7.92}$$

Together with (7.25) and (7.26) we obtain three conditions which determine some point λ_0, β_0, T_0 on the line of stability. This point is actually an isolated point of instability on the isotherm. Let us consider a small region in the neighborhood of this point: $T = T_0$, $\lambda = \lambda_0 + \delta\lambda$, $\beta = \beta_0 + \delta\beta$. Then α will be small, and placing this in (7.24) and taking (7.92) into consideration, we obtain

$$-2\delta\lambda^2 + \lambda_0^3(\delta\beta^2 - \alpha^2)L''(\beta_0) + \lambda_0^3\left(\frac{\partial^2 L}{\partial\lambda^2}\right)_0 \delta\lambda^2 + \lambda_0^3\left[\frac{\partial L'(\beta_0)}{\partial\lambda}\right]_0 \delta\beta\,\delta\lambda + \ldots = 0, \quad (7.93)$$

$$L''(\beta_0)\,\delta\beta + \left[\frac{\partial L'(\beta)}{\partial\lambda}\right]_0 \delta\lambda + \ldots = 0.$$

Solving these equations for α and $\delta\beta$, we obtain

$$|\alpha| = \text{const}\,|\lambda - \lambda_0|, \qquad \beta = \beta_0 + \text{const}(\lambda - \lambda_0). \quad (7.94)$$

We will not bother to write out the cumbersome expressions for the constants that enter here. Thus, when $\lambda = \lambda_0$ we have $\alpha = 0$, i.e., this state is unstable, but in any neighborhood of the point λ_0, $\alpha \neq 0$, and, actually, we have an isolated point of instability.

Therefore, the combination of equations (7.25), (7.26), and (7.92) are the conditions defining the approach to the critical point in the theory developed:

$$\lambda_0 L(\beta_0) = 1, \qquad L'(\beta_0) = 0, \qquad \lambda_0^2\left(\frac{\partial L}{\partial\lambda}\right)_0 = -1. \quad (7.95)$$

If there exists a derivative $(\partial L/\partial T)_0$, then it is easy to obtain from it the dependence of α and β on temperature.

Assuming that $\beta = \beta_0 + \delta\beta$, $T = T_0 + \delta T$, and $\lambda = \lambda_0$, placing this in (7.24), and taking (7.95) into consideration, it is not difficult to find that in the region of stable states

$$\alpha = \text{const}\sqrt{(T - T_0)}, \qquad \beta = \beta_0 + \text{const}(T - T_0). \quad (7.96)$$

In connection with (7.10) we find that the thickness of the surface (or boundary) layer of a liquid on approaching the critical point increases without limit, in accordance with the law

$$d = \frac{\text{const}}{|v - v_0|}, \quad (7.97)$$

if we move along the isotherm, and

$$d = \frac{\text{const}}{\sqrt{(T - T_0)}}, \quad (7.98)$$

if we move along the isochore.

Now let us consider the change of λ_0, β_0, and T_0 on moving along the line of limit of stability in the neighborhood of the critical point. In this case $\alpha(\lambda_0) = 0$, always. Differentiating the identity

$$\lambda_0 L[\beta(\lambda_0), \lambda_0, T(\lambda_0)] \equiv 1\,, \tag{7.99}$$

we obtain

$$1 + \lambda_0^2\left[L'(\beta_0)\frac{d\beta}{d\lambda_0} + \left(\frac{\partial L}{\partial \lambda}\right)_0 + \left(\frac{\partial L}{\partial T}\right)_0 \left(\frac{dT}{d\lambda_0}\right)_{\text{lim}}\right] = 0\,, \tag{7.100}$$

where $(\ldots)_0$ means "on the line" of the limit of stability, while $(\ldots)_{\text{lim}}$ means "along the line" of limit of stability. Using (7.95), at the same critical point we obtain $[(dT/d\lambda)_{\text{lim}}]_{\text{crit}} = 0$, or

$$\left(\frac{dT}{dv}\right)_{\text{lim crit}} = 0\,. \tag{7.101}$$

If in $L(\beta_0)$ the temperature is eliminated through the equation of state, and differentiating the identity

$$\lambda_0 L[\beta(\lambda_0), \lambda_0, p(\lambda_0)] \equiv 1\,, \tag{7.102}$$

we obtain

$$\left(\frac{dp}{dv}\right)_{\text{lim, crit}} = 0\,. \tag{7.103}$$

Thus, from our determination of the critical point (7.92) it follows that the limiting line of stability in the $T - v$ or $p - v$ planes at the limiting point has an extremum as defined by the thermodynamic theory.

If we also assume the existence of higher derivatives of $L(\beta_0)$ with respect to λ and T, then it is not difficult to show that the locus of the limiting line of stability in the neighborhood of the critical point in the $T - v$ or $p - v$ planes corresponds to a parabola as in the thermodynamic theory of the critical point [7]. There is, however, no assurance of the existence of these derivatives. For a complete analysis of the problem it is essential to know the behavior of $g(r; v, T)$ not only at large distances, but everywhere, and this knowledge is not at present available.

But even without a more complete analysis it is possible to delineate one point at which the above theory differs significantly from the classical theory. In the classical theory it is assumed that the critical point itself is a point corresponding to stable states, and this guarantees the supposed non-zero value of the derivative $(-\partial^3 p/\partial v^3)_T$ [7]. It follows from the above discussion that this is not so. At the critical point, as on the whole limiting line of stability, $\alpha_1 = 0$, and therefore the substance is absolutely unstable. In addition, the substance is also unstable in some small neighborhood of the critical point, surrounding it on all sides; on the side of the stable states α_1, although not equal to zero, is still very small. Strictly speaking, equilibrium thermodynamic functions and their derivatives do not exist at the critical point. One can only speak of them in the sense of limiting values on approaching from the side of the stable states, and the problem of determining the limiting line of stability and the thermodynamic properties of the substances in the neighborhood of the critical point must be solved with great care.

REFERENCES

[1] B. T. Geilikman, *Statisticheskaya teoriya fazovykh prevrashchenii*, Gostekhizdat (*Statistical Theory of Phase Transformations*), State Technical Press, 1954.
[2] I. Z. Fisher, *Zh. Eksperim. i. Teor. Fiz.* **28** (1955), 171.
[3] I. Z. Fisher, *ibid.*, p. 437.
[4] I. Z. Fisher, *ibid.*, p. 447.
[5] M. A. Leontovich, *Statisticheskaya fizika*, Gostekhizdat (Statistical Physics), State Technical Press, 1945.
[6] M. Born and H. Green, *Proc. Roy. Soc., ser. A*, **189** (1947), 455.
[7] L. D. Landau and E. M. Lifshits, *Statisticheskaya fizika*, Gostekhizdat (Statistical Physics), State Technical Press, 1951.
[8] S. V. Tyablikov, *Zh. Eksperim. i Teor. Fiz.*, **17** (1947), 386.
[9] V. G. Levich, *Vvedenie v statisticheskuyu fiziku*, Gostekhizdat (Introduction to Statistical Physics), State Technical Press, 1954.
[10] I. Z. Fisher, *Dissertatsiya*, Belorusskii Gosudarstvennyi Universitet, Minsk. (Dissertation), Belorussian State University, Minsk, 1958.
[11] R. Dzhons and V. Farri, *Razdelenie isotopov metodom termodiffuzii*, IL (Separation of Isotopes by the Thermal Diffusion Method), IL, 1947.
[12] F. Simon, M. Ruhemann, and A. Edwards, *Z. Phys. Chem., ser. B*, **6** (1930), 331.
[13] P. Bridgman, *Fizika vysokikh davlenii*, ONTI (The Physics of High Pressures), ONTI, 1935.
[14] R. Fowler and E. Guggenheim, *Statisticheskaya termodinamika*, IL (Statistical Thermodynamics), IL, 1949.

CHAPTER 8

NUMERICAL METHODS IN THE THEORY OF LIQUIDS

1. THE USE OF NUMERICAL METHODS

In the preceding chapters we have considered the status and success of the theory of the liquid state based on a study of correlation functions and integral equations for them. In doing so we repeatedly had occasion to be convinced of the great mathematical difficulties encountered in solving various problems, which seriously hamper the further development of the theory. The only possible circumvention currently available is the extensive application to the theory of liquids of the powerful modern methods of computer mathematics. In chapter 5 we gave two examples of the use of computers in problems of the theory of liquids. There we were concerned with the numerical solution of the nonlinear Bogolyubov integral equation for the radial distribution function of the particles of a liquid, $g(r)$. Analogous use of numerical methods of solution, using computers, is also possible and desirable for other integral equations arising in the theory. In all these cases, however, the use of complex calculational procedures is implied for equations which in themselves are only approximate, in consequence for example, of the use of the superposition approximation or other approximations. Naturally the question arises as to whether these complex calculational techniques should not be used directly in rigorous variants of the theory. An ideal case would be the possibility of calculating directly the configurational integral Q_N of a system of a large number of particles.

It appears that in principle such a calculation is possible; this type of calculation has led to the introduction of the Monte Carlo method into statistical physics. The use of Monte Carlo methods in classical statistical physics was suggested for the first time by J. E. Mayer. It was used first in papers [1, 2] for very simplified models of a system of particles, and then in papers [3, 4, 5] after considerable refinement of the method for more complex and interesting systems (see also the review [6]).

For a comparatively long time, some workers [7, 8] have been using direct integration of the equations of motion in a system containing large numbers of hard spheres. Such direct dynamical calculations for a system with a large number of particles is very interesting. From the results it is possible to draw many conclusions regarding both the kinetic and the equilibrium-statistical properties of the system.

In the present chapter we shall briefly consider the ideas and the results found in these calculations, with reference to the theory of liquids and gases. Principal attention will be focused on the Monte Carlo method. The underlying basis of the Monte Carlo method still needs more thorough study, but we shall not be concerned with that problem here.

The Monte Carlo method, in general, refers to a technique of numerical calculation in which specific probability elements are introduced. This is in contrast with the classical techniques of calculation, which depend on the successive development of completely determined algebraic operations. In its different variants the Monte Carlo method has recently found application in many problems of physics, technology, etc. In our case we are principally concerned with the calculation of multiple integrals of the type of the configuration integral. The nature of the Monte Carlo method will be analyzed in greater detail below.

The results obtained by the Monte Carlo method up to the present, although very interesting, are still fairly modest. It is essential to take into account, however, that the purpose of the first papers published was primarily to test the usefulness of the method itself and to refine it, and not to obtain new results. At the present time, it must be acknowledged that the Monte Carlo method has completely justified itself, and after further refinement may be extremely useful not only for problems in the theory of liquids, but also for many other problems in statistical physics. If we take into consideration the rapid growth in technical facilities and methods of calculational mathematics, these hopes are justified. It appears likely that it is precisely in this direction that we may expect the greatest successes in statistical physics in the very near future, at least in the field of classical theory. In addition, many of the ideas that have arisen in the Monte Carlo method (for example, the idea of introducing periodic boundary conditions for a disordered system; see below) may be useful in statistical physics regardless of the methods used.

2. THE MONTE CARLO METHOD IN STATISTICAL PHYSICS

The basic idea of the Monte Carlo method consists of the replacement of direct integration in the expression for the configuration integral,

$$Q_N = \int_V \cdots \int_V \exp\left[-\frac{U_N(\mathbf{q}_1, \ldots, \mathbf{q}_N)}{kT} \right] d\mathbf{q}_1 \ldots d\mathbf{q}_N \,, \quad (8.1)$$

or in analogous integral expressions which determine the average values of functions of the coordinates,

$$\bar{F} = Q_N^{-1} \int_V \cdots \int_V F(\mathbf{q}_1, \ldots, \mathbf{q}_N) \exp\left[-\frac{U_N(\mathbf{q}_1, \ldots, \mathbf{q}_N)}{kT} \right] \times d\mathbf{q}_1 \ldots \mathbf{q}_N \,, \quad (8.2)$$

by averaging over a great number of random events (configurations) which form a Markov chain with constant transition probabilities.

Consider the $3N$ dimensional configuration space of the system under investigation, and consider a discrete subdivision into an arbitrary large number s of equal cells. Let the cells be numbered in any order. We shall say that the system is in the ith state if the point which describes it is in the ith cell. In each state we may assign to the system a definite numerical value F_i of any function of the coordinates of the system $F(q_1, \ldots, q_N)$, having taken the values $q_1, \ldots, q_N$ as corresponding, for example, to the centers of the cells. In particular, the energy of interaction of the particles of the system is now also described by the set of possible values U_i, $i = 1, \ldots, s$. It is clear that if s is sufficiently large, the replacement of a continuous configuration space by a discrete space does not materially affect the average values of the functions of the coordinates. Then, instead of (8.1) and (8.2), we will have

$$Q_N \sim Q_N' = \sum_{1 \le i \le s} \exp\left(-\frac{U_i}{kT} \right), \quad (8.3)$$

$$\bar{F} = Q_N'^{-1} \sum_{1 \le i \le s} F_i \exp\left(-\frac{U_i}{kT} \right). \quad (8.4)$$

Now let us turn to the following formal scheme. We shall consider the set of all s possible states of the system as a set of chance events A_i that form a Markov chain with constant transition probabilities

$A_i \to A_j$ equal to $p_{ij} \geq 0$. The p_{ij} satisfy the normalization condition

$$\sum_{1 \leq j \leq s} p_{ij} = 1 \,, \qquad i = 1, 2, \ldots, s \,. \quad (8.5)$$

Later we shall need some simple information from the theory of uniform Markov chains (see, for example, eq. [9]). Let us designate by $p_{ij}^{(n)}$ the probability of realizing the transition $A_i \to A_j$ for n steps (so that $p_{ij}^{(1)} \equiv p_{ij}$). If all A_i, $i = 1, \ldots, s$, form one ergodic class, i.e., all states of A_i are not periodic, and if from any state A_i any state A_j is attainable within some finite number of transitions n, then the following limiting probabilities exist:

$$\lim_{n \to \infty} p_{ij}^{(n)} = u_j \,, \qquad j = 1, 2, \ldots, s \,, \quad (8.6)$$

for all i, and

$$u_j > 0 \,, \qquad \sum_{1 \leq j \leq s} u_j = 1 \,, \qquad (8.7)$$

so that u_j defines some distribution of probabilities for A_j. In addition, in the Markov chain theory it is demonstrated that the values u_j are unambiguously defined through normalization by (8.7) and by the values of p_{ij} through a system of linear equations

$$u_j = \sum_{1 \leq i \leq s} u_i p_{ij} \,, \qquad j = 1, 2, \ldots, s \,, \quad (8.8)$$

and that the distribution determined by the numbers u_j is the stationary distribution of the probabilities of the events A_j, i.e., their distribution is such that being taken as initial, they would not change during the course of the Markov process. Equation (8.6) expresses the passage of the system toward a stationary (equilibrium) state independent of the choice of the initial state.

If, therefore, we consider a chain with an unlimited number of steps, the average value of some function of state F_i, taken along the chain, will in the limit obviously be equal to

$$\bar{F} = \sum_{1 \leq i \leq s} F_i u_i \,. \qquad (8.9)$$

If we choose

$$u_i = Q_N'^{-1} \exp\left(-\frac{U_i}{kT}\right), \qquad (8.10)$$

the limiting average of F_i along the unlimited Markov chain will correspond to the canonical average value of the function F as in (8.4).

The necessity remains of selecting the probabilities of the transitions, p_{ij}. It is obvious that this may be done in many ways, since for given values of u_j the p_{ij} are not unambiguously determined from $2s$ of the equations (8.5) and (8.8). Therefore in the space of these events there exists a large number of Markov chains which possess the required limiting property (8.6) and (8.10). We note that the relationships

$$u_i p_{ij} = u_j p_{ji} \, , \tag{8.11}$$

which obviously express the principle of microscopic reversibility in the system, turn equations (8.8) into identities. Therefore, in the practical construction of the Markov chains with the limiting property which we need, it is possible to start from conditions (8.5) and (8.11) instead of (8.5) and (8.8). In connection with (8.10) this gives us relationships for p_{ij} of the form

$$p_{ij} \exp\left(-\frac{U_i}{kT}\right) = p_{ji} \exp\left(-\frac{U_j}{kT}\right). \tag{8.12}$$

Thus the Markov chain, all the states of which form one ergodic class with transition probabilities which satisfy conditions (8.5) and (8.12), coincides with the Gibbs canonical ensemble in the sense that for a sufficiently long chain various states appear with frequencies which are proportional to the Boltzmann factor $\exp[-(U_i/kT)]$. The convergence does not depend on the choice of the initial state, and the average of a function along the chain tends to the average over the canonical ensemble.

Let us now turn to concrete physical systems and consider the problem of the maintenance of the requirement of ergodicity. For the sake of simplicity, let the total energy of interaction of the particles of a system be represented in the form of a sum of pair interactions:

$$U_N(q_1, \ldots, q_N) = \sum_{1 \leq i < j \leq N} \Phi(|q_i - q_j|). \tag{8.13}$$

If the potential $\Phi(r)$ nowhere becomes $+\infty$ then the values of $\exp[-(U_i/kT)]$ will nowhere become zero, so that all u_i in (8.6) will also be different from zero. Therefore, for any transition $A_i \rightarrow A_j$ between the states in discrete configuration space, there exists a non-zero probability of a transition, $p_{ij}^{(n)}$, in some finite number of steps n. All the states of the system are thus attainable from one another, and their totality forms one ergodic class [9]. In this case, any Markov chain with transition probabilities defined by (8.5) and (8.12) converges to the canonical ensemble in the sense mentioned above.

In the theory of liquids and gases a model intermolecular potential $\Phi(r)$, which when $r \to 0$ becomes $+\infty$, is often used. An example of such a potential is

$$\Phi(r) = \frac{A}{r^m} - \frac{B}{r^n}; \qquad A, B > 0; \qquad m > n, \qquad (8.14)$$

which, when $m = 12$ and $n = 6$, becomes the Lennard-Jones potential. In this case $\exp[-(U_i/kT)] = 0$ for configurations in which two particles of the system completely coincide. For these configurations then $u_i = 0$. If we exclude a finite number of these special states, the Markov chain formed by the transitions between all the remaining states of the system in discrete configurational space will again have the property of ergodicity. (In continuous configurational space the majority of points where $U_N = +\infty$ are of zero measure and hence are unimportant.)

Difficulty with ergodicity will only occur if $\Phi(r)$ becomes $+\infty$ in a finite region. Thus, for example, in the model of hard spheres we found that

$$\begin{aligned} \Phi(r) &= +\infty \qquad \text{when} \qquad r < a, \\ \Phi(r) &= 0 \qquad \text{when} \qquad r > a, \end{aligned} \qquad (8.15)$$

where a is the diameter of a sphere; the same will be true in any model of particles with a hard core. When $r < a$ the first equation (8.15) holds. At very high densities, close to the maximum possible density for hard spheres of a given diameter, rearrangements of the particles may be impossible and then we might expect the appearance of configurations of the system between which transitions are impossible. If this occurs, the majority of all possible states of the system break up into isolated ergodic classes without transitions between them, and then the limiting behavior of some definite Markov chain, described above, will depend on which of the ergodic classes the initial state of this chain belongs to. The equivalence of the limiting behavior of the Markov chain and of the Gibbs canonical ensemble will be lost in this case. It should be mentioned, however, that this possible difficulty is not due to the introduction of Markov chains, but to the properties of the system itself, and has to do with fundamental problems at the basis of classical statistical physics. As a matter of fact, if we go over from a description of states in configurational space to a dynamic description of the behavior of a system in the full phase space, the same difficulty is experienced. The specific multiconnectedness of phase space will correspond to the multiconnectedness of configuration space that has appeared, and it is necessary once again to analyze the validity of the canonical distribution for an ensemble of such systems.

Thus we encounter fundamental problems in studying the attainability of states in statistical mechanics. These problems require further study, and we will not discuss them here. In any case it is clear that difficulties with ergodicity of the Markov chains that are of interest to us may arise only for very special types of intermolecular potential $\Phi(r)$ and for very high densities which correspond to an extremely compressed crystalline state of the system.

We should state, in conclusion, that the assumption of pairwise additivity of the intermolecular forces in the system (8.13) is not essential. The Monte Carlo method described above is valid for any law of interaction between the particles depending only on the coordinates of the particles, provided the ergodicity is maintained.

It should also be mentioned that if we disregard the doubtful cases where the conditions of ergodicity possibly break down, the equivalence of the limiting behavior of the Markov chains studied above and the Gibbs canonical ensemble is exact. Therefore, the physical results which may be obtained on this basis (in the case of a sufficiently accurate practical application of the method), will contain no other inaccuracies than the ordinary statistical errors. In this respect the new method differs in principle from the methods of the theory of free volume or the theory based on the superposition approximation. Both these theories, as we have seen, are essentially approximate, and furthermore the degree of approximation cannot be evaluated in advance.

3. IMPLEMENTATION OF THE MONTE CARLO METHOD

The reduction of canonical averaging to averaging along some Markov chain with some supplementary limitations may actually be realized by reproducing the corresponding Markov chains on computers. In papers [1, 2, 3, 4, 5] such a program has actually been carried out for some simple models of systems.

The first and principal difficulty that occurs is the practical impossibility of carrying out the calculation for a system with a number of particles of the order of the Avogadro number, which would be desirable. If a reasonable time is allotted the machine calculations and the requirement is made that a sufficiently long chain be generated so that statistical errors will be within reasonable limits, actual possibilities at the present time do not exceed the calculation of the properties of a system with several hundred particles. In a typical case one has to be limited to a still smaller number of particles. This may lead to an appreciable distortion of the results anticipated, not only due to the inadequacy of the statistics, but also to the large role of surface effects, especially in a condensed state of the system.

A way out of this situation was pointed out in paper [1]. It consists in the imposition of periodic boundary conditions on the boundaries of the small volume under consideration. All three-dimensional space is divided into equal cells of volume V with N particles in each. One of them is arbitrarily considered basic, and the relative configurations of particles that occur in it and their motion are repeated in all the remaining cells, so that the displacement of the entire system by a distance of the length of the edge of the basic cell along this edge will change nothing in the general configuration of the system. Furthermore, it appears that if one of the particles of the basic cell goes out of it through a side due to its motion, it will again enter the same cell through the opposite side (and the same will occur in all cells). Thus, although we are considering an unlimited system, the computer must only take into consideration the motion of N molecules in the basic cell, inasmuch as, together with this motion, there is a defined motion in the system as a whole. Moreover, it is assumed that calculation of the energy of any configuration of particles is achieved by the summation of the interactions of all the particles in the system as a whole and not only of the interactions of the particles of the basic cell, so that marginal effects at the boundaries of the cells do not result. In the calculations that have been carried out up to the present, the basic cell has been chosen in the form of a cube with 32, 108, or 256 particles.

It is clear that only a small part of all the possible configurations of particles is taken into consideration by the method of periodic boundary conditions. All the remaining configurations for the system as a whole, which have not been taken into consideration, may roughly be divided into two groups according to whether the number of particles and the configuration of particles in each cell is close to or far from the number of particles and the possible configurations in the basic cell. In the first case, the statistical weights of the configurations not taken into consideration are close to the statistical weights of the configurations taken into consideration, and this very fact in the method presented gives an approximate calculation. In the second case, we are concerned with "large scale" fluctuations of density in volumes that are comparable with or exceed the volume of the elementary cell V, and with an amplitude comparable with or exceeding the average value of the density

N/V. If the dimensions of the basic cell and the number of particles N in it are not too small, such fluctuations are events of comparatively small probability (for the system as a whole) and their contribution to the statistical integral and to the evaluation of the average equilibrium values of the physical properties is negligible. As regards "small scale" fluctuations of density, they are taken into consideration in this method at fairly large values of V and N. One might, therefore, think that the method of periodic boundary conditions, used for large cells and large numbers of particles in them, should lead to fairly reliable results. This very interesting problem requires further study.

Preliminary data along these lines were obtained in paper [10], where the influence of periodic boundary conditions on the properties of a gaseous system was studied. The following values of the second and third virial coefficients were obtained:

$$B_N = B_\infty\left(1 - \frac{1}{N}\right), \tag{8.16}$$

$$C_N = C_\infty\left(1 + \frac{1}{5N} - \frac{6}{5N^2}\right), \tag{8.17}$$

where the subscripts ∞ and N refer to the usual unlimited system and to a system with periodic boundary conditions with N particles in the basic cell, respectively. Paper [11] considers a one-dimensional model of a condensed system, and it was shown that the distortions of estimates for pressure and energy due to periodic boundary conditions were also of the order of $1/N$. For a condensed three-dimensional system the problem has not yet been studied, but it is very probable that in general a correction of the order of $1/N$ will be necessary.

The necessity of working with a small number of particles in a small elementary cell also involves the inconvenience that, in the case of the "hard" particles, the possible difficulties with ergodicity considered above may arise at lower average densities than in a system of very large dimensions. For example, with a high density of hard spheres in a small, rigid volume, rearrangements of the spheres may be impossible, although in a larger volume and at the same average density the rearrangements would be facilitated by fluctuations in density. Now, however, if N is not too small—say of the order of hundreds—this difficulty is only relevant to the extremely condensed crystalline states of the system. What the authors of paper [3] call the "quasi-ergodic" problem is apparently more serious. This is the possibility of the appearance, in some cases, in the configuration space of the system with which we are concerned, of two or more regions which make comparable contributions to the full configurational integral but such that, although they formally are members of one and the same ergodic class of states, the probability of transitions between them is very small. For a finite-length Markov chain such transitions cannot be realized at all. Inasmuch as any practically realizable Markov chain must be finite, if such a situation occurs, the Monte Carlo method may lead to erroneous results. If this difficulty actually exists, it is clear that it must also refer to the very dense states of the system under consideration and above all to the case of hard particles. Practical means for avoiding this possible difficulty may involve either the lengthening of the Markov chain as much as possible, or variations within certain limits of the initial state of the chain (by generating a series of chains instead of one).

Now let us consider the problem of the actual construction of Markov chains. In the studies that have been completed up to the present, one-step transition probabilities were selected as follows. Let $x_r^{\alpha(i)}$, where $\alpha = 1, 2, 3$; $r = 1, 2, \ldots, N$; $i = 1, 2, \ldots, s$, designate the αth Cartesian coordinate of the rth particle in the ith state (configuration) of the system. The Cartesian axes are chosen along the edge of the basic cell. A single step in the Markov chain consists of the transfer by a certain distance of only one particle, so that

$$p_{ij} = 0 \,, \tag{8.18}$$

if the configurations i and j differ by the positions of two or more particles. Moreover, there is introduced an arbitrary (but fixed) length δ, appreciably less than the length of the edge of the basic cell, which is the possible change in position of one particle in a single step. The transition probability satisfies equation (8.18) again if the change of position of a particle which causes a change in the configurations in a given transition is such that $|x_r^{\alpha(i)} - x_r^{\alpha(j)}| > \delta$.

If, however,

$$|x_r^{\alpha(i)} - x_r^{\alpha(j)}| \leq \delta \,, \qquad x_s^{\beta(i)} - x_s^{\beta(j)} = 0 \,, \tag{8.19}$$

while $\alpha, \beta = 1, 2, 3$; $r = 1, 2, \ldots, N$; $s = 1, 2, \ldots, r-1, r+1, \ldots, N$, then the probability of a one-step transition is chosen equal to

$$\begin{aligned} p_{ij} &= C \qquad \text{when} \qquad U_j \leq U_i \,, \\ p_{ij} &= C \exp\left(-\frac{U_j - U_i}{kT}\right) \quad \text{when} \quad U_j > U_i \,, \quad \text{for} \quad j \neq i \end{aligned} \tag{8.20}$$

and

$$p_{ii} = 1 - \sum_{\substack{1 \leq j \leq s \\ j \neq i}} p_{ij} \,, \qquad \text{for} \qquad j = i \,. \tag{8.21}$$

It is easy to see that the basic equations (8.5) and (8.12) for p_{ij} are identically satisfied in this case with any choice of the constant C which does not lead to $p_{ij} < 0$. Actually the choice of C is made in such a way that, on discarding the experimental weight factor in (8.20), the expression $p_{ij} = C$, assumed for all i and j including the case $j = i$ with correct normalization, would indicate the equal probability of all transitions of any particle within the limits of a cube with a volume of $(2\delta)^3$ (see below).

The above is accomplished in the following manner [1, 3]. Let the ith state of a system be fixed. Special equipment in the computer will produce both an arbitrary choice of three independent random variables ξ^α, $\alpha = 1, 2, 3$, the values of which may be changed within the interval $-1 \leq \xi^\alpha \leq 1$, and the arbitrary choice of the integral number r which may assume the values $r = 1, 2, \ldots, N$. To the resultant of these chance events the possible movement of the rth particle to a new position is compared, where

$$x_r^{\alpha(i)} \rightarrow x_r^{\alpha(j)} = x_r^{\alpha(i)} + \xi^\alpha \delta \tag{8.22}$$

and the energy U_j in this possible state is calculated. If $U_j \leq U_i$ then new coordinates are assigned to the rth particle which are shown at the right in (8.22) and the system is considered as having gone over to a new jth state. If, however, $U_j > U_i$ the computer will produce a supplementary arbitrary choice of one more random variable, ξ^4, within the interval $0 \leq \xi^4 \leq 1$ and the result of the new selection is compared with $\exp[-(U_j - U_i)/kT]$. If $\xi^4 < \exp[-(U_j - U_i)/kT]$, a transition of the system to a new jth state according to (8.22) will occur; if, however, $\xi^4 > \exp[-(U_j - U_i)/kT]$, the rth particle will remain in its old place and the transition to the new jth state will not occur. In the latter case, however, it is considered that one step $A_i \rightarrow A_i$ occurred in the Markov chain with a probability of p_{ii}. After this the entire procedure is repeated from the beginning, starting from the new jth state if a transition did occur. It is easy to see that the frequencies of the transitions under these conditions actually correspond to the probabilities (8.18) to (8.21).

The set of possible values of the parameters $\xi^\alpha(\alpha = 1, 2, 3)$ is discrete and their density determines the number s of subdivisions of the entire configuration space of the system into discrete cells about which we spoke in the preceding section. As regards the choice of the constant parameter δ, this is arbitrary since the probabilities of transitions (8.18) to (8.21) satisfy the basic equations (8.5) and (8.12) independently of the value of δ. In actual practice, however, the choice of δ is very important, since too small values of δ result in very small steps and in the necessity of generating very long chains, while for too large values of δ and a given set of possible values of ξ^a, many states of the system may be passed through.

4. RESULTS OF CALCULATIONS FOR A MODEL OF A REAL SYSTEM

A study by the Monte Carlo method of a model of a real system through choice of the potential of intermolecular forces in the Lennard-Jones form

$$\Phi(r) = \epsilon\left[\left(\frac{a}{r}\right)^{12} - 2\left(\frac{a}{r}\right)^{6}\right] \qquad (8.23)$$

is of great interest. Such a study of a two-dimensional case was carried out in one of the early papers [1]. The more interesting three-dimensional case was investigated in papers [3, 5]. In order to compare the results of calculations with experimental data, the following values were chosen for the constants ϵ and a in (8.23).

$$\epsilon = 1.653 \cdot 10^{-14}\ \text{erg}, \qquad a = 3.822 \cdot 10^{-8}\ \text{cm}, \qquad (8.24)$$

which result from studies of the second virial coefficient of argon [12]. Comparison with the data for other noble gases may be derived by use of the principle of corresponding states. It should be noted that the length a in (8.23) is the distance to the minimum of $\Phi(r)$ and not the diameter of a particle.

In papers [3, 5] Markov chains for a system with 32 and 108 molecules in the basic cell were studied. All calculations were carried out for only one isotherm, $T = 328°$ K, which corresponds approximately to double the critical temperature of argon, and for the range of reduced volumes from $v/v^* = 0.75$ to $v/v^* = 7.5$. Here v is the volume per particle in the actual system and $v^* = a^3/\sqrt{2}$ is the volume per particle in a close packed system of spheres of diameter a. Altogether 31 Markov chains for 13 values of the reduced volume were realized. The length of the chain in various cases varied from 30,000 to almost half a million transitions. Seven of the chains corresponded to 108 particles in the basic cell, the remainder to 32 particles in the cell.

The greatest difficulty (which was also significant in principle) was presented by the evaluation of the total energy of interaction of molecules according to (8.13) and (8.23). If we calculate the energy of interaction of one molecule with all the others, beginning with the closest neighbors and then going on to all the more distant ones, then, due to the presence of the term with r^{-6} in (8.23), such a sum will converge very slowly. The ultimate speed of a computer and the necessity of completing the entire calculation of the chain during not too long a period seriously limit the precision of the calculation of these sums which for each transition in the chain must be calculated anew. In fact, these sums were broken into a small number of terms, taking into consideration the interaction of several layers of the nearest neighbors of each particle (in various cases this corresponded to the calculation of from 12 to 54 interactions for one particle), and then corrections of a different type were introduced. More detailed information about this is available in paper [3]. We shall note only that the summation of the interactions was extended not only over the particles of the basic cell, but for each particle its neighbors in adjacent cells were also taken into consideration.

In each configuration, knowledge of the energy of interaction of the particles makes possible the determination of all thermodynamic functions of the system. The energy and the heat capacity C_V of the system, referred to one mole, will be equal to

$$E = \tfrac{3}{2}RT + \bar{U}_{N_A}, \qquad (8.25)$$

$$C_V = \tfrac{3}{2}R + \frac{1}{kT^2}\left(\langle U^2_{N_A}\rangle - \bar{U}^2_{N_A}\right), \qquad (8.26)$$

where $\bar{U}_{N_A}$ designates the energy of interaction (8.13) of N_A particles, with N_A the Avogadro number, and the overbar indicates averaging along the length of the Markov chain. The well-known expression from the thermodynamic theory of fluctuations is used here for the heat capacity. Calculation of the expressions for $\bar{U}_{N_A}$ and $\langle U^2_{N_A}\rangle$ from (8.13) is carried out according to the equation

$$\bar{U}_{N_A} = \frac{1}{2}\frac{N_A}{N}\left\langle \sum_{1\leq i\leq N}\ \sum_{\substack{1\leq k\leq\infty \\ k\neq i}} \Phi(|q_i - q_k|)\right\rangle \qquad (8.27)$$

and analogously for $\langle U^2_{N_A}\rangle$. Here N is the number of particles in a basic cell. The pressure in the system may be calculated from

$$pv = kT - \frac{1}{6N}\left\langle \sum_{1\leq i\leq N}\ \sum_{\substack{1\leq k\leq\infty \\ k\neq i}} r_{ik}\Phi'(r_{ik})\right\rangle, \qquad (8.28)$$

$$r_{ik} = |q_i - q_k|,$$

which, for our case, is a natural analogue of the general equation (2.39) or (2.40). In fact, as has already been mentioned, the infinite sums in

(8.27) and (8.28) were calculated approximately by calculation of a small number of terms and the introduction of supplementary corrections.

For each configuration of the system the total number of particles $N_i(r)$ contained in a sphere of given radius r surrounding the ith particle was also calculated, and the average integral distribution function for the number of particles was worked out:

$$N(r) = \frac{1}{N}\left\langle \sum_{1 \leq i \leq N} N_i(r) \right\rangle . \tag{8.29}$$

These calculations were carried out for a large set of values of r (small mesh) from zero to values of the order of several a. The usual radial distribution function $g(r)$ is obtained from this by differentiating with respect to r:

$$g(r) = \frac{v}{4\pi r^2} \frac{dN(r)}{dr} . \tag{8.30}$$

Knowledge of the functions $\Phi(r)$ and $g(r)$ permits the independent determination of the energy E and the pressure p in the system according to the general theory presented in chapter 2. Comparison of the results of both methods of calculation makes it possible to introduce supplementary corrections during the course of the calculations, in particular in the calculation of the sums of the energies of interaction of the particles.

The results of the calculations are presented in papers [3, 4, 5] in the form of tables and diagrams. Three theoretical radial distribution functions for the value of the reduced volume $v/v^* = 2.5$ are shown in Figure 16 which was taken from paper [5]. Experimental radial distribution functions in this region of temperatures ($T = 328°$ K) and density are lacking for argon. One of the curves corresponds to one in the paper of Kirkwood and co-workers [13] discussed in chapter 5 in which calculations were carried out with the aid of the superposition approximation with the modified Lennard-Jones potential (5.71), which is now written in the form

$$\begin{aligned} \Phi(r) &= +\infty \quad \text{when} \quad r < 2^{-1/6}a , \\ \Phi(r) &= \epsilon\left[\left(\frac{a}{r}\right)^{12} - 2\left(\frac{a}{r}\right)^{6}\right] \quad \text{when} \quad r > 2^{-1/6}a . \end{aligned} \tag{8.31}$$

The two remaining curves were obtained by the Monte Carlo method for the same modified potential and for the potential (8.23). It can be seen from the graph that the introduction of a hard "core" appreciably distorts the shape of the radial distribution function. For the same intermolecular potential, the results of the theory based on the superposition approximation differ somewhat from the results of the Monte Carlo theory, which should be considered to be more precise. From the data of paper [13] it can be seen that at higher densities the discrepancy between the results of the two theories increases even more.

In paper [5], for the sake of direct comparison between theory and experiment, the radial distribution function for a system with the

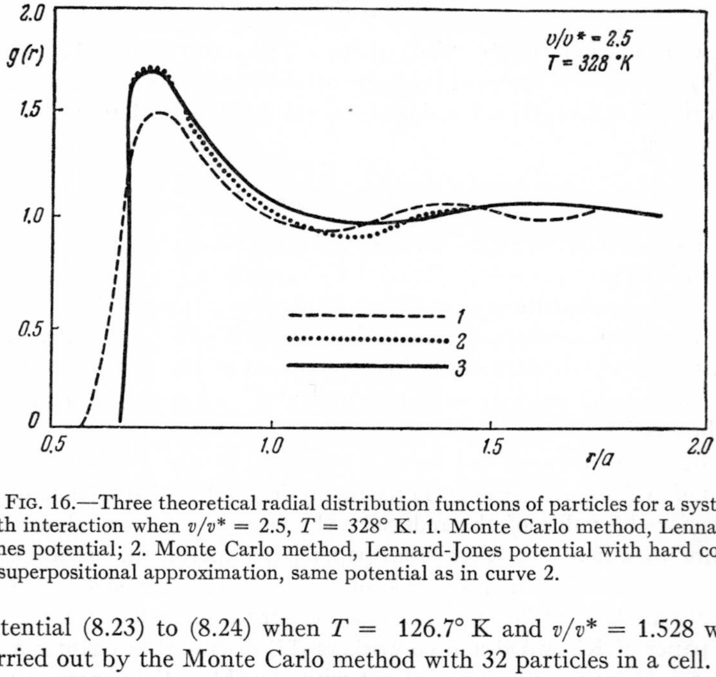

FIG. 16.—Three theoretical radial distribution functions of particles for a system with interaction when $v/v^* = 2.5$, $T = 328°$ K. 1. Monte Carlo method, Lennard-Jones potential; 2. Monte Carlo method, Lennard-Jones potential with hard core; 3. superpositional approximation, same potential as in curve 2.

potential (8.23) to (8.24) when $T = 126.7°$ K and $v/v^* = 1.528$ was carried out by the Monte Carlo method with 32 particles in a cell. In Figure 17 the results of these calculations are compared with the experimental radial distribution function for liquid argon at the same values of thermodynamic parameters as those used in paper [14]. The figure shows that the qualitative agreement is entirely satisfactory. The slight divergence is due to the crudeness of the calculation of the experimental radial distribution function from X-ray data, to statistical errors of the Monte Carlo method and, possibly, to the inaccuracy of the Lennard-Jones potential.

To examine the thermodynamic results we consider the equation of state of the system. Figure 18 shows the results of calculations of the equation of state when $T = 328°$ K according to the Monte Carlo theory, according to the free-volume theory, and according to the theory based on the superposition approximation. Also shown are the experimental data for argon from [12] and [15]. The figure shows that in the region of volumes larger than 1.5 v^*, the agreement of the results of the Monte Carlo method with experimental data from [12] is very good. The agreement with experimental data from [15] at smaller vol-

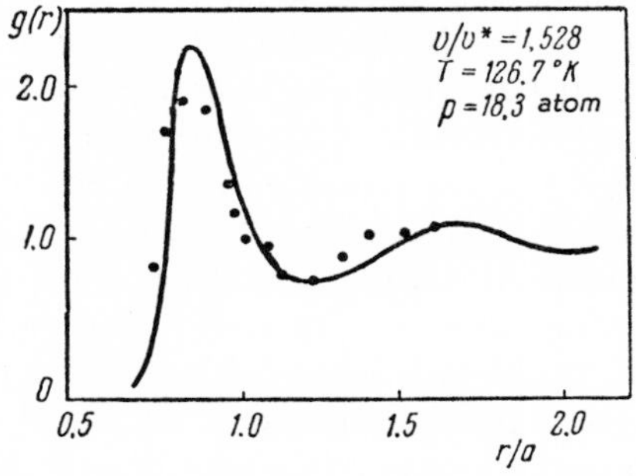

FIG. 17.—Experimental (dots) and theoretical (according to the Monte Carlo method; solid line) radial distribution functions of particles for liquid argon at 126.7° K, pressure 18.3 atm, $v/v^* = 1.528$.

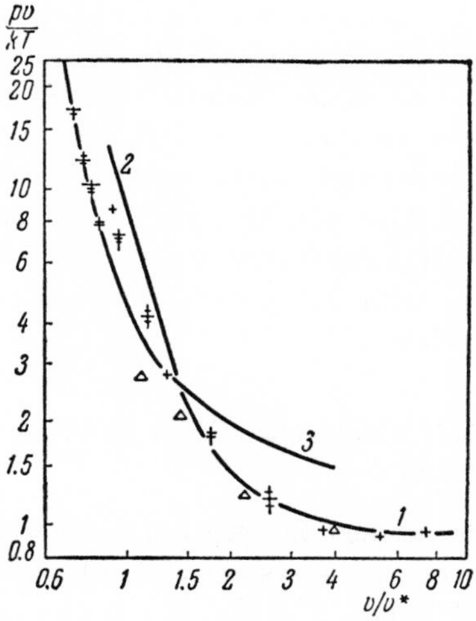

FIG. 18.—Equation of state of argon; isotherm at 328° K. 1. Experimental data [12]; 2. experimental data [15]; 3. theory of free volume; Δ. superposition approximation. Short horizontal lines, the Monte Carlo method for 108 particles in a cell; long horizontal lines, the Monte Carlo method for 32 particles in a cell. Vertical lines show the probable error in the Monte Carlo method.

umes is not so good. It is possible that the results of the older paper [15] are in need of revision. Comparison of the three theoretical results with each other shows inapplicability of the free-volume theory at average and large specific volumes and of the superposition approximation at small specific volumes.

The most interesting peculiarity of the results of the Monte Carlo method shown in Figure 18 is the appearance in the region between $v/v^* = 0.90$ and 0.95 of a break in the pressure isotherm. The same peculiarity occurs on the isotherm of the energy of the system. This should be interpreted as an indication of a phase transition from the dense gaseous to the crystalline state. Although the pressure isotherm in the neighborhood of the transition region has, unfortunately, not been studied in detail, it is impossible to doubt the presence of a phase transition. This is confirmed by comparison of the radial distribution functions of particles that refer to states lying on both sides of the transition region. In one case these functions have a typically "crystalline" form with sharp peaks separated by deep minima which go down to zero; in the other they have a typically "liquid" form with smeared and poorly separated peaks (for more detail see [3]). In addition, special analysis of the configurations of particles of the system along the Markov chain on both sides of the transition region showed that on the right of the break in the isotherm in Figure 18 there is self-diffusion of particles; on the left, however, self-diffusion is practically absent. Thus, in a model of a real system, the Monte Carlo method for the first time clearly demonstrates the liquid-crystal phase transition contained in Gibbs statistical physics and simultaneously describes both phases.

We shall not consider here the other thermodynamic results of papers [3, 4, 5]. Let us mention only the interesting fact that the results obtained with 32 or with 108 particles in an elementary cell hardly differ from one another.

5. RESULTS OF CALCULATIONS FOR A SYSTEM OF HARD SPHERES

In chapter 5 we mentioned the great interest which a study of the simplest possible system—a system of hard spheres—offers for the theory of gases and liquids. Therefore it was natural to use the Monte Carlo method for the study of such a system. This was done in the first paper [1] for a two-dimensional system, and then in papers [2, 4, 5] for the more interesting three-dimensional system. In paper [2] a system with $N = 256$ spheres in the basic cell was studied. In the case of comparatively large N one might expect to obtain results of very high precision. But it is not difficult to see that in order to obtain reliable results in the limit of large N, a significant increase of the length of the Markov chain is required. In paper [8] this was not done, and due to insufficient length of the chains realized, the results were not completely accurate. In particular, the phase transition between the ordered and disordered phases was not detected. In papers [4, 5], to which we will give major attention below, the basic cell contained only up to 32 particles; however, the great accuracy of the calculations gave more reliable and more interesting results. We should mention, by the way, that the study of hard spheres by the Monte Carlo method is capable of greater precision than in the case of attracting particles, since the complex problem of obtaining a reliable summation of the particle interactions is avoided.

Now, inasmuch as for any U_i and U_j in (8.20) $\exp[-(U_j - U_i)/kT] = 0$ or 1, all the transitions determined by equations (8.19) and (8.22) are equally probable if only they do not lead to the overlapping of spheres, and the transitions are forbidden otherwise. Therefore, the generation of Markov chains is now greatly simplified: for any choices of random variables r and ξ^a, $a = 1, 2, 3$, which do not lead to overlapping of the particles, the transition (8.22) is accomplished; otherwise the rth particle returns to its place. Using the same computers and the same calculation time as in the preceding problem allows the calculation of much longer Markov chains. Many chains in papers [4, 5] attained lengths of a million or even several million transitions.

At first, in all the papers mentioned, the radial distribution functions were calculated as described in the preceding section, and then the pressure was determined from the equation

$$\frac{pv}{kT} = 1 + \frac{2\pi a^3}{3v} g(a+0). \tag{8.32}$$

In all the papers all Markov chains had an ordered face-centered cubic distribution of particles in their initial states, or else had such a distribution which was only slightly disturbed (in the case of control chains).

Figure 19, which was taken from paper [5], shows the equation of state of a system of hard spheres in accordance with various theories and the Monte Carlo method. Here $v_0 = a^3/\sqrt{2}$ is the volume per particle in a close packed system of spheres of diameter a. The crosses show the results of the dynamical calculations, described in the following section, and the two thicker lines in the figure refer to the same paper. It is evident that the results of the theory of free volume and of the theory based on the superposition approximation, deviate greatly from the more precise results of the Monte Carlo method, according to papers [4, 5]. The five-term virial equation of state (5.59), found in paper [2], is more precise at large volumes than the superposition approximation and the theory of free volume. The excellent precision of the five-term virial equation of state at very small volumes which is apparent in the figure is deceptive.

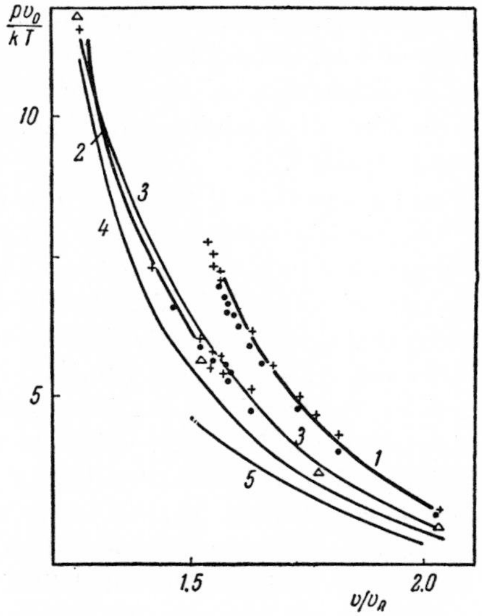

FIG. 19.—Equation of state of a system of hard spheres. 1 and 2. Results of dynamic calculation for 108 particles in a cell (crosses); 3. five-term equation of state; 4. theory of free volume; 5. superposition approximation; Δ. Monte Carlo method according to [2]; dots. Monte Carlo method according to [4, 5].

The most noteworthy peculiarity of Figure 19 is the appearance in it of two branches of the isotherm with a break between them, which doubtless indicates a phase transition in the system. As in the case of particles with a Lennard-Jones potential, a study of the form of the radial distribution functions of particles and of self-diffusion of particles on both sides of the transition region indicates a dense gas-crystal transition. The theory of free volume and the five-term virial equation of state, as can be seen from the chart, do not contain even a hint of a phase transition, which is their significant defect. From this it is also evident that the accuracy of the five-term virial equation of state is fortuitous, since this equation, in terms of its meaning, can only refer to a gas, while a fall in pressures lies in the crystalline region. In contrast to this, the superposition approximation theory of liquids, although it gives low values for the pressure, correctly predicts the existence of the limit of stability of the uniform phase. We saw in chapter 7 that, the superposition approximation leads to a limit of stability of the uniform phase of a system of hard spheres at a volume per particle which is twice the volume of a particle. In the notation of Figure 19, this corresponds to a value of $v/v_0 = 1.48$, which agrees fairly well with the results of the Monte Carlo method, although somewhat low. According to paper [5] the transition region between the phases of a system of hard spheres lies on both sides of the value $v/v_0 = 1.55$.

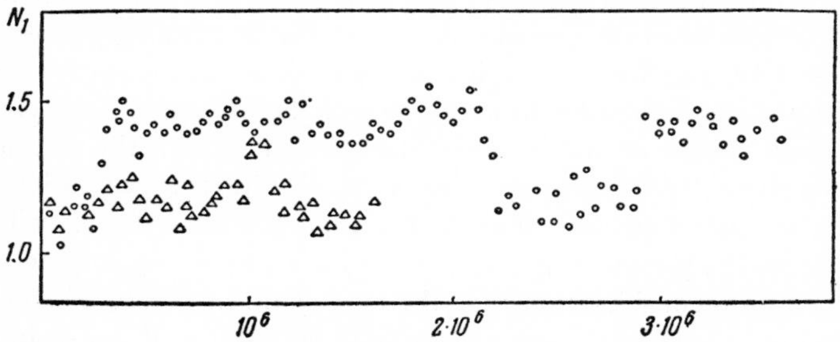

FIG. 20.—Convergence of two Markov chains (triangles and circles) in the transition region when $v/v_0 = 1.55$.

It is interesting to emphasize that Figure 19 leaves no doubt about the fact that the transition between ordered and disordered phases in a system of hard spheres is the usual phase transition of the first type. In the figure one can clearly see the "superheated" and "supercooled" states. It is obvious that inasmuch as interaction of particles is lacking, the latent heat connected with the phase transition is purely of entropic origin in this case.

In a rigorous theory one would expect the appearance of a horizontal portion of the pressure isotherm in the region of the phase transition. This was not obtained in papers [4, 5] because of the very slow convergence of the Markov chains near the region of the phase transition. This is shown in Figure 20, which was taken from [5], and depicts the average number N_1 of molecules in a very thin spherical layer close to some arbitrarily chosen particle. There are considered various configurations of the system for two Markov chains when $v/v_0 = 1.55$. Qualitatively, according to (8.32), the term N_1 corresponds to the pressure in the system, since it is proportional to $g(a + 0)$. It can be seen that all the values of N_1 are grouped about two values which correspond to the two branches of the isotherm in Figure 19. In the case of a shorter chain with a million and a half transitions, the values of N_1 that occurred fluctuated fairly stably about the lower of the values, with the exception of one jump to the upper of the values of N_1 which were then observed for approximately 10^5 transitions in the chain. In the second and longer chain, with more than three million transitions, both upper and lower values of N_1 (primarily the upper) with three jumps between them were alternately observed. It is clear that averaging along the shorter chain leads (fairly precisely) to the magnitude of the pressure in the crystalline phase of the system when $v/v_0 = 1.55$. However, averaging along the longer chain gives a result which differs greatly both from the pressure in each of the metastable phases when $v/v_0 = 1.55$, and from the value of the pressure in a two-phase equilibrium system. In order to obtain one of the first results the chain is too long; for the second it is too short. Calculation of the pressure in a two-phase equilibrium system would require the generation of a chain not less than ten times longer than the longest shown in the chart. At the present time, however, this is completely impractical if we take into consideration that the long chain in Figure 20 was generated on a very advanced computer in the course of approximately 40 hours.

The data on pressure in the neighborhood of $v/v_0 = 1.55$, shown in Figure 19, were obtained by the authors of papers [4, 5] by averaging along one group of values of N_1. In consequence of this it became possible to separate each of the metastable phases which continued up to the point $v/v_0 = 1.55$. With such a calculation the portion included within the transition region where each of the phases individually is absolutely unstable does not appear.

6. DYNAMICAL CALCULATIONS IN A SYSTEM OF HARD SPHERES

In conclusion we will briefly consider the results of two very interesting papers [7, 8] in which the classical equations of motion for a system of a very large number of particles in the form of hard spheres were integrated on high-speed computers. The results of these papers are interesting both for statistical thermodynamics and for the theory of the structure and the kinetic properties of liquids and dense gases.

As in the Monte Carlo method, systems of N particles occupying a volume in the form of a cube with periodic boundary conditions at its edges were examined, so that in fact unlimited systems were studied. The following cases were studied: at low to average densities, $N = 32$ and 100; at higher densities, $N = 32$, 108, 256, and 500 particles in a basic cell, i.e., the case where $N = 4n^3$, which permits the densest face-centered cubic packing of spheres in the cube.

In addition, in some cases at higher densities, a system was studied with 96 particles in a basic cell which had the form of a right-angled parallelopiped with sides that permit very dense hexagonal packing of the spheres. The results of the latter cases do not differ from those of the former. As in the Monte Carlo method, the requirements of a reasonable length of computer times and the assembly of adequate statistics lead at present to preference for a system with small values of N in the basic cell. The most reliable results were obtained when $N = 32$, 100, and 108; moreover, control calculations showed that the results, which refer to the statistical characteristics of the system as a whole when $N = 32$, do not differ appreciably in any way from the results when $N = 108$.

At the initial moment for each system all particles of the basic cell were arranged at the points of a face-centered cubic lattice (or a very dense hexagonal lattice when $N = 96$), uniformly distributed over the whole volume of the cell, and all had velocities that were identical in magnitude, but different in direction. The distribution of the directions of the initial velocities of various particles was completely random. Integration of the equations of motion for subsequent times showed that all particles were shifted uniformly and in a straight line in the direction of their initial velocities up to the moment of the first collision of a pair of particles in the system. Next, following the laws of elastic collision, the velocities of the corresponding pair of particles after collision were calculated, and the entire system of particles again shifted uniformly and in a straight line with these new velocities until the next collision between some pair of particles, etc. In this way the motions in a large number of systems were calculated for 24 values of the average density of particles, and for many of them the results were calculated over again for various values of N. The extent of the motion studied in all cases was very great, and in many cases reached half a million and more collisions in one cell.

The values of the coordinates and velocities of particles in the basic cell in the course of its motion (i.e., for all collisions) were placed in the memory of the computer for each system, and the statistical characteristics of the system were calculated from these data. A large number of kinetic and of equilibrium-statistical properties of the system of hard spheres was studied in this way.

We shall consider the kinetic properties of the system only very briefly. In the first place, although the initial distribution of velocities was markedly non-equilibrium, the equilibrium Maxwellian distribution was attained very quickly and then maintained unchanged. The corresponding relaxation time was very small—of the order of the time necessary for achieving from two to four collisions per particle, depending on the average density of the system being studied. The same result was obtained from the calculation of the Boltzmann H function as a function of the number of collisions. In all cases the H function steadily decreased, and after two or three collisions per particle, attained a constant value, about which only very weak fluctuations occurred; these fluctuations were related to the smallness of the number of particles in the system. For the same reason the Maxwellian distribution of velocities was attained only in the region of small and average values of the velocities. For a short period of computer operation and in the case of a small number of particles in the basic cell, the "tail" of the Maxwellian distribution for very large velocities could, of course, not be observed. Of the kinetic properties, the autocorrelation function for velocity and the coefficient of self-diffusion at various densities of the system were also studied. It should be noted that at high densities a large correlation between the present and past states of the velocities of the particles, brought about through neighboring particles, was detected. For details paper [8] should be referred to. Below we shall go over to an examination of the equilibrium properties of a system of hard spheres.

In all cases the pressure was calculated by two methods: by means of the radial distribution function from equation (8.32), and by means of the virial theorem through substitution in the "virial" of a force acting between the particles due to the change of momentum of the colliding particles. In all cases, within the limits of accuracy of the calculation, the results of both methods were coincident. The equation of state thus obtained for a system of hard spheres is shown in Figure 19 in the form of two thick lines for the system with 108 particles in the basic cell, and by means of crosses for the system with 32 particles in the basic cell. As can be seen from the diagram, there is good agreement between these results and the results of the Monte Carlo method for the same system of particles. The presence of a phase transition of the first sort, of the melting-crystallization type, is also fully confirmed in this method. Identification of the type of transition follows from the value of the coefficient of self-diffusion on both sides of the transition region.

According to papers [7, 8] the transition region between phases extends from $v/v_0 = 1.525$ to approximately $v/v_0 = 1.7$. The existence of two phases and of a transition region between them appeared in the method described in approximately the same way as in the Monte Carlo method: at corresponding densities and with the passage of time, the system remained alternately in two different states. The jumps between the two states occurred comparatively rarely, and for finite observation of the evolution of the system, averaging did not give any definite and reasonable results for the pressure. As in the Monte Carlo method, it was necessary to separate both types of states from one

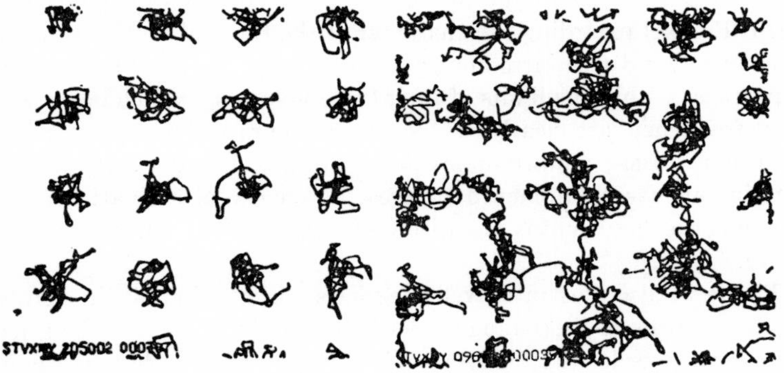

a *b*

FIG. 21.—Plane projections of the motion of 16 particles in a system with 32 particles in a cell when $v/v_0 = 1.525$.

another and to carry out the averaging for each of them individually. The data for the transition region that are shown in Figure 19 were obtained in this way.

Thus, due to the extreme smallness of the number of particles in the baisis cell ($N = 32$ or 108) the dense gas-crystal phase transition was not observed in the form of two coexisting phases, but in the form of alternating fluctuations of the system between these phases. However, the authors of paper [8] believe that even when $N = 500$ the realization in each cell of two phases coexisting with a transition region between them, would be possible.

In order to make the motion of the particles in the system visible, an oscillograph was coupled with the computer and the x, y-coordinates of some 16 particles of the system, as calculated by the computer, were simultaneously projected on the screen. Sections *a* and *b* of Figure 21 show the results obtained. They both refer to a system with 32 particles in the basic cell when the volume $v/v_0 = 1.525$. Figure 21*a* shows the projections of traces of particles in the course of 1,000 collisions (in the entire cell). During this period the system "melted," i.e., it went over from an ordered phase to a disordered one. Figure 21*b* shows the projections of traces of particles during 3,000 collisions when the system was already in the "liquid" state. Paper [8] gives many other photographs of this type that refer both to the "crystalline" and to the gaseous states of the system.

In many respects Figure 21 is very interesting for the theory of liquids. First of all, the kinetics of molecular motion in a liquid is distinctly visible in it. In full accord with the concepts introduced by Ya. I. Frenkel regarding the character of the thermal motion of molecules in a liquid (see introductory chapter), the irregular fluctuations of particles within the limits of their "free volumes," which occur with great frequency, are clearly visible, as are the rarer jumps of particles from some quasi-equilibrium positions to others. It is perfectly obvious that in this example of hard spheres the energy of activation corresponding to these jumps is entirely of entropic and not of energetic origin.

Figure 21 also illustrates well the views, discussed above in chapter 3, on the nature of short-range order in liquids. If we neglect the traces of long-range order that exist here, it is clearly noticeable that the instantaneous and average short-range order can be distinguished.

The relative positions of the average volumes containing the individual particles are highly ordered. This is precisely the average short-range order in liquids which is indicated by the experimentally obtained radial distribution functions $g(r)$. However, one can also see clearly from the figure that the average amplitudes of the irregular fluctuations of the particles near their quasi-equilibrium positions is approximately the same in magnitude as the average distance between the particles; consequently order in the instantaneous positions of particles is practically absent even in the very smallest group of particles. Moreover, it should be taken into consideration that Figure 21 refers directly to the melting point, where, in accordance with the ideas of short-range order in liquids, one should expect the greatest "quasi-crystallinity." If we go away from the melting point, the density of particles decreases and the absence of order in the instantaneous positions of the particles will become even greater, although the arrangement of the near neighboring volumes containing particles will be maintained in some measure.

The material presented in this chapter shows how great the possibilities are of applying the powerful methods of computer calculation to the problems of the theory of liquids and dense gases. It may be assumed that further development of these methods and application to the problems of statistical physics will lead to new and significant results.

REFERENCES

[1] N. Metropolis, M. Rosenbluth, A. Rosenbluth, A. Teller, and E. Teller, *J. Chem. Phys.*, **21** (1953), 1087.
[2] M. Rosenbluth and A. Rosenbluth, *J. Chem. Phys.*, **22** (1954), 881.
[3] W. Wood and F. Parker, *J. Chem. Phys.*, **27** (1957), 720.
[4] W. Wood and J. Jacobson, *J. Chem. Phys.*, **27** (1957), 1207.
[5] W. Wood, F. Parker, and J. Jacobson, *Nuovo Cimento, suppl.*, **9**, No. 1 (1958), 133.
[6] I. Z. Fisher, *Uspekhi Fiz. Nauk*, **69** (1959), 349.
[7] B. Alder and T. Wainwright, *J. Chem. Phys.*, **27** (1957), 1208.
[8] T. Wainwright and B. Alder, *Nuovo Cimento, suppl.*, **9**, No. 1 (1958), 116.
[9] W. Feller *Vvedenie v teoriyu veroyatnostei i ee prilozheniya*, IL (Introduction to the Theory of Probabilities and Its Application), IL, 1952.
[10] I. Oppenheim and P. Mazur, *Physica*, **23** (1957), 197.
[11] I. Z. Fisher, *Doklady Akad. Nauk Belorusskoi SSR*, **4** (1960), 148.
[12] A. Michels, H. Wijker, and H. Wijker, *Physica*, **15** (1949) 627.
[13] J. Kirkwood, V. Lewinson, and B. Alder, *J. Chem. Phys.*, **20** (1952), 929.
[14] A. Eisenstein and N. Gingrich, *Phys. Rev.*, **62** (1942), 261.
[15] P. Bridgman, *Proc. Amer. Acad. Arts and Sci.*, **70** (1935), 1.

SUPPLEMENT

STUART A. RICE and PETER GRAY

OTHER ASPECTS OF THE EQUILIBRIUM PROPERTIES OF LIQUIDS

S1. INTRODUCTION

In the few years since the publication of the Russian version of this book there has been considerable development of the theory of liquids. In this Supplement we present a survey of the newer work on the equilibrium properties of liquids. An extensive treatment of this subject, and of the non-equilibrium theory, will be found in the *Proceedings of the General Motors Conference on the Liquid State.* We wish to thank the Elsevier Press for permission to use part of that material herein.

It seems pertinent to add a few words about the material covered in this Supplement. The two most fruitful approaches to the theory of the equilibrium properties of liquids can be traced to the middle 1930's: the cluster-expansion methods all derive from the classical work of J. E. Mayer, and the distribution-function approach owes much to the incisive analyses of Kirkwood and Yvon. In the main body of the text Professor Fisher makes reference to the results of both types of analysis, but uses primarily a formulation of the distribution-function approach which was introduced by Bogolyubov. Moreover, the analysis in the text is carried out in the formalism of the Canonical Ensemble. Since much of the contemporary research on the theory of liquids uses the formalism of the Grand Canonical Ensemble, and extensive use is made of diagrammatic expansions and cluster-integral techniques, we have given in this Supplement an extended survey of both the distribution-function and cluster-integral theories. Occasionally results are derived here which duplicate results in the main text, but the methods used are different. The purpose of including such material is to show the power and range of the various analytic tools available, and to establish connections between the various techniques.

S1.1. Correspondence of Sections and Notation

Sections of this Supplement correspond to sections of the book in the following way: sections S1 to S3 correspond to sections 1.1 and 1.4, S4.1–S4.3 to 2.1–2.3, S5 to 4.1 and 4.2, S6 to chapter v, and S7 to 3.1 and chapter viii.

The notation used in the main text does not entirely conform with common usage. In the Supplement we have, therefore, retained the conventional symbols; the few differences are shown in the Table.

Main Text	Supplement	Meaning
Q_N	Z_N	configurational partition function
$F_s(q_1, \ldots, q_s)$	$g^{(s)}(\{s\})$	*specific* s-particle correlation function
E	$\langle U \rangle$	average internal energy
F	A	(Helmholtz) free energy
Φ	u	interparticle potential
a	σ	range parameter for interparticle potential
λ	ξ	Kirkwood coupling parameter

In addition, it should be noted that the s-particle correlation potential Ψ_s (eq. [2.83]) is not a common one. In the case $s = 3$, it can be seen to correspond to the series expansion $\Sigma_{n=1}^{\infty} \rho^n \delta_{n+3}$ (1, 2, 3) in equation (S6.34).

S2. SUMMARY OF THE PROPERTIES OF ENSEMBLES

S2.1. General Remarks [1]

It is convenient at the outset to introduce the most general ensemble with which we shall be dealing. By an ensemble is meant a collection of replica systems so large that the proportion of all replica systems in each state available to the particular system under discussion may be identified with the probability of finding the particular system in that state at an arbitrary instant. The most general ensemble used herein is known as the Grand Canonical Ensemble (G.C.E.). It is supposed to consist of a large number, M, of systems, each of volume V, and each separated from the other systems by membranes permeable to energy and matter. The state of each system is specified by its volume V (which is fixed), its composition $\boldsymbol{N}$, and its energy E_k. The composition $\boldsymbol{N}$ is the set of numbers $(N_1, \ldots, N_i, \ldots)$ of molecules of type 1, . . . , type i, . . . , respectively, in the volume V. For each composition, $\boldsymbol{N}$, a certain set of energy levels is available to the system, and these are imagined grouped into levels of width ΔE, such that $E \leq E_k \leq E + \Delta E$ contains ω_k states. We have, of course,

$$E_k = E_k(\boldsymbol{N}), \qquad \omega_k = \omega_k(\boldsymbol{N}). \tag{S2.1}$$

Following Mayer, we suppose that, of the M systems, m are in the kth energy level for a particular composition $\boldsymbol{N}$. The number of ways this can arise is denoted by $\Omega(m)$, and is given by

$$\Omega(m) = \binom{M}{m} \omega_k^m \Omega_r(M - m). \tag{S2.2}$$

Here, $\binom{M}{m}$ is the number of ways m systems may be chosen from M, ω_k^m is the number of ways the m systems may be distributed among the ω_k states if the states have equal weight, and $\Omega_r(M - m)$ is the number of ways of distributing the $M - m$ remaining systems among the states available to them. $\Omega_r(M - m)$ must be evaluated subject to the constraints that the total energy and the total number of molecules of each type in the ensemble is constant. It is, of course, assumed that $m < \omega_k$ in equation (S2.2). We can define an entropy for the ensemble, for this arrangement, by

$$S(m) = k \ln \Omega(m). \tag{S2.3}$$

Since the equilibrium configuration is defined as that for which the entropy is a maximum under conditions of constant energy and volume, the value which m must assume in equilibrium is that for which

$$\Delta S(m) = S(m) - S(m-1) = 0, \tag{S2.4}$$

or

$$k \ln\left[\frac{\omega_k}{m}(M - m + 1)\right] = -[S_r(M - m) - S_r(M - m + 1)], \tag{S2.5}$$

where

$$S_r = k \ln \Omega_r. \tag{S2.6}$$

The change from $(m - 1)$ to m in the number of systems in the ω_k states in the kth level involves, in the rest of the system, a *decrease* of V in the volume, a *decrease* of $\boldsymbol{N}$ in the number of molecules, and a decrease E_k in the energy. If $M \gg m \gg 1$ and M approaches infinity, in conformity with the initial definition of the ensemble, S_r may be equated with the entropy of the system, so that

$$S_r(M-m)-S_r(M-m+1)$$

$$=-V\left(\frac{\partial S_r}{\partial V}\right)_{N\ E}-N\cdot\left(\frac{\partial S_r}{\partial N}\right)_{V\ E}-E_k\left(\frac{\partial S_r}{\partial E}\right)_{V,N}, \qquad (S2.7)$$

$$=k\beta(-pV+N\cdot\mathbf{\mu}-E_k),$$

where k is Boltzmann's constant, β the inverse temperature in energy units, p is the pressure, and $\mathbf{\mu}=(\mu_1,\ldots,\mu_i,\ldots)$ are the chemical potentials per molecule of the various species. From (S2.5) and (S2.7), in the limit of large M, we obtain

$$\frac{m}{M\omega_k}=\exp[\beta(-pV+N\cdot\mathbf{\mu}-E_k)], \qquad (S2.8)$$

which can be interpreted as the probability that a system will, for given pressure, volume, temperature, and composition, occupy a given state of energy E_k. After multiplication by the degeneracy ω_k, it is also the probability that, in an infinitely large system of known pressure, temperature, and composition, an arbitrary volume V will be found to have a composition N and an energy E_k. Defining this probability by $P(E_k, N, V)$, we have

$$\frac{m}{M}=P(E_k,N,V),$$
$$=\omega_k\exp[\beta(-pV+N\cdot\mathbf{\mu}-E_k)]. \qquad (S2.9)$$

Since we shall have occasion to deal only with one-component systems, the vector notation for N and $\mathbf{\mu}$ will be dropped from now on.

It is now convenient to introduce the Grand Partition Function (G.P.F.) by

$$\Xi=\sum_{k,\ N}\omega_k\exp[\beta(N\mu-E_k)]. \qquad (S2.10)$$

Since, by definition,

$$\sum_{k,\ N}P(E_k,N,V)=1,$$

we have, from (S2.9),

$$\Xi=\exp(\beta pV), \qquad (S2.11)$$

whereupon

$$P(E_k,N,V)=\Xi^{-1}\omega_k\exp[\beta(N\mu-E_k)];\ \text{G.C.E.} \qquad (S2.12)$$

One can now write down expressions for the entropy, mean energy, and composition according to the G.C.E.:

$$S = -k \sum_{k,\, N} P(E_k, N, V) \ln P(E_k, N, V) + \text{const}, \quad \text{(S2.13)}$$

$$\langle E \rangle = \sum_{k,\, N} E_k P(E_k, N, V), \quad \text{(S2.14)}$$

$$\langle N \rangle = \sum_{k,\, N} N P(E_k, N, V). \quad \text{(S2.15)}$$

The constant term in (S2.13) represents the somewhat arbitrary nature of the grouping of states into levels performed earlier.

Let us now consider the special case in which the members of the ensemble are constrained to have the same number of molecules. Such an ensemble is called the Canonical Ensemble (C.E.). The sum over N disappears and equation (S2.12) becomes

$$P(E_k, N, V) = Q_N^{-1} \omega_k \exp(-\beta E_k); \ \text{C.E.}, \quad \text{(S2.16)}$$

where

$$Q_N = \sum_k \omega_k \exp(-\beta E_k). \quad \text{(S2.17)}$$

If we further restrict the possible energies to one level E_k only, then the sum over k disappears, and we have the microcanonical ensemble, for which

$$P(E_k, N, V) = 1. \quad \text{(S2.18)}$$

The probability of finding the system in one of the ω_k *states* of energy E_k is then ω_k^{-1} in the Microcanonical Ensemble.

S2.2. Transition to a Classical Phase-Space Description [1]

Hitherto, we have discussed the properties of the ensembles in terms of energy levels, a feature arising essentially from the necessity of describing microscopic phenomena in terms of quantum mechanics. In discussing the properties of liquids, such as argon, krypton, etc., whose important properties can be explained in classical terms, we shall find it more convenient to introduce the phase-space description of the system. In this description we represent the state of the system by the set of momenta $\boldsymbol{P}^N = (\boldsymbol{p}_1, \boldsymbol{p}_2, \ldots, \boldsymbol{p}_N)$ and coordinates $\{N\} = (\boldsymbol{R}_1, \boldsymbol{R}_2, \ldots, \boldsymbol{R}_N)$ of its N constituent molecules. It is conventional to regard the microscopic state of a system as being represented by a single point $(\boldsymbol{P}^N, \{N\})$ in a 6 N-dimensional phase space. In this context we remark that the addition or removal of molecules to or from the system *changes the dimensionality of the phase space*, so that a phase space of a given dimensionality cannot describe the G.C.E.

In setting up the classical equivalent of the Canonical and Microcanonical ensembles, we are led to the question: how precisely may we define the energy level in the continuous spectrum of states? According to the uncertainty principle, a point in the phase space of a particle constrained to one-dimensional motion cannot be located more closely than a "cell" of size h:

$$\Delta p \Delta R \backsim h \,, \tag{S2.19}$$

and we suppose that the finest subdivision of phase space allowable in quantum mechanics is a cell of size h^{3N}. Classically, we can conceive of integrating over such a cell, but according to (S2.19) we cannot distinguish any variation in a phase function. Turning to equation (S2.17), we see that each term in the summation must correspond to the integral of $\exp[-\beta H(\boldsymbol{P}^N, \{N\})]$ over the region of the phase space for which the classical Hamiltonian $H(\boldsymbol{P}^N, \{N\}) = E_k$ and $E \leq E_k \leq E + \Delta E$, where ΔE is subject to (S2.19). This region, or shell, has volume $N!h^{3N}$, because there are $N!$ permutations of the molecules among the momenta and positions for a single-phase cell, for which the energy E_k is unchanged. In a rigorous treatment of the transition to a phase-space description, the leading (classical) term is found to be independent of the symmetry of the molecular wave functions. Thus, the volume of the shell is *not* associated with the quantum-mechanical permutation factor $(-)^P$, P being zero or unity according as the permutation is even or odd. The weighting factor, ω_k, originally chosen to represent the number of quantum-mechanically distinct states with energies in the interval $E \leq E_k \leq E + \Delta E$, is taken to be unity because ΔE is now the smallest distinguishable energy difference. As a result, for a single term in (S2.17), we have

$$N!h^{3N} \exp(-\beta E_k) = \underset{E \leq E_k \leq E+\Delta E}{\int \cdots \int} \exp(-\beta H)\, d\boldsymbol{P}^N d\{N\} \tag{S2.20}$$

and

$$Q_N = \frac{1}{N!h^{3N}} \int \cdots \int \exp(-\beta H)\, d\boldsymbol{P}^N d\{N\}, \tag{S2.21}$$

where the integral is now over the entire region of phase space accessible to the system.

If the Hamiltonian can be expressed in the form

$$H = (\boldsymbol{P}^N, \{N\}) = \sum_{i=1}^{N} \frac{1}{2m} p_i^2 + U(\{N\}), \qquad (S2.22)$$

where $U(\{N\})$ is the potential energy of the system and is assumed to depend only on the coordinates of the N molecules, then

$$Q_1 = V\left(\frac{2\pi m}{\beta h^2}\right)^{3/2}$$

and

$$Q_N = \frac{1}{N!}\left(\frac{Q_1}{V}\right)^N \int \cdots \int \exp[-\beta U(\{N\})]\, d\{N\}, \qquad (S2.23)$$

where, as before, V is the volume of the system.

S3. THE THEORY OF IMPERFECT GASES

The theory of imperfect gases has played an important role in the development of our general understanding of the properties of systems of interacting molecules. In addition, the formal structure of the theory is fundamental to the derivation of some of the most recent liquid theories. For these reasons we shall examine the statistical mechanics of imperfect gases in some detail. However, no attention will be devoted to the study of critical phenomena and attendant problems; we confine our discussion solely to the behavior of one-phase fluid systems.

S3.1. Preliminary Study [2]

From (S2.11) and (S2.17) we see that the Grand Canonical and Canonical ensembles are related to each other by

$$\Xi = \sum_N Q_N(N, \beta, V)\exp(\beta N\mu). \qquad (S3.1)$$

Consider now new quantities λ (absolute activity) and z (fugacity) defined by

$$\lambda = \exp(\beta\mu), \qquad z = \frac{Q_1}{V}\lambda.$$

In these variables equation (S3.1) may be written

$$\begin{aligned}\Xi &= 1 + Q_1\lambda + Q_2\lambda^2 + \ldots \\ &= \sum_{N\geq 0} \frac{Z_N z^N}{N!}, \qquad (S3.2)\end{aligned}$$

where Z_N is the configurational partition function, which will be discussed in detail in section S4.1. By comparing equations (S3.1) and (S3.2), we find that

$$Z_N = \left(\frac{V}{Q_1}\right)^N N! Q_N , \tag{S3.3}$$

using the fact that $Q_0 = 1$.

The pressure can be related to the configurational partition functions by means of equations (S2.11), (S3.2), and (S3.3). We have

$$\beta p V = \ln\left(\sum_{N\geq 0} \frac{Z_N z^N}{N!}\right), \tag{S3.4}$$

so that if the right side of (S3.4) is expanded in a power series in z,

$$\beta p = \sum_{j\geq 1} b_j z^j . \tag{S3.5}$$

The quantities $j!b_jV$ are well known in statistics as the semi-invariants of Thiele, or, cumulants. They are closely related to the cumulant functions discussed in section S3.3 and are given, in terms of the partition function, by

$$j!b_jV = j! \sum_{\mathbf{n}} (-)^q q! \prod_i \left[\frac{1}{n_i!}\left(\frac{Z_i}{i!}\right)^{n_i}\right], \tag{S3.6}$$

where $q = \Sigma_i n_i - 1$ and $\Sigma_{\mathbf{n}}$ is the sum over all positive or zero integers such that $\Sigma_i i n_i = j$. The first few terms are

$$\begin{aligned} b_1 V &= Z_1 (= V), \\ b_2 V &= \tfrac{1}{2}(Z_2 - Z_1^2), \\ b_3 V &= \tfrac{1}{6}(Z_3 - 3Z_1Z_2 + 2Z_1^3), \ldots . \end{aligned} \tag{S3.7}$$

It is seen from the form of equation (S3.7) that the semi-invariant of order j is expressed in terms of a set of configurational partition functions of order not greater than j. Equation (S3.5) is, therefore, an expansion in terms of the properties of clusters of molecules of increasing size, and the quantities b_j are called the cluster integrals. Z_N may also be expressed in terms of these cluster integrals as follows. Substitution of (S3.5) in (S2.11) gives

$$\begin{aligned} \exp(\beta p V) &= \prod_{j\geq 1} \exp(b_j V z^j), \\ &= \prod_{j\geq 1} \left[\sum_{m_j \geq 0} \frac{1}{m_j!} (b_j V)^{m_j} z^{j m_j}\right], \\ &= \sum_{N\geq 0} \sum_{\mathbf{m}} \left[\prod_{j=1}^{N} \frac{(b_j V)^{m_j}}{m_j!}\right] z^N , \end{aligned} \tag{S3.8}$$

so that, by comparison with (S3.2),

$$Z_N = N! \sum_m \left[\prod_{j=1}^{N} \frac{(b_j V)^{m_j}}{m_j!} \right], \qquad \text{(S3.9)}$$

where Σ_m means the summation over all sets of $m_1, m_2, \ldots, m_j \ldots$ compatible with $\Sigma_j j m_j = N$. Equation (S3.9) is an expression for the configurational partition function for N molecules in terms of the cluster integrals for smaller numbers of molecules.

The derivation given is rigorous and valid for quantum-mechanical systems insofar as the expansion of (S3.4) is valid. This is generally accepted to be the case if the expansion is applied to an imperfect gas, but difficulties with convergence are encountered when one attempts to apply the expression to the study of condensation phenomena, critical phenomena, and the liquid phase. The derivation is very general because it does not depend upon pairwise additivity for the intermolecular potentials, or any other property. However, the generality of the formalism hides many interesting details and much of the physics. For this reason we next consider a much more detailed derivation of the expansion (S3.9). In particular, the relation between the cluster integrals, b_j, the intermolecular potential, and the character of the simultaneous interactions of j molecules will be displayed. A great simplification will be obtained by the introduction of certain "irreducible" cluster integrals.

It is convenient here to assume, as we do throughout the rest of the book, that the total potential energy of interaction is pairwise decomposable,

$$U(\{N\}) = \sum_{i>j} u(i, j),$$

whereupon

$$\begin{aligned} \exp[-\beta U(\{N\})] &= \prod_{i>j} \exp[-\beta u(i, j)] \\ &= \prod_{i>j} (1 + f_{ij}) \end{aligned} \qquad \text{(S3.10)}$$

and

$$f_{ij} = \exp[-\beta u(i, j)] - 1 . \qquad \text{(S3.11)}$$

This technique, which enables the exponential function of N coordinates to be separated into the sum of products of functions of smaller numbers of coordinates, is due to Mayer. A one to one correspondence (mapping) between the terms in (S3.10) and a set of graphs may be established. The graphs are defined by stating that a point defines a molecule, and a line between points i and j represents the term f_{ij}. For example, the figure

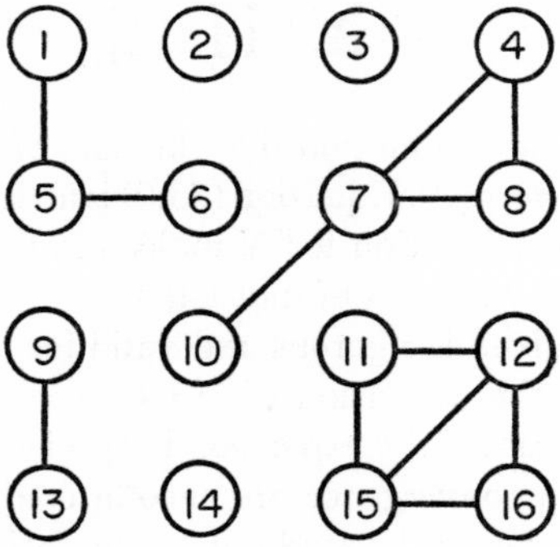

is a mapping of the product

$$f_{1,5}f_{5,6}f_{4,7}f_{4,8}f_{7,8}f_{7,10}f_{9,13}f_{11,12}f_{11,15}f_{12,15}f_{12,16}f_{15,16}$$
$$= (f_{1,5}f_{5,6})(f_{4,7}f_{4,8}f_{7,8}f_{7,10})(f_{9,13})(f_{11,12}f_{11,15}f_{12,15}f_{12,16}f_{15,16}).$$

An irreducible cluster is defined by a mapping in which each point (molecule) is connected by a bond (f_{ij}) to at least two other points. For completeness, the exceptional case of two interacting molecules is included as the lowest irreducible cluster. In this classical case, the cluster integrals, b_j, are related to the cluster mappings by

$$b_j = \frac{1}{j!V} \int S_{1,2\,\ldots\,j+1} d\{j\}, \qquad \text{(S3.12)}$$

where $S_{1,2,\ldots,j}$ is the sum of all terms which connect in a cluster molecules 1, 2, . . . , j, no other molecules being connected. For example,

$$b_3 = \frac{1}{6V} \int S_{1,2,3} d\{3\}$$
$$= \frac{1}{6V} \int (f_{1,3}f_{1,2} + f_{2,3}f_{1,3} + f_{2,3}f_{1,2} + f_{1,3}f_{2,3}f_{1,2})\, d\{3\} \qquad \text{(S3.13)}$$
$$= \tfrac{1}{2}\beta_1^2 + \tfrac{1}{3}\beta_2\,.$$

Equation (S3.13) is derived in the following way. Each of the products of two f_{ij} factors may be represented graphically by, for instance,

$$\equiv \frac{1}{6V} \int f_{1,2}f_{2,3} d\{3\}, \qquad \text{(S3.14)}$$

since the numbering of the molecules is immaterial. Now, $f_{1,2}$ and $f_{2,3}$ depend on $\boldsymbol{R}_{12} = \boldsymbol{R}_2 - \boldsymbol{R}_1$ and $\boldsymbol{R}_{23}$, respectively. The integration, which is over the space of $\boldsymbol{R}_1$, $\boldsymbol{R}_2$, $\boldsymbol{R}_3$, may be changed to an integration over $\boldsymbol{R}_{12}$, $\boldsymbol{R}_{13}$, $\boldsymbol{R}_{33}$. Consequently, (S3.14) contains the product of two integrals of the type

$$\int f_{ij} d\boldsymbol{R}_{ij} = \beta_1 , \tag{S3.15}$$

and one of the type

$$\int d\boldsymbol{R}_i = V . \tag{S3.16}$$

The three terms in the general form of equation (S3.14), therefore, give rise to the term $\frac{1}{2}\beta_1^2$, where β_1 is the irreducible cluster integral for two molecules. The remaining term in the integrand, $f_{1,2}\, f_{1,3}\, f_{2,3}$, is the most highly connected arrangement of factors for three molecules and gives rise to the irreducible cluster β_2. Quite generally, the largest irreducible cluster for a group of n molecules is of the order $(n - 1)$, since the last variable of integration ($\boldsymbol{R}_{23}$ in the 3-molecule case) is always expressible in terms of the other variables (e.g., $\boldsymbol{R}_{23} = \boldsymbol{R}_{13} - \boldsymbol{R}_{12}$). Hence, the final integration is an unweighted integral over the center of mass, giving rise to a factor V. In the case of four molecules, we have, according to the definition of irreducible clusters, three types of integrals contributing. These are:

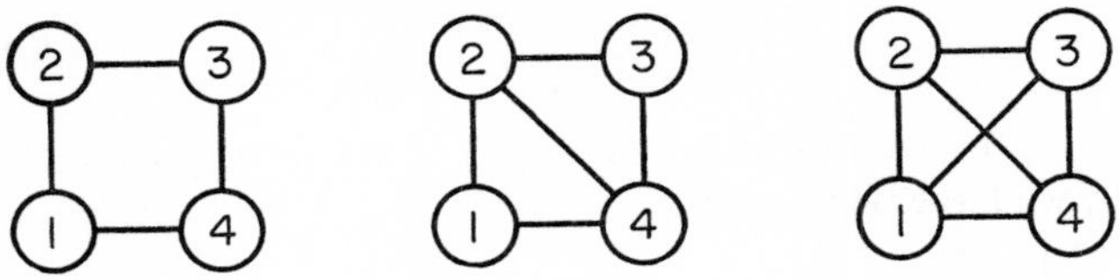

For different orderings of the molecules, there can be seen to arise three distinct graphs of the first kind, six of the second, and one of the third. Finally, we remark that the irreducible cluster integrals are defined in an analogous way to the b_j; namely,

$$\beta_j = \frac{1}{j!V} \int \mathfrak{S}_{1,2,\ldots,j+1}\, d\{j+1\}, \tag{S3.17}$$

where $\mathfrak{S}_{1,2,\ldots,j+1}$ is the sum of all irreducible connections between j molecules.

It is clear that the irreducible clusters form a much smaller set than do the reducible (general) clusters. Indeed, it can be shown that the equation of state of the imperfect gas is

$$pV = NkT\left(1 - \sum_{k=1}^{N} \frac{k}{k+1}\, \beta_k \rho^k\right), \tag{S3.18}$$

where ρ is the density, N/V, and T is the temperature.

S3.2. A Different Expansion [2]

The expansion (S3.18) of the equation of state in powers of the density is equivalent to that given earlier in powers of the activity (eq. [S3.5]) since, in the low-density limit, the activity tends to the density. In this section we sketch a different method of expansion which does not require the assumption of pairwise-additive potentials. Indeed, this method is also valid for quantum-mechanical systems, and provides a bridge between the Mayer f-function expansion and the simple evaluation of the Grand Partition Function outlined in the first discussion of the imperfect gas.

We begin by defining a set of probability distributions $W(\{k\})$ by

$$W(\{k\}) = \prod_{i<j=2}^{k} (1 + f_{ij}) = \sum_{G_k} \prod^{(k)} f_{ij}, \qquad \text{(S3.19)}$$

the sum going over *all* graphs G_k of k labeled points. The W_k are normalized in such a way that they approach unity when the k molecules become distant from one another. We next define a class of related functions, the Ursell cluster functions, or $\mathfrak{U}$-functions, by

$$\mathfrak{U}(\{k\}) = \sum_{(C_k)} \prod^{(k)} f_{ij}, \qquad \text{(S3.20)}$$

the sum going over all *connected* graphs of k labeled points, C_k. From (S3.20), we have, for example,

$$\begin{aligned} &\mathfrak{U}(\{1\}) = 1 , \\ &\mathfrak{U}(\{2\}) = f_{1\,2} , \\ &\mathfrak{U}(\{3\}) = f_{1.2}f_{1,3} + f_{1,3}f_{2,3} + f_{1,2}f_{2,3} + f_{1,2}f_{1,3}f_{2,3} , \\ &\qquad \ldots . \end{aligned} \qquad \text{(S3.21)}$$

It is seen that the last displayed member of (S3.21) is identical with the integrand of b_3 in (S3.13), and so forth.

The relation between the $\{W\}$ and the $\{\mathfrak{U}\}$ is called the Ursell development:

$$\begin{aligned} &\mathfrak{U}(\{1\}) = W(\{1\}), \\ &\mathfrak{U}(\{2\}) = W(\{2\}) - W(1)W(2), \\ &\mathfrak{U}(\{3\}) = W(\{3\}) - W(1,\,2)W(3) - W(2,\,3)W(1) \\ &\qquad - W(1,\,3)W(2) + 2W(1)W(2)W(3), \qquad \ldots , \end{aligned} \qquad \text{(S3.22)}$$

where we have used the notation (i) to represent the coordinates of the ith labeled point (while retaining the notation $\{i\}$ to represent the set of coordinates of all i labeled points). The coefficients of the terms are $(-)^{n-1}(n-1)!$, where n is the number of W factors in the term. In the absence of an external field we can choose the energy zero such that $W(\{1\}) = 1$. Equation (S3.22) then may be inverted to give

$$\begin{aligned} W(\{1\}) &= \mathfrak{U}(\{1\}) = 1, \\ W(\{2\}) &= \mathfrak{U}(1)\mathfrak{U}(2) + \mathfrak{U}(\{2\}), \\ W(\{3\}) &= \mathfrak{U}(1)\mathfrak{U}(2)\mathfrak{U}(3) + \mathfrak{U}(1,2)\mathfrak{U}(3) \\ &\quad + \mathfrak{U}(1,3)\mathfrak{U}(2) + \mathfrak{U}(2,3)\mathfrak{U}(1) + \mathfrak{U}(\{3\}), \quad \ldots. \end{aligned} \tag{S3.23}$$

The coefficients before all terms in this expression are $+1$. What we have achieved, formally, is a representation of the Boltzmann factor for N molecules, $W(\{N\})$, as a sum of products of $\mathfrak{U}$-functions. Suppose that any of these products contains m_1 groups of 1 molecule, m_2 groups of 2 molecules, . . . , m_l of l molecules, subject to the conservation condition: $\Sigma_l l m_l = N$. We now note the following: The function $\mathfrak{U}(\{l\})$ is zero for separated configurations, i.e., for all configurations wherein the l molecules are separated into two or more groups at such distances that no interaction exists between the molecules of the several groups.

The proof of this theorem is based on the product property of exponentials. For a separated configuration of molecules in sets $\{i\}$, $\{j\}$, $\{k\}$, etc., we have

$$\begin{aligned} \exp[-\beta U(\{N\})] &= \exp[-\beta U(\{i\})] \\ &\quad \times \exp[-\beta U(\{j\})]\exp[-\beta U(\{k\})]\ldots. \end{aligned} \tag{S3.24}$$

Let the theorem be proved for all functions for which $k < l$. Both sides of (S3.24) are now expressed in terms of $\mathfrak{U}$-functions. On the right-hand side no terms appear containing $\mathfrak{U}$-functions sharing molecules of different groups. The sum of such terms, *which must occur on the left-hand side*, is, therefore, zero. This sum includes a large number of terms containing $\mathfrak{U}$-functions, with $k < l$, which were assumed to be zero, and, therefore, the term $\mathfrak{U}(\{l\})$, which occurs once, must be zero also. The theorem can be immediately verified for the special cases $\mathfrak{U}(\{2\})$ and $\mathfrak{U}(\{3\})$, and the general proof follows by induction. The theorem is also valid in quantum statistics, where the W functions are now Slater sums. The product property used for the exponentials also holds for Slater sums because, for a separated configuration, the Hamiltonian operator separates into a sum and the wave function factorizes into a product. The proof then follows directly, as in the classical case.

Having expressed the Boltzmann factor for the system of N molecules as the sum of products of $\mathfrak{U}$-functions, we may now formally integrate the configurational partition function. From (S3.20), we have

$$b_l = \frac{1}{l!V}\int \mathfrak{U}(\{l\})\,d\{l\}. \tag{S3.25}$$

The general expression for any product of $\mathfrak{U}$-terms is then

$$(1!b_1V)^{m_1}(2!b_2V)^{m_2}\ldots(l!b_lV)^{m_l} = \prod_j (j!b_jV)^{m_j}, \quad \text{(S3.26)}$$

where there are m_j clusters (non-separated groups) of j molecules in the product of $\mathfrak{U}$-functions. The constraint is, again, $\Sigma_j jm_j = N$. Other terms can be obtained by permutation of molecules, except those within a subgroup, and also by permutation of groups of unequal size. The total number of these terms is

$$N!\prod_{j=1}^{N}\frac{1}{(j!)^{m_j}m_j!}, \quad \text{(S3.27)}$$

whereupon

$$Z_N = N!\sum_{(\sum_j jm_j=N)}\prod_{j=1}^{N}\frac{(Vb_j)^{m_j}}{m_j!}, \quad \text{(S3.28)}$$

which is, again, the same as (S3.9).

Alternatively, the terms in the development of $W(\{N\})$ [eq. (S3.23)] may be reordered in the following way. First, all terms are collected in which molecule 1 occurs in a group by itself, i.e., which contain the factor $\mathfrak{U}(1)$; the coefficient of this term is $W(2, \ldots, N)$. Next, all terms in which molecule 1 occurs in a group with one other molecule [i.e., $\mathfrak{U}(1, 2)$] are collected; the coefficient of each one is $W(3, \ldots, N)$, and so on. We finally obtain

$$W(\{N\}) = \mathfrak{U}(1)W(\{N-1\}) + \sum_P \mathfrak{U}(1, i)W(\{N-2\}) + \ldots, \quad \text{(S3.29)}$$

where Σ_P means the sum over all ways of choosing molecule i, molecules i and j, etc. Equation (S3.29) is now integrated over $\{N\}$, and from the definition of the cluster integrals (S3.25) we find

$$Z_N = \sum_{j=1}\binom{N-1}{j-1}(j!b_jV)Z_{N-j}. \quad \text{(S3.30)}$$

Thus, there is achieved a decomposition of Z_N into sums of products of disjoint clusters of j molecules, and systems of $N - j$ molecules. The first few terms of the decomposition may be understood in the following way. Since

$$W(\{N\}) = \prod_{i<j=2}^{N}(1+f_{ij}),$$

the product may be separated into

$$W(\{N\}) = \prod_{\substack{i<j=3 \\ (\text{not } 1)}}^{N} (1+f_{ij}) \prod_{k=2}^{N} (1+f_{1k}), \qquad \text{(S3.31)}$$

where the condition (not 1) on the first product means that all terms in which molecule 1 appears are put into the second product. On expanding the second product, (S3.31) becomes

$$\begin{aligned} W(\{N\}) &= \prod_{\substack{i<j=3 \\ (\text{not } 1)}}^{N} (1+f_{ij}) \\ &\quad \times\left(1+\sum_{k=2}^{N} f_{1k} + \sum_{k<l=2}^{N}\sum^{N} f_{1k}f_{1l} + \ldots\right) \\ &= W(\{N-1\}) + \prod_{\substack{i<j=3 \\ (\text{not } 1)}}^{N} (1+f_{ij}) \\ &\quad \times\left(\sum_{k=2}^{N} f_{1k} + \ldots\right). \end{aligned} \qquad \text{(S3.32)}$$

In the second term of equation (S3.32) we have a sum of terms

$$f_{1k} \prod_{\substack{i<j=3 \\ (\text{not } 1)}}^{N} (1+f_{ij}) \qquad (k=2, \ldots, N),$$

and each may be separated into

$$\begin{aligned} f_{1k} \prod_{\substack{i<j \\ (\text{not } 1,\, k)}}^{N} (1+f_{ij}) \prod_{m=2}^{N} (1+f_{km}) &= f_{1k}W[1, 2, \ldots, (k-1), (k+1), \ldots, N] \\ &\quad + f_{1k} \prod_{\substack{i<j \\ (\text{not } 1,\, k)}}^{N} (1+f_{ij})\left(\sum_{m=2}^{N} f_{km} + \ldots\right). \end{aligned}$$

As there are $(n-1)$ terms of this type, (S3.31) may be written

$$\begin{aligned} W(\{N\}) &= W(\{N-1\}) \\ &\quad + \sum_{k=2}^{N} f_{1k}W[1, 2, \ldots, (k-1), (k+1), \ldots, N] + \cdots, \\ &= W(\{N-1\}) + (N-1)\mathfrak{U}(1, 2)W(3, \ldots, N) + \cdots \end{aligned}$$

as before.

S3.3. Kubo's Method of Cumulants [3] [15]

S3.3.1. *General Formulation.*—In the preceding sections we have demonstrated the relationship between the equation of state of a fluid and a set of irreducible integrals. These irreducible integrals have a graphical representation (in the classical case) in which each point (molecule) is connected by a bond (f_{ij}) to at least two other points. By the introduction of irreducible integrals, economy is achieved in accounting for all possible molecular interactions. In this section we consider in greater detail the meaning of the graphical representation and its connection to the invariant expansion of equation (S3.6). To establish this connection we must examine the properties of cumulants.

Given a random variable X, the moments and cumulants (semi-invariants), of X are defined by the moment generating function, $M(\xi)$, and the cumulant function, $K(\xi)$. These are

$$M(\xi) \equiv \langle \exp \xi X \rangle = \sum_{n=0}^{\infty} \frac{\xi^n}{n!} \mu_n$$
$$= \exp\left(\sum_{n=1}^{\infty} \frac{\xi^n}{n!} \kappa_n\right) \equiv \exp[K(\xi)]. \tag{S3.33}$$

Equation (S3.6) follows directly from (S3.33). As usual, the broken bracket ($\langle\ \rangle$) indicates the expectation value of the variable, and μ_n and κ_n are defined to be the nth moment and nth cumulant, respectively. For the case of N random variables, $X_1, \ldots, X_N$, we have, by analogy,

$$M(\xi_1, \ldots, \xi_N) \equiv \left\langle \exp\left(\sum_{j=1}^{N} \xi_j X_j\right)\right\rangle$$
$$= \sum_{\nu_1=0}^{\infty} \cdots \sum_{\nu_N=0}^{\infty} \left(\prod_j \frac{\xi_j^{\nu_j}}{\nu_j!}\right) \mu(\nu_1 \ldots \nu_N) \tag{S3.34}$$
$$= \exp\left[\sum_{\nu_1 \ldots \nu_N}{}' \left(\prod_j \frac{\xi_j^{\nu_j}}{\nu_j!}\right) \kappa(\nu_1 \ldots \nu_N)\right]$$
$$\equiv \exp[K(\xi_1 \ldots \xi_N)],$$

where the prime indicates that the summation is carried over all values of $\nu_1 \ldots \nu_N$, except the single term $\nu_1 = \nu_2 = \ldots = \nu_N = 0$. It will be convenient to use the notation

$$\mu(\mathbf{v}) \equiv \mu(\nu_1 \ldots \nu_N) \equiv \mu(X_1^{\nu_1} \ldots X_N^{\nu_N}) \equiv \langle X_1^{\nu_1} \ldots X_N^{\nu_N} \rangle$$
$$\kappa(\mathbf{v}) \equiv \kappa(\nu_1 \ldots \nu_N) \equiv \kappa(X_1^{\nu_1} \ldots X_N^{\nu_N}) \qquad \text{(S3.35)}$$
$$\equiv \langle X_1^{\nu_1} \ldots X_N^{\nu_N} \rangle_c ,$$

where the subscript c indicates "connected" in the graphical sense already introduced. More generally, the subscript c indicates a *cumulant average*, which is not a simple average. For example,

$$\langle X_1 X_2 \rangle_c = \langle X_1 X_2 \rangle - \langle X_1 \rangle \langle X_2 \rangle. \qquad \text{(S3.36)}$$

Using (S3.35), (S3.34) may be rewritten in the form

$$\left\langle \exp\left(\sum_{j=1}^{N} \xi_j X_j\right)\right\rangle = \sum_{\nu_1=0}^{\infty} \cdots \sum_{\nu_N=0}^{\infty} \prod_j \frac{\xi^{\nu_j}}{\nu_j!} \langle X_1^{\nu_1} \ldots X_N^{\nu_N} \rangle$$
$$= \exp\left(\sum_{\nu_1 \ldots \nu_N}{}' \prod_j \frac{\xi_j^{\nu_j}}{\nu_j!} \langle X_1^{\nu_1} \ldots X_N^{\nu_N} \rangle_c \right). \qquad \text{(S3.37)}$$

We can also write, by summation of the above,

$$\left\langle \exp\left(\sum_{j=1}^{N} \xi_j X_j\right)\right\rangle = \exp\left\langle \exp\left(\sum_{j=1}^{N} \xi_j X_j\right) - 1 \right\rangle_c . \qquad \text{(S3.38)}$$

An important property of cumulants which makes them useful in the treatment of interacting systems is the following: a cumulant can be explicitly represented only by the lower (*not higher*) moments, and vice versa. Equation (S3.34) can be inverted to read

$$\kappa(\mathbf{v}) = -\left(\prod_{j=1}^{N} \nu_j!\right) \sum_{\{m_i\}} \left(\sum_{i=1}^{\infty} k_i - 1\right)! \, (-)^{\Sigma_{i=1}^{\infty} k_i}$$
$$\times \prod_{i=1}^{\infty} \frac{1}{k_i!} \left[\frac{\mu(\mathbf{m}_i)}{\prod_{j=1}^{N} m_{ij}!} \right]^{k_i}, \qquad \left(\sum_{i=1}^{\infty} k_i m_{ij} = \nu_j \right). \qquad \text{(S3.39)}$$

Equation (S3.39) is seen to be a generalization of equation (S3.6). As displayed, (S3.39) is a relation for $\kappa(\mathbf{v})$ in terms of moments $\mu(\boldsymbol{\omega})$, for each of which $\omega_i \leq \nu_i$, for all i. That this is so is implied by the restriction $\Sigma_{i=1}^{\infty} k_i m_{ij} = \nu_j$ on the sum over all sets of moments $\mu(\mathbf{m}_i)$. If, for any i, $m_{ij} > \nu_j$, then the restriction implies that $k_i = 0$, so that the corresponding term in the product $\Pi_{i=1}^{\infty}$ is unity. Also, of course, while the product $\Pi_{j=1}^{N}\nu_j!$ formally includes every variable, any $\nu_j = 0$ gives a factor unity.

Equation (S3.39) is of sufficient importance that we digress to discuss its derivation. Consider first the case of a single variable. Equation (S3.33) can be rearranged to read

$$\sum_{n=1}^{\infty} \frac{\xi^n}{n!} \kappa_n = \ln\,(1+X), \tag{S3.40}$$

where

$$X = \sum_{m=1}^{\infty} \frac{\xi^m}{m!} \mu_m . \tag{S3.41}$$

Since ξ is arbitrary, the right-hand side of (S3.40) may always be expanded in a non-divergent series

$$\begin{aligned} \ln(1+X) &= X - \frac{X^2}{2} + \frac{X^3}{3} - \dots, \\ &= \sum_{l=1}^{\infty} (-)^{l-1} \frac{X^l}{l}, \end{aligned} \tag{S3.42}$$

for some ξ. Since, in a multinomial expansion of $X^l = (\Sigma_{i=1}^{\infty} x_i)^l$, the general term is

$$l! \prod_{i=1}^{\infty} \frac{x_i^{n_i}}{n_i!}; \qquad \sum_{i=1}^{\infty} n_i = l,$$

the coefficient of ξ^m in the nth term of equation (S3.42) is

$$\frac{(-)^{n-1}}{n} n! \prod_{i=1}^{\infty} \frac{1}{n_i!} \left(\frac{\mu_i}{i!}\right)^{n_i}; \qquad \sum_{i=1}^{\infty} i n_i = m, \qquad \sum_{i=1}^{\infty} n_i = n,$$

and, from (S3.40), we find

$$\begin{aligned} \kappa_m = -m! \sum (-)^{\Sigma_{i=1}^{\infty} n_i} \left(\sum_{i=1}^{\infty} n_i - 1\right)! \\ \times \prod_{i=1}^{\infty} \frac{1}{n_i!} \left(\frac{\mu_i}{i!}\right)^{n_i}; \quad \left(\sum_{i=1}^{\infty} i n_i = m\right). \end{aligned} \tag{S3.43}$$

Again, because of the restriction on the summation over sets $\mathbf{n}$, no μ_i $(i > m)$ appears on the right-hand side.

We now derive equation (S3.39) following Meeron. In the notation

$$\boldsymbol{\nu}! = \prod_{i=1}^{N} \nu_i!, \qquad \boldsymbol{\xi}^{\boldsymbol{\nu}} = \prod_{i=1}^{N} \xi_i^{\nu_i}, \qquad \left(\frac{\partial}{\partial \boldsymbol{\xi}}\right)^{\boldsymbol{\nu}} = \prod_{i=1}^{N} \left(\frac{\partial}{\partial \xi_i}\right)^{\nu_i},$$

equation (S3.41) may be written

$$\phi(\boldsymbol{\xi}) = \exp[\gamma(\boldsymbol{\xi})], \tag{S3.44}$$

where

$$\phi(\boldsymbol{\xi}) = \sum_{\mathbf{v}\geq \mathbf{o}} \frac{\boldsymbol{\xi}^{\mathbf{v}}}{\mathbf{v}!}\mu(\mathbf{v}) \tag{S3.45}$$

and

$$\gamma(\boldsymbol{\xi}) = \sum_{\mathbf{v}> \mathbf{o}} \frac{\boldsymbol{\xi}^{\mathbf{v}}}{\mathbf{v}!}\kappa(\mathbf{v}); \tag{S3.46}$$

$\mathbf{v} > \mathbf{o}$ means that the summation includes all vectors $\mathbf{v}$ with *at least* one element different from zero. By differentiation,

$$\left[\left(\frac{\partial}{\partial \boldsymbol{\xi}}\right)^{\mathbf{v}} \phi(\boldsymbol{\xi})\right]_{\boldsymbol{\xi}=0} = \mu(\mathbf{v}); \qquad \mathbf{v}\geq \mathbf{0}, \tag{S3.47}$$

$$\left[\left(\frac{\partial}{\partial \boldsymbol{\xi}}\right)^{\mathbf{v}} \gamma(\boldsymbol{\xi})\right]_{\boldsymbol{\xi}=0} = \kappa(\mathbf{v}); \qquad \mathbf{v}> \mathbf{0}. \tag{S3.48}$$

We now seek a formula for the $\mathbf{v}$th derivative of an exponential function. This is

$$\left(\frac{\partial}{\partial \mathbf{x}}\right)^{\mathbf{v}} \exp[g(\mathbf{x})] = \exp[g(\mathbf{x})]\mathbf{v}! \sum_{\{\mathbf{m}_i\}} \prod_i \frac{1}{k_i!} \left[\frac{1}{\mathbf{m}_i!}\left(\frac{\partial}{\partial \mathbf{x}}\right)^{\mathbf{m}_i} g(\mathbf{x})\right]^{k_i}, \tag{S3.49}$$

$$\sum_i k_i \mathbf{m}_i = \mathbf{v},$$

which may be verified when x is the only variable and proved, in general, by induction. The function $\phi(\boldsymbol{\xi})$ may now be differentiated $\mathbf{v}$ times with respect to $\boldsymbol{\xi}$. If $\boldsymbol{\xi}$ is then set equal to zero and equations (S3.47–48) are used, we find

$$\mu(\mathbf{v}) = \mathbf{v}! \sum_{\{\mathbf{m}_i\}} \prod_{i=1}^{\infty} \frac{1}{k_i!} \left[\frac{\kappa(\mathbf{m}_i)}{\mathbf{m}_i!}\right]^{k_i}; \qquad \left(\sum_{i=1}^{\infty} k_i \mathbf{m}_i = \mathbf{v}\right). \tag{S3.50}$$

It is now necessary to invert (S3.49) to read

$$\left(\frac{\partial}{\partial \mathbf{x}}\right)^{\mathbf{v}} \ln f(\mathbf{x}) = -\nu! \sum_{\{\mathbf{m}_i\}} \left(\sum_{i=1}^{\infty} k_i - 1\right)! \prod_{i=1}^{\infty} \frac{1}{k_i!} \times \left[\frac{(-)}{\mathbf{m}_i! f(\mathbf{x})}\left(\frac{\partial}{\partial \mathbf{x}}\right)^{\mathbf{m}_i} f(\mathbf{x})\right]^{k_i}; \qquad \left(\sum_{i=1}^{\infty} k_i \mathbf{m}_i = \mathbf{v}\right). \tag{S3.51}$$

When (S3.51) is used to differentiate the inverse of (S3.50) we find

$$\kappa(\mathbf{v}) = -\mathbf{v}!\sum_{\{m_i\}}\Big(\sum_{i=1}^{\infty} k_i - 1\Big)!\prod_{i=1}^{\infty}\frac{1}{k_i!}\Big[-\frac{\mu(m_i)}{m_i!}\Big]^{k_i}; \qquad \Big(\sum_{i=1}^{\infty} k_i m_i = \mathbf{v}\Big). \tag{S3.52}$$

The most important property of cumulants (for our present purposes) is the following: a cumulant, $\kappa(X_i, X_j, \ldots)$, is zero if the elements $X_i, X_j, \ldots$ may be divided into groups which are statistically independent. As a corollary, we note that a cumulant is zero if one of the variables in it is independent of the others. Conversely, a cumulant is non-zero *if and only if* the variables in it are statistically connected.

Let the variables $(X_i, X_j, \ldots)$ be divided into two groups

$$\{X\} = \{X'\} + \{X''\}, \tag{S3.53}$$

which are statistically independent. Then,

$$\langle \exp(\Sigma\xi X)\rangle = \langle \exp(\Sigma\xi' X')\rangle\,\langle \exp(\Sigma\xi'' X'')\rangle, \tag{S3.54}$$

because of the assumed independence. Further, using (S3.34),

$$K\{\xi\} = K_1\{\xi'\} + K_2\{\xi''\}, \tag{S3.55}$$

so that powers of ξ' and ξ'' never mix. Thus, any cumulant in which variables from the two groups do appear must vanish.

The important simplification brought about by the use of cumulants is in the explicit recognition of the kind of averages which are used in statistical mechanics. To establish a deeper connection we now consider a rearrangement of the cumulant expansion into a cluster expansion. Define

$$K(\xi_1, \ldots, \xi_N) = \sum{}' \prod_{i=1}^{N} \frac{\xi_i^{\nu_i}}{\nu_i!}\,\kappa(\mathbf{v}) = \sum_l K_l. \tag{S3.56}$$

First, collect all the terms in the cumulant series which contain the particular variable X_i. This term, denoted by $K_1(X_i)$, is given by the moment-generating function of the single variable, $M_1(X_i)$,

$$M_1(X_i) \equiv \langle \exp(\xi_i X_i)\rangle = \exp[K_1(X_i)], \tag{S3.57}$$

and, therefore, the first term in the expansion $K = \Sigma_l K_l$ may be chosen to be

$$K_1 = \sum_i K_1(X_i). \tag{S3.58}$$

The next term, K_2, will be of the form

$$K_2 = \sum_{i,\,j} K_2(X_i,\, X_j), \tag{S3.59}$$

where $K_2(X_i,\, X_j)$ is the collection of all terms in the cumulant series that contain two variables, X_i and X_j. Now the two-variable moment-generating function can be written in the form

$$\begin{aligned} M_2(X_i,\, X_j) &= \langle \exp(\xi_i X_i + \xi_j X_j) \rangle \\ &= \exp[K_1(X_i) + K_1(X_j) + K_2(X_i,\, X_j)], \end{aligned} \tag{S3.60}$$

and, therefore,

$$\exp[K_2(X_i,\, X_j)] = \frac{M_2(X_i, X_j)}{M_1(X_i) M_1(X_j)}. \tag{S3.61}$$

Let $\{n\}_N$ denote a set of n variables selected from N variables $X_1, \ldots,$ X_N. Then we may proceed as outlined to obtain the expansion

$$K = \sum_{n=1}^{N} \sum_{\{n\}_N} K_n(\{n\}_N), \tag{S3.62}$$

where $K_n(\{n\}_N)$ is the collection of all terms involving the cumulants which contain any of the variables $\{n\}_N \equiv (X_{i_1}, \ldots, X_{i_n})$ at least once. The series (S3.62) converges since N is finite, and the convergence of the moments is assured. The same principle of rearrangement also applies to more complex cases where we have a hierarchy of functions $U(\{n\}_N)$, which are functions of n variables, $\{n\}_N = (X_{i_1}, \ldots,$ $X_{i_n})$ selected from a given set of N variables, $\{N\} = (X_1, \ldots, X_N)$. The analogs of the relations given are

$$M_n(\{n\}_N) = \langle \exp[U(\{n\}_N)] \rangle, \tag{S3.63}$$

$$M(\{N\}) = \langle \exp[U(\{N\})] \rangle = \exp[K(\{N\})], \tag{S3.64}$$

$$K(\{N\}) = \sum_{n=1}^{N} \sum_{\{n\}_N} K_n(\{n\}_N). \tag{S3.65}$$

We now seek to show that in the cluster expansion of a cumulant function, $K(\{N\})$, the cluster cumulant function $K_n(\{n\}_N)$ for a set of n variables is given explicitly by

$$K_n(\{n\}_N) = \sum_{l=1}^{N} (-)^{n-l} \sum_{\{l\}_n} \ln M_l(\{l\}_N), \tag{S3.66}$$

or, if n is even,

$$\exp[K_n(\{n\}_N)] = \frac{M_n(\{n\}_N)\prod M_{n-2}(\{n-2\}_N)\ldots\prod_{i<j} M_2(i,j)}{\prod M_{n-1}(\{n-1\}_N)\ldots\prod_i M_1(i)}; \quad \text{(S3.67)}$$

and, if n is odd,

$$\exp[K_n(\{n\}_N)] = M_n(\{n\}_N)\frac{\prod M_{n-2}(\{n-2\}_N)\ldots\prod_i M_1(i)}{\prod M_{n-1}(\{n-1\}_N)\ldots\prod_{i<j} M_2(i,j)}. \quad \text{(S3.68)}$$

In conformity with the notation introduced, $\{l\}_n$ is a set of l variables selected from the set $\{n\}_N$. To prove this, consider a set of variables, $\{n+1\}_N$. From the definition of K_n,

$$\begin{aligned}\ln M_{n+1}(\{n+1\}_N) &= \sum_{m=1}^{n+1}\sum_{\{m\}_{N+1}} K_m(\{m\}_N)\\ &= \sum_{m=1}^{n}\sum_{\{m\}_{N+1}} K_m(\{m\}_N)\\ &\quad + K_{n+1}(\{n+1\}_N).\end{aligned} \quad \text{(S3.69)}$$

Substitute (S3.66) into (S3.67) to give

$$\begin{aligned}K_{n+1}(\{n+1\}_N) &= \sum_{m=1}^{n}\sum_{\{m\}_{n+1}}\sum_{l=1}^{m}(-)^{m-l}\sum_{\{l\}_m}\ln M_l(\{l\}_N)\\ &\quad + \ln M_{n+1}(\{n+1\}_N).\end{aligned} \quad \text{(S3.70)}$$

On the right-hand side, collecting terms, the coefficient of $\ln M_l(\{l\}_N)$ is found to be

$$\begin{aligned}&1-\binom{n-l+1}{1}+\binom{n-l+1}{2}+\ldots\\ &\quad +(-)^{n-l}\binom{n-l+1}{n-l}\\ &= (1-1)^{n-l+1}-(-)^{n-l+1}=(-)^{n-l},\end{aligned} \quad \text{(S3.71)}$$

which verifies (S3.66).

An important property of cumulants can be demonstrated by considering the case where the set $\{n\}_N$ is divided into two independent sets, $\{n'\}_N$ and $\{n''\}_N$, such that

$$\{n\}_N = \{n'\}_N + \{n''\}_N . \tag{S3.72}$$

Then it is clear that (cf. eq. [S3.54])

$$M_n(\{n\}_N) = M_{n'}(\{n'\}_N) M_{n''}(\{n''\}_N), \tag{S3.73}$$

whereupon

$$K_n(\{n\}_N) \equiv K_{n'+n''}(\{n'+n''\}_N) = 0 , \tag{S3.74}$$

and, even more generally,

$$K_{m'+m''}(\{m'\}_{n'} + \{m''\}_{n''}) = 0 , \tag{S3.75}$$

provided that neither $\{m'\}_{n'}$ nor $\{m''\}_{n''}$ is empty. The proof that (S3.74) is valid follows directly from

$$\begin{aligned} &M_{n'+n''}(\{n\}_N) \\ &= \exp\Big[\sum_{m=1}^{n} \sum_{\{m'\}_{n'}} \sum_{\{m''\}_{n''}} K_{m=m'+m''}(\{m'\}_{n'} + \{m''\}_{n''})\Big] \\ &M_{n'}(\{n'\}_N) M_{n''}(\{n''\}_N) \\ &\qquad = \exp\Big[\sum_{m'=1}^{n'} \sum_{\{m'\}_{n'}} K_{m'}(\{m'\}_{n'})\Big] \\ &\qquad \times \exp\Big[\sum_{m''=1}^{n''} \sum_{\{m''\}_{n''}} K_{m''}(\{m''\}_{n''})\Big] . \end{aligned} \tag{S3.76}$$

The sum over m in the first line of equation (S3.76) contains contributions in which $\{m'\}_{n'}$ and $\{m''\}_{n''}$ may be empty, while in the second line we see that only terms for which neither $\{m'\}_{n'}$ nor $\{m''\}_{n''}$ are empty contribute. Equation (S3.75) then follows from a comparison with equation (S3.73).

S3.3.2. *The Mayer Cluster Theory.*—In general, a set of variables $\{n\}$ is called connected if there is no way of dividing it into two or more subsets $\{n'\}$, $\{n''\}$ such that (S3.73) is satisfied; otherwise it is called unconnected. The importance of the cumulant cluster expansion is that it consists only of connected cluster cumulant functions, since the unconnected ones vanish. This is the clearest demonstration of the physical content of the elaborate algebraic techniques used in the original derivation by Mayer. It is in the nature of the averaging process that unconnected clusters do not appear, and it is only because the older methods do not take advantage of this fact that elaborate analysis is required to establish it.

To demonstrate how the virial expansion follows easily from the cumulant averaging it is convenient to introduce a generalized exponential function. We define

$$\begin{aligned}\exp_L\left(\sum_{i=1}^{N} X_i\right) &= \sum_{n=0}^{\infty}\frac{1}{n!}L\left(\sum_{i=1}^{N} X_i\right)^n \\ &= 1+\sum_i X_i+\sum_{i,\,j} X_iX_j+\ldots \\ &\quad +\sum_{\{n\}_N} X_{i_1}\ldots X_{i_n}+\ldots \\ &= \prod_{i=1}^{N}(1+X_i).\end{aligned} \tag{S3.77}$$

The operation L is called leveling (and $\exp_L\,[\Sigma\, X_i]$ is called a leveled exponential) because, by definition, it levels off a product of X_i's by erasing those terms in which any X's appear with a power greater than unity. Obviously,

$$\begin{aligned}\exp_L\left(\sum_{i=1}^{N} X_i+\sum_{j=1}^{M} Y_j\right) \\ &= \exp_L\left(\sum_{i=1}^{N} X_i\right)\exp_L\left(\sum_{j=1}^{M} Y_j\right) \\ &= \prod_{i=1}^{N}(1+X_i)\prod_{j=1}^{M}(1+Y_j).\end{aligned} \tag{S3.78}$$

We also have the following example:

$$\left\langle \exp_L\left(\sum_{i=1}^{N}\xi_iX_i\right)\right\rangle = \exp\left\langle \exp_L\left(\sum_{i=1}^{N}\xi_iX_i\right)-1\right\rangle_c, \tag{S3.79}$$

using (S3.38). But

$$\left\langle \exp_L\left(\sum_{i=1}^{N}\xi_iX_i\right)\right\rangle = \exp\,[K(\xi)], \tag{S3.80}$$

whereupon

$$K(\xi) = {\sum_{\nu_1 \cdots \nu_N}}' \prod \frac{\xi_i^{\nu_i}}{\nu_i!} \langle LX_1^{\nu_1} \dots X_N^{\nu_N} \rangle_c, \quad (S3.81)$$

which leads to the explicit forms:

$$\langle LX_i \rangle_c = \langle X_i \rangle$$

$$\langle LX_i^2 \rangle_c = \langle LX_i^2 \rangle - \langle LX_i \rangle^2 = - \langle X_i \rangle^2$$

$$\langle LX_i^3 \rangle_c = \langle LX_i^3 \rangle - 3\langle LX_i^2 \rangle \langle LX_i \rangle + 2\langle LX_i \rangle^3$$

$$= 2\langle X_i \rangle^3 .$$

(S3.82)

In terms of the cluster cumulants,

$$\exp_L \left(\sum_{i=1}^N \xi_i X_i \right) = \prod_{i=1}^N \exp_L (\xi_i X_i) = \prod_{i=1}^N (1 + \xi_i X_i), \quad (S3.83)$$

and so

$$M_n(\{n\}_N) = \left\langle \prod_{\{n\}_N} (1 + \xi_i X_i) \right\rangle. \quad (S3.84)$$

Introducing equation (S3.66),

$$\left\langle \exp_L \left(\sum_{i=1}^N \xi_i X_i \right) \right\rangle = \exp (K_N) = \exp \left(\sum_{n=1}^N \sum_{\{n\}_N} K_n \right), \quad (S3.85)$$

where

$$K_1 = \sum_{j=1}^N \ln M_1(X_j)$$

$$= \sum_{j=1}^N \ln (1 + \xi_j \langle X_j \rangle)$$

$$= \sum_{j=1}^N \sum_{r=1}^\infty (-)^{r-1} \xi_j^r \frac{\langle X_j \rangle^r}{r} \quad (S3.86)$$

$$K_2 = \sum_{i,j=1}^N \ln \left[\frac{M_2(X_i, X_j)}{M_1(X_i)M_1(X_j)} \right]$$

$$= \sum_{i,j=1}^N \ln \left[1 + \frac{\xi_i \xi_j \langle X_i X_j \rangle}{(1 + \xi_i \langle X_i \rangle)(1 + \xi_j \langle X_j \rangle)} \right],$$

and so forth.

We are now ready to study the imperfect gas, once again. Consider the classical case for which we write (pairwise-additive potentials)

$$\begin{aligned}\exp[-\beta U(\{N\})] &= \exp\Big[-\beta\sum_{i<j} u(i,\ j)\Big]\\ &= \prod_{i<j=2}^{N}(1+f_{ij}) = \exp_L\Big(\sum_{i<j=2}^{N} f_{ij}\Big).\end{aligned} \tag{S3.87}$$

The interaction contribution to the configurational free energy, A'_N, is then, by (S3.80), just

$$\begin{aligned}-\beta A'_N &= \ln\langle\exp[-\beta U(\{N\})]\rangle\\ &= \ln\exp\Big\langle\exp_L\Big(\sum_{i<j=2}^{N} f_{ij}\Big)-1\Big\rangle_c\\ &= \Big\langle\exp_L\Big(\sum_{i<j=2}^{N} f_{ij}\Big)-1\Big\rangle_c.\end{aligned} \tag{S3.88}$$

The general term of the expansion has the form $\langle\Pi_{i<j=2}^{(n)} f_{ij}\rangle_c$, with the product over a specified set of bonds. The set of these bonds must be connected or the term vanishes (see eqs. [S3.73–74]). Now the set of bonds is unconnected unless the bonds connect all of the particles involved. What about the set of connected bonds? If n molecules are involved in the set of bonds,

$$\begin{aligned}\Big\langle\prod_{i<j=2}^{(n)} f_{ij}\Big\rangle_c &= V^{-N}\int\cdots\int\Big(\prod^{(n)} f_{ij}\Big)_c d\{N\}\\ &= V^{-n}\int\cdots\int\Big(\prod^{(n)} f_{ij}\Big)_c d\{n\}\\ &= V^{-n+1}\int\cdots\int\Big(\prod^{(n)} f_{ij}\Big)_c d\{n-1\},\end{aligned} \tag{S3.89}$$

where we have introduced the definition of the average, and, in the last term, changed to relative coordinates and integrated over the volume V. Equations (S3.88) and (S3.89) lead to

$$-\beta A'_N = \sum_{n=1}^{N-1}\binom{N}{n+1}\sum_{(C_{n+1})}\Big\langle\prod^{(n+1)} f_{ij}\Big\rangle_c, \tag{S3.90}$$

where $\binom{N}{n+1}$ is the number of arrangements of N molecules in groups of $(n+1)$, and the sum is over all graphs of $(n+1)$ labeled points, each of which is connected to at least two others. Taking the limit $N \to \infty$, $V \to \infty$, $(N/V) = \rho =$ constant, we have

$$-\beta A'_N = N \sum_{n=1} \frac{\beta_n}{n+1} \rho^n, \tag{S3.91}$$

where the irreducible cluster integral β_n is defined by (cf. eq. [S3.17])

$$\sum_{(C_{n+1})} \left\langle \prod^{(n+1)} f_{ij} \right\rangle_c = \frac{n!}{V^n} \beta_n. \tag{S3.92}$$

With the usual thermodynamic relation between p' and A'_N, it is found that

$$p' = -\left(\frac{\partial A'_N}{\partial V}\right)_{N\ T} = -\rho k T \sum_{n=1} \frac{n}{n+1} \beta_n \rho^n, \tag{S3.93}$$

which is in agreement with (S3.18).

S3.4. Some Topological Arguments [4]

In previous sections we have established a relationship between the thermodynamic properties of a fluid and a set of defined irreducible integrals. For the classical case, where the total intermolecular potential is pairwise decomposable and there is a one to one mapping of the various interaction terms, we have seen that

$$\beta p V = V\left[z + \sum_{N=2}^{\infty} \frac{z^N}{N!} \left(\sum_{\substack{\text{(all clusters} \\ \text{of } n \text{ molecules)}}} \int \ldots \int \prod f_{ij} d\{N\} \right)\right], \tag{S3.94}$$

where the second summation on the right is over all products Πf_{ij} whose corresponding graph is a cluster, i.e., a connected graph in which no pair of points is joined by more than one line. We now wish to consider the topological properties of these clusters and examine how they may be reduced to the irreducible clusters. This argument is inserted here because of its role in the method of summation of infinite subclasses of terms in series defined by diagrams. It is just these summation techniques that have proven very useful in recent theories of the liquid state.

To proceed we must introduce some definitions and concepts from the theory of linear graphs. Consider the following graphs:

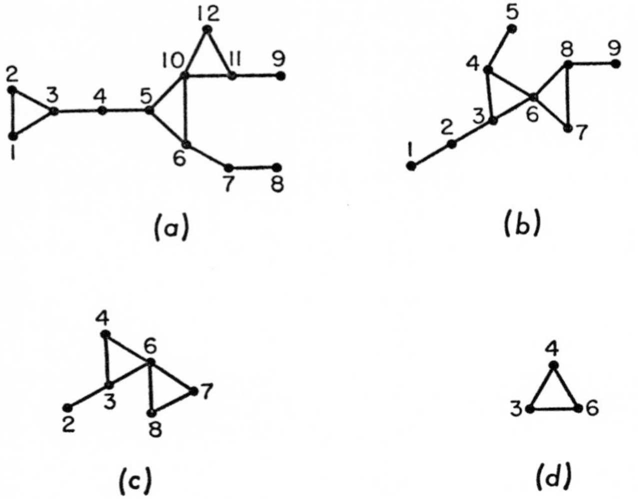

(S3.95)

i) Points such as 10 in equation (S3.95a) are called articulation points. The removal of 10, and all lines connected to it, severs the graph into two disjoint parts. Note that this is not true of 12, which is, therefore, not an articulation point.

ii) A connected graph without articulation points is called a star [e.g., the groups (10, 11, 12) or (4, 5), considered as isolated from the other points].

iii) An arbitrary cluster is divided by its articulation points into a collection of stars. For example, in (S3.95b) the articulation points are 2, 3, 4, 6, and 8. These divide the diagram into the stars (1, 2), (2, 3), (3, 4, 6), (4, 5), (6, 7, 8), and (8, 9).

iv) Because of (iii) any cluster can be considered to be a collection of stars joined together at articulation points. From this point of view the cluster is called a star tree. A star tree with some point singled out is called a rooted star tree, and the cited point is called the root. A star tree may have a number of disjoint branches except for the root. In equation (S3.95b), if 3 is designated as the root, we obtain a rooted tree with the branches (1, 2, 3) and (3, 4, 5, 6, 7, 8, 9).

A cluster may be subdivided in a number of different ways into stars, rooted star trees, and branches at articulation points. For each such subdivision the corresponding integral can be written as a product of integrals referring to the component stars, rooted star trees, and branches. The integral over the integrand represented by (S3.95b) is then

$$\int f_{12}f_{23}f_{34}f_{36}f_{45}f_{46}f_{67}f_{68}f_{78}f_{89}d\{9\} = V\int d(1)f_{12}\int d(2)f_{23}\int d(5)$$
$$\times f_{45}\int d(9)f_{89}\int d(3)d(4)f_{34}f_{36}f_{46}\int d(7)d(8)f_{67}f_{68}f_{78},$$

with the factor V arising from $d(6)$. Alternatively, this same integral may be written as the product of an integral referring to one of the stars, and integrals referring to each one of the rooted star trees, which are attached to this star through articulation points. For example,

$$\int f_{12}f_{23}f_{34}f_{36}f_{45}f_{46}f_{67}f_{68}f_{78}f_{89}d\{9\} = V\int d(1)d(2)f_{12}f_{23}\int d(5)$$
$$\times f_{45}\int d(3)d(4)f_{34}f_{36}f_{46}\int d(7)d(8)d(9)f_{67}f_{68}f_{78}f_{89},$$

where, again, the factor V arises from $d(6)$.

We shall now prove that it is possible to express pV in terms of integrals referring only to stars.

Consider equation (S3.95b). The three stars (8, 9), (4, 5), and (1, 2) are attached to the remainder of the graph by only one articulation point. If these stars are removed, we obtain (S3.95c). Now (S3.95c) has two stars [(2, 3) and (6, 7, 8)] each attached by only one articulation point. Removing these stars leads to the graphs of equation (S3.95d). Thus, (S3.95b) can be considered to be constructed from the fundamental star (3, 4, 6) by the attachment of the rooted trees (*3*, 2, 1), (*4*, 5), and (*6*, 7, 8, 9) where the italicized point is the root. The process of successive removal of all stars attached at only one point is called the reduction process. All stars containing a single articulation point must be completed before the new graph is examined and the reduction process repeated. The application of the reduction process to (S3.95a) yields, not a fundamental star, but rather a fundamental point, which in this case is 5. It is easily seen that the application of the reduction process to an arbitrary cluster will yield, after a finite number of steps, either a fundamental star or a fundamental point. Any graph can, therefore, be considered to be built of a fundamental star with a number of attached rooted trees, or of a number of branches joined at a fundamental point.

What distinguishes a fundamental star or a fundamental point from all other stars and points in the graph? Define the order of a rooted star tree as follows: The order of a rooted star tree is the number of steps in the reduction process required to reduce it to a point. Then the following theorem is easily proved: All clusters can be divided into two disjoint classes: those with a unique fundamental point and those with a unique fundamental star. If a graph has a fundamental point, no branch attached to this point has an order greater than the rest. If a graph has a fundamental star, no rooted star tree attached to this star has an order greater than the rest.

The theorem is proved by assuming a violation and deducing a contradiction. Suppose, for example, that a graph with a fundamental star has an attached rooted star tree, of order n, greater than the order of all the others. After $n - 1$ steps in the reduction process, all the other rooted star trees will have been reduced to points, while the given one will have been reduced to one or more stars attached to the fundamental star at one point. If this is so, however, one further application of the reduction process should result in a point. This contradicts the hypothesis that the graph has a fundamental star. A similar argument applies to the case of the fundamental point.

We can now proceed to examine the connected diagrams of the integrand of equation (S3.94). Consider some cluster term which has a fundamental star σ and attached rooted star trees, $\tau_1, \ldots, \tau_r$. Let m be the number of points in σ and let $m_1, \ldots, m_r$ be the number of points besides the root in $\tau_1, \ldots, \tau_r$. The total number of points is $N = m + m_1 + \ldots + m_r$. Of course, there are a number of clusters which differ from the selected cluster only in the labeling. All of these clusters make the same contribution to pV, and computation of the contribution of all clusters is identical except for labeling.

Let the fundamental star be labeled $1, 2, \ldots, m$, and let $\tau_1, \ldots, \tau_r$ be labeled with integers from the sets $\{m_1\}, \ldots, \{m_r\}$. The sum over all labelings of the selected graph is the sum over all labelings which do not interchange labels among σ and $\tau_1, \ldots, \tau_r$, multiplied by the number of ways of choosing sets of $m, m_1, \ldots, m_r$ integers out of N integers. Thus, the total contribution of this cluster is

$$\frac{z^N}{N!}\frac{N!}{m!m_1!\ldots m_r!}\sum_{\substack{\text{(all labelings of } \sigma \\ \text{with integers from} \\ 1\ldots m)}}\int\prod f_{ij}d\{m\}$$

$$\times\prod_{s=1}^{r}\sum_{\substack{\text{(all labelings of } \tau_s \\ \text{with integers from} \\ 1\ldots m_s)}}\int\prod f_{ij}d\{m_s\}. \tag{S3.96}$$

There are, of course, $N!$ different labelings of any particular N-point graph. Equation (S3.96) represents the decomposition for a graph of the structure described. Consider now all clusters which have the same fundamental star. All such clusters can be built up by attaching various collections of trees to the points of the star, but the way in which the trees are added is restricted by the requirement that at any stage at least two must be of the same order. Consider now the *definition*

$$\rho = z + \sum_{N\geq 1} \frac{z^{N+1}}{N!} \sum_{\substack{\text{(all rooted star trees}\\ \text{with root 1 from points}\\ 2,\dots,N+1)}} \times \int \prod f_{ij} d(2)\dots d(N+1), \tag{S3.97}$$

where z arises only when no rooted star tree is attached to σ. We now define a quantity Σ by

$$V\Sigma = \sum_{m=2}^{\infty} \frac{\rho^m}{m!} \sum_{\substack{\text{(all stars of}\\ m \text{ points)}}} \int \prod f_{ij} d\{m\}. \tag{S3.98}$$

Σ contains all possible clusters built up by adding m rooted star trees of any order to fundamental stars of order m. For all terms in which the highest order rooted star tree occurs only once, the requirement of dependence cited is violated; in other words, such terms refer to *different* fundamental stars. Consequently Σ contains many clusters more than once. Since we have added trees independently, the sum of products in (S3.98) is equal to the product of the sums. Now, there is a one to one correspondence between labeled rooted star trees with root one formed from $N+1$ points and labeled clusters formed from $N+1$ points. From the definition of the Grand Partition Function (eqs. [S2.15] and [S3.2]), we have

$$\langle N \rangle = \frac{\partial \ln \Xi}{\partial \ln z}$$

$$= V\left[z + \sum_{N\geq 1} \frac{z^{N+1}}{N!} \sum_{\substack{\text{(all clusters of}\\ N+1 \text{ molecules)}}} \times \int \prod f_{ij} d(2)\dots d(N+1) \right]; \tag{S3.99}$$

and, therefore, from equations (S3.97) and (S3.99),

$$\rho = \frac{\langle N \rangle}{V}, \tag{S3.100}$$

so that ρ is just the average density.

We now must examine the overcounted terms. The contributions to be subtracted are those from clusters formed from σ (now no longer the fundamental star of the cluster) by attaching a number of rooted star trees, one of which has greater order than the rest. If s is the articulation point at which the tree of largest order (τ_s) is attached to σ, the remaining trees $\tau_i (i \neq s)$ together with σ form a branch β. The contributions to be subtracted from those clusters are formed by joining a branch of order p to a rooted star tree of order q, with $p \leq q$.

Consider now the contributions to pV from clusters with fundamental points. These are formed by attaching a number of branches at a point, taking care that at least two branches have orders greater than the rest (and equal to each other). The contribution of all clusters constructed from a fundamental point without the above restriction is

$$z + \sum_{N \geq 1} \frac{z^{N+1}}{N!} \sum_{\substack{\text{(all clusters} \\ \text{constructed by} \\ \text{adding branches} \\ \text{to one point)}}} \int \prod f_{ij} d(2) \ldots d(N+1), \tag{S3.101}$$

which, by virtue of (S3.97) is just ρ.

The only contribution to be subtracted (the overcounted terms) is that from clusters formed by joining one or more branches ($\beta_1, \beta_2, \ldots, \beta_s$) to a common root, such that one, say β_s, has order p greater than the rest. The remaining branches, $\beta_i (i \neq s)$, form a tree of order q, with $q < p$. The case when β_s is the only tree must also be included. If we call a point a tree of order zero, the overcounted contributions arise from joining a rooted star tree of order q and a branch of order p with $p > q \geq 0$. The overcounted configurations from both types of clusters comprise contributions from all graphs formed by joining a branch and a tree to a common root, with no restrictions on the order of the branch or the rooted tree. A given cluster appears in this collection as many times as the number of ways it can be constructed by attaching a tree and a branch at a common root.

Consider a particular cluster formed by joining a particular branch β, with a root 1 and remaining points labeled $2, \ldots, N+1$, and a particular tree τ, with a root 1 and remaining points labeled $N+2, \ldots, N+M+1$. The contribution of this cluster together with all distinct clusters formed by permutation of labels among points within the rooted star tree and branch may be written

$$\begin{aligned} V & \sum_{\substack{\text{(all labelings of} \\ \beta \text{ with integers} \\ 2, \ldots, N+1)}} \int \prod f_{ij} d(2) \ldots d(N+1) \\ \times & \sum_{\substack{\text{(all labelings of} \\ \tau \text{ with integers} \\ N+2, \ldots, N+M+1)}} \int \prod f_{ij} d(N+2) \ldots d(N+M+1). \end{aligned} \tag{S3.102}$$

(Note that integration over $d(1)$ leads to the factor V.) Multiply by the number of ways of choosing N integers to label the points of the branch, M integers to label the points of the rooted star tree, and one integer to label the common root; sum over all branches and rooted star trees. The result is

$$V\sum_{N\geq 1}^{\infty}\frac{z^N}{N!}\sum_{(\text{all branches})}\int\prod f_{ij}d(2)\dots d(N+1)$$
$$\times\left[z+\sum_{M\geq 1}^{\infty}\frac{z^{M+1}}{M!}\sum_{\substack{(\text{all rooted star trees with}\\ \text{root 1 and other points}\\ N+2,\dots,N+M+1)}}\right. \qquad (S3.103)$$
$$\left.\times\int\prod f_{ij}d(N+2)\dots d(N+M+1)\right].$$

Note that the term z comes from the rooted star trees of order zero and the factorials from the combinatorial factors. Now, every branch can be represented in one and only one way, as a rooted star with a number of rooted star trees attached at points other than the root. Therefore, the first factor in (S3.103) is seen to be equivalent to the series

$$\sum_{N\geq 1}^{\infty}\frac{\rho^N}{N!}\sum_{\substack{(\text{all rooted stars}\\ \text{with root 1 and}\\ \text{points }2,\dots,N+1)}}\int\prod f_{ij}d(2)\dots d(N+1), \qquad (S3.104)$$

whereas the second factor is just ρ, by (S3.97). Noting the change in summation, (S3.104) is seen to be the derivative of (S3.98) with respect to ρ. Setting (S3.98) equal to $V\Sigma$ we finally have, for the equation of state,

$$\beta p V = V\left(\Sigma+\rho-\rho\,\frac{\partial\Sigma}{\partial\rho}\right). \qquad (S3.105)$$

By noting that

$$-\rho^2\frac{\partial}{\partial\rho}\left(\frac{\Sigma}{\rho}\right)=\Sigma-\rho\,\frac{\partial\Sigma}{\partial\rho}, \qquad (S3.106)$$

we return to the familiar relationship

$$\beta p=\rho-V\sum_{m=2}^{\infty}\frac{m-1}{m!}\,\rho^m\sum_{\substack{(\text{all stars}\\ \text{with }m\\ \text{points})}}\int\prod f_{ij}d\{m\}. \qquad (S3.107)$$

The relabeling $\nu = m - 1$, and the definition

$$\beta_\nu = \frac{1}{\nu! V} \int \sum_{\substack{\text{(stars with} \\ \nu+1 \text{ points)}}} \prod f_{ij} d\{\nu\}, \qquad \text{(S3.108)}$$

leads to

$$\beta p = \rho - \sum_{\nu=1}^{\infty} \frac{\nu}{\nu+1} \beta_\nu \rho^\nu, \qquad \text{(S3.109)}$$

a form more familiar than equation (S3.105).

S4. DISTRIBUTION FUNCTIONS [1]

The goal of the statistical theory of matter is the formulation of relationships between the macroscopic properties of matter and the presumed known properties of the molecules composing the system. For the case of the imperfect gas we have shown how the equation of state can be represented in terms of the contributions from isolated molecules, isolated pairs of molecules, isolated triplets of molecules, etc. This sequential analysis of the effect of intermolecular interactions is best suited to the discussion of a dilute system (such as a gas) but becomes relatively intractable for dense systems. For this reason, we now discuss an alternative representation of the molecular-statistical properties of matter. Instead of analyzing the equation of state in terms of the additive effects of groups of isolated molecules, we seek a description of the behavior of small groups of molecules which are in interaction with the remainder of the system. We are thereby led to the study of molecular distribution functions.

S4.1. Definitions

S4.1.1. *Canonical Ensemble.*—Consider a closed system containing N molecules. We denote by $\rho_N^{(n)}(\{n\})d\{n\}$ the probability of finding a molecule in $d\mathbf{R}_1$ at $\mathbf{R}_1$, another in $d\mathbf{R}_2$ at $\mathbf{R}_2$, . . . , and another in $d\mathbf{R}_n$ at $\mathbf{R}_n$, irrespective of where the remaining $N - n$ molecules are located. The function $\rho_N^{(n)}(\{n\})$ is defined by

$$\rho_N^{(n)}(\{n\}) = \frac{N!}{(N-n)!} \frac{\int \ldots \int \exp[-\beta U(\{N\})] d\{N-n\}}{Z_N}, \qquad \text{(S4.1)}$$

where Z_N is given by equations (S2.23) and (S3.3):

$$Z_N = \int \ldots \int \exp[-\beta U(\{N\})] d\{N\}. \qquad \text{(S4.2)}$$

The factor $[N!/(N-n)!] = \binom{N}{n} n!$ is the number of ways of placing n molecules selected from N in $d\{n\}$. The $\rho_N^{(n)}$ is known as the generic-probability density, or distribution function, where the term generic implies that the molecules at the positions in the argument of $\rho_N{}^{(n)}$ are not specifically chosen. From (S4.1) we have

$$\int \ldots \int \rho_N^{(n)}(\{n\})\, d\{n\} = \frac{N!}{(N-n)!}. \qquad (S4.3)$$

In particular,

$$\int \rho_N^{(1)} d(1) = N, \qquad \int \rho_N^{(2)} d(1)\, d(2) = N(N-1). \qquad (S4.4)$$

We may define a completely random distribution in the limit for which $T \rightarrow \infty$, or alternatively, in the limit in which the system is so dilute that the most likely configurations are those for which the molecules are widely enough separated that $\beta U(\{N\}) = 0$. For this case,

$$Z_N = V^N,$$

so that

$$\rho_N^{(n)} = \frac{1}{V^n} \frac{N!}{(N-n)!} = \rho^n \frac{N!}{N^n (N-n)!}, \qquad (S4.5)$$

with

$$\rho_N^{(1)} = \rho = \frac{N}{V}, \qquad \rho_N^{(2)} = \frac{N(N-1)}{V^2} = \rho^2 \left(1 - \frac{1}{N}\right). \qquad (S4.6)$$

S4.1.2. *Correlation Functions.*—Because of molecular interactions, no real system exhibits a random distribution in configuration space. We define $g_N^{(n)}$, the correlation function corresponding to an n-molecule generic distribution function, by

$$\rho_N^{(n)} = \left[\prod_{i=1}^{n} \rho_N^{(1)}(i)\right] g_N^{(n)}(\{n\}). \qquad (S4.7)$$

Clearly, these functions represent the extent to which the distributions of n molecules are not completely random. The normalization properties of $g_N^{(n)}$ are such that

$$\int \ldots \int g_N^{(n)} d\{n\} = \frac{V^n}{N^n} \frac{N!}{(N-n)!} = V^n \left[1 + O\left(\frac{1}{N}\right)\right]. \qquad (S4.8)$$

In particular,

$$g_N^{(1)} = 1 \, . \tag{S4.9}$$

From (S4.4) we see that

$$\int g_N^{(2)} d(1) d(2) = V^2 \left(1 - \frac{1}{N}\right). \tag{S4.10}$$

For a fluid, the pair distribution is spherically symmetric, so that

$$\begin{aligned} \rho_N^{(2)}(\boldsymbol{R}_1, \boldsymbol{R}_2) &= \rho_N^{(2)}(R_{12}), \\ g_N^{(2)}(\boldsymbol{R}_1, \boldsymbol{R}_2) &= g_N^{(2)}(R_{12}), \end{aligned} \tag{S4.11}$$

whereupon equation (S4.10) may be integrated over $\boldsymbol{R}_1$, and over the angular part of $\boldsymbol{R}_{12}$, to give

$$4\pi \rho \int g_N^{(2)}(R_{12}) R_{12}^2 dR_{12} = N - 1 \, , \tag{S4.12}$$

which shows that $g_N^{(2)}$ appears in the role of the experimental radial distribution function $g(R_{12})$. For this reason, we shall sometimes denote it without either the superscript or subscript.

S4.1.3. *Grand Canonical Ensemble.*—If the system is open, the generic distribution function for n molecules, $\rho^{(n)}$, is the average of (S4.1) over systems containing n or more molecules. That is,

$$\rho^{(n)} = \sum_{N \geq n} \rho_N^{(n)} P_N(V, T), \tag{S4.13}$$

where P_N is defined by

$$\sum_{N \geq 0} P_N(V, T) = 1 \, .$$

From sections S2.1 and S2.2 we see that

$$\begin{aligned} P_N(V, T) &= \sum_k P(E_k, V, N) \\ &= \Xi^{-1} \left(\frac{Vz}{Q_1}\right)^N Q_N \\ &= \frac{z^N Z_N}{\Xi N!}, \end{aligned} \tag{S4.14}$$

whence

$$\rho^{(n)} = \frac{1}{\Xi} \sum_{N \geq n} \frac{z^N}{(N-n)!} \int \ldots \int \exp[-\beta U(\{N\})] \, d\{N-n\}. \tag{S4.15}$$

Equation (S4.13), or (S4.15) with (S4.3), leads to the normalization relation

$$\int \rho^{(n)} d\{n\} = \sum_{N \geq n} \frac{N!}{(N-n)!} P_N = \left\langle \frac{N!}{(N-n)!} \right\rangle . \quad \text{(S4.16)}$$

Thus,

$$\int \rho^{(1)} d(1) = \langle N \rangle , \quad \text{(S4.17)}$$

so that

$$\rho^{(1)} = \rho = \frac{\langle N \rangle}{V} . \quad \text{(S4.18)}$$

Also,

$$\int \rho^{(2)} d(1) d(2) = \langle N^2 \rangle - \langle N \rangle . \quad \text{(S4.19)}$$

Equation (S4.19) is important in the discussion of thermodynamic properties in the next section. Note the general differences between equations (S4.16–19) and the corresponding equations for the Canonical Ensemble, in that the latter relations do not involve averages.

In the limit that the system becomes large with z and T fixed, that is $V \to \infty$, $\langle N \rangle \to \infty$, while $\langle N \rangle / V = \rho =$ constant, the two sets of equations become identical. This is because the probability distribution for N becomes very sharply peaked about $\langle N \rangle$ (it can be shown that the relative width $\propto \langle N \rangle^{-1} [\langle N^2 \rangle - \langle N \rangle^2]^{1/2} \sim \langle N \rangle^{-1/2}$), so that effectively only one value of N, namely $\langle N \rangle$, is found. Then (S4.16) may be written

$$\int \rho^{(n)} d\{n\} = \langle N^n \rangle \left[1 + O\left(\frac{1}{\langle N \rangle} \right) \right] . \quad \text{(S4.20)}$$

For a completely random distribution, we may write $\beta U(\{N\}) = 0$, and find that

$$\rho^{(n)} = z^n = \rho^n . \quad \text{(S4.21)}$$

This result differs from those for the Canonical Ensemble, (S4.5–6), in that no terms of $O(1/\langle N \rangle)$ appear.

S4.1.4. *Correlation Functions.*—The correlation function $g^{(n)}$ may be defined analogously to equation (S4.7) by

$$\rho^{(n)} = \rho^n g^{(n)} , \quad \text{(S4.22)}$$

so that

$$\int g^{(n)} d\{n\} = \frac{V^n}{\langle N \rangle^n} \left\langle \frac{N!}{(N-n)!} \right\rangle , \quad \text{(S4.23)}$$

and in the limit $\langle N \rangle$, $V \to \infty$ while z and T remain constant,

$$\lim_{\langle N \rangle, V \to \infty} \int g^{(n)} d\{n\} = V^n . \quad \text{(S4.24)}$$

If we rewrite (S4.15) as

$$\rho^{(n)} = \frac{z^n}{\Xi} \sum_{N \geq n} \frac{z^{N-n}}{(N-n)!} \int \ldots \int \exp[-\beta U(\{N\})] d\{N-n\}$$

$$= \frac{z^n}{\Xi} \sum_{m \geq 0} \frac{z^m}{m!} \int \ldots \int \exp[-\beta U(\{n+m\})] d\{m\}, \qquad (S4.25)$$

it is seen that, in the limit of infinite dilution, $z \to \rho \to 0$, and

$$\rho^{(n)} = \rho^n \exp[-\beta U(\{n\})],$$
$$g^{(n)} = \exp[-\beta U(\{n\})]. \qquad (S4.26)$$

We shall have occasion to use these results later.

S4.2. Thermodynamic Properties of a Fluid

We shall now examine the representation of the thermodynamic properties of a fluid in terms of the molecular distribution functions. This representation has a compact form and is an exact and rigorous alternative to the virial expansion formalism.

It is convenient to start with the normalization conditions, (S4.19), written for the two-body distribution function. These are

$$\int \rho^{(2)}(1, 2) d(1) d(2) = \langle N^2 \rangle - \langle N \rangle, \qquad (S4.27)$$

$$\int \rho^{(1)}(1) \rho^{(1)}(2) d(1) d(2) = \langle N \rangle^2. \qquad (S4.28)$$

By subtracting (S4.28) from (S4.27), we obtain

$$\int [\rho^{(2)}(1, 2) - \rho^{(1)}(1) \rho^{(1)}(2)] d(1) d(2)$$
$$= \langle N^2 \rangle - \langle N \rangle^2 - \langle N \rangle. \qquad (S4.29)$$

To evaluate the right-hand side of (S4.29), we return to the definition of the Grand Partition Function. It is easily seen from (S3.2) that

$$\langle N \rangle = \frac{1}{\Xi} \sum_{N \geq 0} N \frac{z^N}{N!} Z_N = \frac{\partial \ln \Xi}{\partial \ln z}, \qquad (S4.30)$$

$$\langle N^2 \rangle = \frac{1}{\Xi} \sum_{N \geq 0} N^2 \frac{z^N}{N!} Z_N = \frac{1}{\Xi} \frac{\partial^2}{\partial \ln z^2} \Xi. \qquad (S4.31)$$

Examination of equations (S4.30) and (S4.31) also shows that

$$\langle N^2 \rangle - \langle N \rangle^2 = \frac{\partial \langle N \rangle}{\partial \ln z} = kT \left(\frac{\partial \langle N \rangle}{\partial \mu} \right)_{T\,V}, \qquad (S4.32)$$

where the last term on the right-hand side of (S4.32) is obtained when it is noted that

$$\mu = kT \ln z + \text{const}\,, \qquad (S4.33)$$
$$(d\mu)_{T\,V} = (kTd \ln z)_{T,V}\,.$$

Now we note that, from (S2.11) and (S3.2),

$$\left(\frac{\partial p}{\partial \mu}\right)_{V,T} = \frac{kT}{V}\cdot\frac{1}{kT}\frac{\partial \ln \Xi}{\partial \ln z} = \frac{\langle N\rangle}{V} = \rho\,, \qquad (S4.34)$$

and thereby

$$\left(\frac{\partial^2 p}{\partial \mu^2}\right)_T = \left(\frac{\partial \rho}{\partial \mu}\right)_T = \left(\frac{\partial \rho}{\partial p}\right)_T\left(\frac{\partial p}{\partial \mu}\right)_T = \rho^2\kappa\,, \qquad (S4.35)$$

where κ is the isothermal compressibility. Using the methods described in equations (S4.30) and (S4.31), we find

$$VkT\left(\frac{\partial^2 p}{\partial \mu^2}\right)_T = \langle N^2\rangle - \langle N\rangle^2 = \rho^2\kappa VkT\,. \qquad (S4.36)$$

Equation (S4.31), when divided by $\langle N\rangle = \rho V$, gives

$$\frac{1}{\rho V}\int[\rho^{(2)} - \rho^{(1)2}]\,d(1)\,d(2) = \frac{\langle N^2\rangle - \langle N\rangle^2}{\langle N\rangle} - 1 \qquad (S4.37)$$
$$= \rho\kappa kT - 1\,.$$

Equation (S4.37) is an equation of state, i.e., a connection between p, V, T and the molecular distribution function. If we introduce the pair correlation function, $g^{(2)}$,

$$4\pi\rho\int_0^\infty [g^{(2)}(R) - 1]R^2dR = \rho\kappa kT - 1\,. \qquad (S4.38)$$

To compute the internal energy, $\langle U\rangle$, we use the thermodynamic relation

$$\langle U\rangle = \langle N\rangle\mu + TS - pV$$
$$= \langle N\rangle\mu + kT^2\left(\frac{\partial \ln \Xi}{\partial T}\right)_{V\,\mu}. \qquad (S4.39)$$

Straightforward evaluation of the derivative of Ξ leads to

$$\left(\frac{\partial \Xi}{\partial T}\right)_{V,\mu} = \frac{1}{kT^2}\sum_{N\geq 2}\frac{z^N}{N!}\int U(\{N\})\exp[-\beta U(\{N\})]\,d\{N\}$$
$$+\sum_{N\geq 0}\frac{z^N}{N!}\left(\frac{3\langle N\rangle}{2T} - \frac{\langle N\rangle\mu}{kT^2}\right)Z_N\,, \qquad (S4.40)$$

where the first summation excludes $N = 0$, $N = 1$ because $U(\{N\}) = 0$, for $N = 0$ and $N = 1$. Since there are $\frac{1}{2}N(N-1)$ equivalent terms in the integral of (S4.40),

$$kT^2\left(\frac{\partial}{\partial T}\ln \Xi\right)_{V\cdot\mu} = \frac{1}{\Xi}\int u(1,2)\Bigg[\sum_{N\geq 2}\frac{z^N}{N!}\frac{N(N-1)}{2} \times \int \exp[-\beta U(\{N\})]\,d\{N-2\}\Bigg]d(1)\,d(2) + \tfrac{3}{2}\langle N\rangle kT - \langle N\rangle \mu . \quad \text{(S4.41)}$$

Using the definitions (S4.15) and (S4.22) easily leads to

$$\begin{aligned}\frac{\langle U\rangle}{\langle N\rangle kT} &= \frac{3}{2} + \frac{\rho}{2kT}\int u(R)\,g^{(2)}(R)\,d\mathbf{R} \\ &= \frac{3}{2} + \frac{2\pi\rho}{kT}\int_0^\infty u(R)\,g^{(2)}(R)R^2 dR,\end{aligned} \quad \text{(S4.42)}$$

expressing the internal energy in terms of the pair correlation function. Although (S4.37) is valid irrespective of the form of $U(\{N\})$, (S4.42) depends on the assumption that $U(\{N\})$ may be represented as the sum of pairwise-additive interaction potentials.

In order to obtain an expression for the pressure we use the relation

$$\left[\frac{\partial}{\partial V}(\beta p V)\right]_{z\,T} = \left(\frac{\partial}{\partial V}\ln \Xi\right)_{z.T} = \beta p, \quad \text{(S4.43)}$$

in which we have used $(\partial p/\partial V)_{z,T} = 0$, which follows because z, T are the two independent thermodynamic variables required to completely determine the state of a system. In differentiating Ξ the variation of the limits of the configuration integral Z_N must be treated carefully. If we are prepared to restrict our calculation to systems large enough that the pressure does not sensibly depend on the shape of the container (this is indeed a weak restriction for most purposes!), it may be assumed that the gas is enclosed in a cubical box of side $V^{1/3}$. It is then possible to render the variables of integration dimensionless by the substitution of $\mathbf{R} = V^{1/3}\mathbf{R}'$, where the range of $\mathbf{R}'$ is $(0, 0, 0) \leq \mathbf{R}' \leq (1, 1, 1)$. The potential now depends explicitly on V, so that

$$Z_N = V^N \int_0^1\!\cdots\!\int \exp[-\beta U(\{N\})]\,d\{N'\} \quad \text{(S4.44)}$$

and

$$\left(\frac{\partial Z_N}{\partial V}\right)_{z\cdot T} = \frac{N}{V}Z_N - \beta V^N \int_0^1\!\cdots\!\int \frac{\partial U}{\partial V}\exp[-\beta U(\{N\})]\,d\{N'\}, \quad \text{(S4.45)}$$

where

$$\{N'\} = (\mathbf{R}'_1, \ldots, \mathbf{R}'_N).$$

Since

$$\begin{aligned}\frac{\partial U}{\partial V} &= \sum_{i=1}^{N} \frac{\partial \mathbf{R}_i}{\partial V} \cdot \nabla_i U \\ &= \frac{1}{3V} \sum_{i=1}^{N} \mathbf{R}_i \cdot \nabla_i U ,\end{aligned} \tag{S4.46}$$

we now have, from (S4.43),

$$\begin{aligned}\beta p &= \frac{1}{\Xi} \sum_{N \geq 0} \frac{z^N}{N!} \Bigg[\frac{N Z_N}{V} \\ &\quad - \frac{\beta}{3V} \sum_{i=1}^{N} \int \ldots \int (\mathbf{R}_i \cdot \nabla_i U) \exp(-\beta U)\, d\{N\} \Bigg] \\ &= \frac{\langle N \rangle}{V} - \frac{\beta}{3V} \left\langle \sum_{i=1}^{N} \mathbf{R}_i \cdot \nabla_i U \right\rangle_{\text{config}} .\end{aligned} \tag{S4.47}$$

The average used in the second term of (S4.47) is seen from the previous line to be a combination of a configurational average and an average in the Grand Canonical Ensemble. If the potential is pairwise decomposable, equation (S4.46) gives rise to $\frac{1}{2}N(N-1)$ similar terms of the form

$$\frac{\beta}{3V} \mathbf{R}_i \cdot \nabla_i u(i, j),$$

so that

$$\begin{aligned}&\frac{\beta}{3V\Xi} \sum_{N \geq 0} \frac{z^N}{N!} \sum_{i=1}^{N} \int \ldots \int (\mathbf{R}_i \cdot \nabla_i U) \exp(-\beta U)\, d\{N\} \\ &\quad = \frac{\beta}{6V} \int\int R u'(R) \Bigg[\frac{1}{\Xi} \sum_{N \geq 0} \frac{z^N}{N!} N(N-1) \int \ldots \int \\ &\qquad \times \exp(-\beta U)\, d\{N-2\} \Bigg] d(1)\, d(2) \\ &\quad = \frac{2\pi\beta\rho^2}{3} \int_0^\infty u'(R)\, g^{(2)}(R) R^3 dR .\end{aligned} \tag{S4.48}$$

Finally, from (S4.47–48), we have

$$p = \rho k T - \frac{2\pi\rho^2}{3} \int_0^\infty u'(R)\, g^{(2)}(R) R^3 dR . \tag{S4.49}$$

This form of the equation of state will prove useful in section S7.

S4.3. A Relationship between the Pair Distribution Function and the Free Energy [5]

There is an interesting relationship between the pair distribution function and the free energy. To develop this relationship, we need to consider the notion of functional differentiation. Consider the following definitions:

a) z is a functional of the function $x(t)$ in the interval (a, b), when it depends on all the values taken by $x(t)$, t varying in the interval (a, b); or alternatively, when a relation is given by which, to every function $x(t)$ defined on the interval (a, b), there can be made to correspond one and only one quantity z, completely determined. A convenient notation is

$$z = F\,[\overset{b}{\underset{a}{x(t)}}]. \tag{S4.50}$$

It is clear that this definition is easily extended to cases where the function x depends on more than one variable, and also to the case where z depends on several functions, $x(t)$, $y(t)$, ...

b) A functional, $F[x(t)]$, of the function $x(t)$ will be defined in general only when $x(t)$ varies within a determinate field of functions. For example,

$$F[x(t)] = \int_a^b x(t)\,dt \tag{S4.51}$$

exists (is definable) only for functions $x(t)$ which are integrable.

c) A functional, $U[A]$, is continuous at an element A if

$$\lim_{n\to\infty} U[A_n] = U[A], \tag{S4.52}$$

where A is the limiting element of the aggregate within which U is defined. A functional is uniformly continuous if, for arbitrary $\epsilon > 0$, there is an $\eta > 0$ such that

$$|U[A] - U[A']| < \epsilon, \tag{S4.53}$$

for $(A, A') < \eta$, whatever A and A' may be.

d) The first derivative of the functional F with respect to the function $y(t)$ at the point ξ is denoted $F'[y(t), \xi]$ and exists if: (1) The ratio $\delta F/\xi h < M$, with M a finite number, and $\delta y(t) = \theta(t)$, $|\theta(t)| < \epsilon$, $\theta(t) = 0$ outside an interval (m, n) of (a, b) of amplitude h and containing ξ in its interior; (2) Putting $\sigma = \int_m^n \theta(t)dt$, there exists a determinate and finite limit of $\delta F/\sigma$, when $\epsilon \to 0$ and $h \to 0$, subject to the condition that ξ is always interior to (m, n); (3) That $\delta F/\sigma$ tends to its limit uniformly with respect to all possible functions $y(t)$ and to all points ξ.

Other higher order and mixed derivatives, differentials, etc., can be similarly defined.

As an example, consider the functional

$$F[y(t)] = k_0 + \sum_{i=1}^{n} \int_a^b \cdots \int_a^b k_i(t_1, \ldots, t_i) \times y(t_1) \ldots y(t_i)\, dt_1 \ldots dt_i , \tag{S4.54}$$

where k_0 is a constant. Then the variation δF corresponding to the increment $\delta y(t)$ is

$$\delta F = \sum_{i=1}^{n} i \int_a^b \delta y(\xi)\, d\xi \int_a^b \cdots \int_a^b k_i(t_1, \ldots, t_{i-1}, \xi) \times y(t_1) \ldots y(t_{i-1})\, dt_1 \ldots dt_{i-1} , \tag{S4.55}$$

and, therefore, the first derivative of F at ξ is

$$F'[y(t), \xi] = k_1(\xi) + \sum_{i=2}^{n} i \int_a^b \cdots \int_a^b \times k_i(t_1, \ldots, t_{i-1}, \xi)\, y(t_1) \ldots y(t_{i-1})\, dt_1 \ldots dt_{i-1} . \tag{S4.56}$$

Note that the factor i arises because there are i functions which can provide the variation δy.

We now consider the Helmholtz free energy to be a functional of the system Hamiltonian. To determine the variation of free energy with Hamiltonian, we add to the Hamiltonian an arbitrary function. Since we are interested in distribution functions for a small number of molecules, we choose the test function to be of the form $\Sigma_{(i_1 \neq i_2 \neq \ldots \neq i_s)} \phi^{(s)}(i_1, \ldots, i_s)$. Now

$$-\beta A_N = \ln Q_N = \ln \left\{ \frac{1}{h^{3N} N!} \int \exp[-\beta H(\mathbf{P}^N, \{N\})]\, d\mathbf{P}^N d\{N\} \right\}, \tag{S4.57}$$

whereupon

$$-\delta(\beta A_N) = \frac{1}{Q_N} \int \Big\{ -\beta [\Sigma \delta \phi^{(s)}] \exp[-\beta \Sigma \phi^{(s)}] \times \int \exp[-\beta H(\mathbf{P}^n, \{N\})]\, d\mathbf{P}^{N-s} d\{N-s\} \Big\}\, d\mathbf{P}^s d\{s\}. \tag{S4.58}$$

From the definition of $\rho^{(s)}$ in the Canonical Ensemble we easily find

$$\rho^{(s)} = \frac{\delta A_N}{\delta \phi^{(s)}}, \tag{S4.59}$$

and in particular

$$\rho^{(2)} = \frac{\delta A_N}{\delta \phi^{(2)}}, \tag{S4.60}$$

where $\phi^{(2)}$ is now considered to be an arbitrary potential depending on the coordinates (1) and (2). This is the desired relationship between the free energy and the distribution function.

The advantage of expressing the functions $\rho^{(s)}$ in the form cited is easily demonstrated when we consider the asymptotic properties of the distribution function. In a large system, for which N, $V \rightarrow \infty$, at constant ρ, the Grand Partition Function is given approximately by one term which is large compared to all the rest. Then the average number of molecules $\langle N \rangle$ may be replaced by the number N corresponding to this term, so that, from equation (S3.2),

$$\Xi \simeq Q_N \left(\frac{Vz}{Q_1}\right)^N. \tag{S4.61}$$

The free energy A_N, calculated in this approximation, is given by

$$-\beta A_N^{(0)} = \ln \Xi - N \ln z + N \ln \left(\frac{Q_1}{V}\right). \tag{S4.62}$$

We have, therefore,

$$\beta \left[\frac{\partial^2 A_N^{(0)}}{\partial N^2}\right]_{V\ T} = \frac{\partial \ln z}{\partial N}. \tag{S4.63}$$

Again ignoring the difference between N and $\langle N \rangle$, we may write

$$\frac{\partial}{\partial N}\left(\frac{\partial \ln \Xi}{\partial \ln z}\right) = 1, \tag{S4.64}$$

since

$$N \simeq \langle N \rangle = \frac{\partial \ln \Xi}{\partial \ln z}, \tag{S4.65}$$

as is easily seen from equation (S3.2). Now, writing (S4.64) as

$$\left(\frac{\partial \ln z}{\partial N}\right)\left(\frac{\partial^2 \ln \Xi}{\partial \ln z^2}\right) = 1,$$

(S4.63) becomes

$$\beta \left[\frac{\partial^2 A_N^{(0)}}{\partial N^2}\right]_{V\ T} = \left(\frac{\partial^2 \ln \Xi}{\partial \ln z^2}\right)^{-1}. \tag{S4.66}$$

A more exact evaluation of Ξ may be obtained by the method of steepest descents. This leads to

$$\Xi = \left[2\pi \left(\frac{\partial^2 \ln \Xi}{\partial \ln z^2}\right)\right]^{1/2} Q_N \left(\frac{Vz}{Q_1}\right)^N, \tag{S4.67}$$

so that a next approximation to A_N is given by

$$\beta A_N = \beta A_N^{(0)} - \tfrac{1}{2} \ln\left[\beta \frac{\partial^2 A_N^{(0)}}{\partial N^2}\right]_{V,T} + \tfrac{1}{2} \ln 2\pi, \quad \text{(S4.68)}$$

where we have used equations (S4.62) and (S4.66). It is easily seen that this extra factor in (S4.67) as compared to (S4.61) is related to the variance $\langle (N - \langle N \rangle)^2 \rangle$ of the number probability distribution $P_N(V, T)$. Now consider the isothermal compressibility κ; we have

$$\kappa^{-1} = -V \left(\frac{\partial p}{\partial V}\right)_{N,T} = V \left(\frac{\partial^2 A_N}{\partial V^2}\right)_{N,T}. \quad \text{(S4.69)}$$

Since our zeroth order of approximation is that of identifying Ξ with its maximum term, we may change the variable in (S4.69) from V to N via the density $\rho = N/V$, and we thereby obtain

$$[\kappa^{(0)}]^{-1} = \left(\rho N \frac{\partial^2 A_N}{\partial N^2}\right)_{T,V}. \quad \text{(S4.70)}$$

We now take a variation of equation (S4.68), and obtain

$$\delta A_N = \delta A_N^{(0)} - \frac{\rho^3 \kappa^{(0)}}{2N\beta} \frac{\partial^2}{\partial \rho^2} [\delta A_N^{(0)}], \quad \text{(S4.71)}$$

where (S4.70) has been used and the derivative of $\delta A_N^{(0)}$ expressed in terms of ρ. Equation (S4.71) may be combined with equation (S4.60) to give

$$\rho^{(s)} = \rho^{(s),(0)} - \frac{\rho^3 \kappa}{2N\beta} \frac{\partial^2}{\partial \rho^2} \rho^{(s),(0)}, \quad \text{(S4.72)}$$

where, in the second term the difference between κ and $\kappa^{(0)}$ has been ignored. For the case $s = 2$, in the limit of large separations, $\rho^{(2),(0)} \to \rho^2$, and (S4.72) becomes

$$\lim_{R_{12}\to\infty} [\rho^{(2)} - \rho^2] = -\frac{\rho^3 \kappa}{N\beta}, \quad \text{(S4.73)}$$

a result equivalent to (S4.37).

S5. SERIES EXPANSIONS FOR THE PAIR DISTRIBUTION FUNCTION

In the introduction to section S4 it was pointed out that distribution functions allow a more economical approach to the calculation of, for instance, the equation of state of a dense fluid, than do the virial expansions discussed in section S3. However, this is not to be taken as implying that the two methods are mutually exclusive. Indeed, they are complementary, and equivalent so long as a virial expansion converges. Before going on to discuss the methods of calculation of distribution functions particularly suited to dense fluids, we give here two different virial expansions.

S5.1. $\mathfrak{U}$-Function Method [6, 7]

The definition of the radial distribution function with which we start is

$$g_N^{(2)}(1, 2) = \frac{V^2}{Z_N} \int \dots \int W(\{N\}) d\{N-2\}, \qquad \text{(S5.1)}$$

where $W(\{N\})$ is defined by (S3.19). Here, we have singled out two molecules, 1 and 2, so that $\{N - 2\} = (3, 4, \dots, N)$, and $g_N^{(2)}(1, 2)$ is the *specific* radial distribution function. It is related to the generic radial distribution function $g_N^{(2)}$ by (cf. eq. [S4.1])

$$g_N^{(2)} = N(N-1) g^{(2)}(1, 2). \qquad \text{(S5.2)}$$

Our procedure is to take equation (S3.29) and study the various types of contribution which arise. We have

$$\begin{aligned} W(\{N\}) &= \mathfrak{U}(1) W(2, \dots, N) \\ &+ \sum_P \mathfrak{U}(1, i) W(2, \dots, i-1, i+1, \dots, N) \\ + \dots &+ \sum_P \mathfrak{U}(1, i_1, \dots, i_{n-1}) W(\underset{(\text{all } j \epsilon 1, \dots, n-1)}{2, \dots, i_{j-1}, i_{j+1}, \dots}, N) \\ + \dots . \end{aligned} \qquad \text{(S5.3)}$$

In the general term of order n two types of contributions may arise depending on whether the set $(i_1, \dots, i_{n-1})$ includes 2. The total number of terms of this order is $\binom{N-1}{n-1}$, while if one $i_j = 2$ $(j \epsilon 1, \dots, n-1)$, there are $\binom{N-2}{n-2}$ terms. Consequently, the number of terms for which $i_j \neq 2$ $(j \epsilon 1, \dots, n-1)$ is

$$\binom{N-1}{n-1} - \binom{N-2}{n-2}.$$

Upon integrating both sides over $d\{N-2\}$, the terms of the first type are

$$\begin{aligned} \int \dots \int & \mathfrak{U}(1, 2, i_1, \dots, i_{n-2}) \\ & \times W(\underset{(\text{all } j \epsilon 1, \dots, n-2)}{3, \dots, i_j - 1, i_j + 1, \dots}, N) d\{N-2\} \\ &= \int \mathfrak{U}(1, 2, i_1, \dots, i_{n-2}) d\{n-2\} \\ & \times \int W(\underset{(\text{all } j \epsilon 1, \dots, n-2)}{3, \dots, i_j - 1, i_j + 1, \dots}, N) d\{N-n\} \\ &= (n-2)! \mathfrak{b}_n Z_{N-n}, \end{aligned} \qquad \text{(S5.4)}$$

where $\{n-2\} = (i_1, \ldots, i_{n-2})$ and $\{N-n\} = (3, \ldots, i_j - 1, i_j + 1, \ldots, N)$ (all $j \epsilon 1, \ldots, n-2$), and we have defined

$$(n-2)!\mathfrak{b}_n = \int \mathfrak{U}(1, 2, i_1, \ldots, i_{n-2})\, d\{n-2\}. \quad \text{(S5.5)}$$

Terms of the second type are

$$\begin{aligned}\int \mathfrak{U}(\underset{(i_j\neq 2,\, j\epsilon 1, \ldots,\, n-1)}{1, i_1, \ldots, i_{n-1}}) W(\underset{(\text{all } j\epsilon 1, \ldots,\, n-1)}{2, \ldots, i_j - 1, i_j + 1, \ldots, N}) \\ \times d\{N-2\} = \int \mathfrak{U}(\underset{(i_j\neq 2,\, j\epsilon 1, \ldots,\, n-1)}{1, i_1, \ldots, i_{n-1}})\, d\{n-1\} \\ \times \int W(\underset{(\text{all } j\epsilon 1, \ldots,\, n-1)}{2, \ldots, i_{j-1}, i_{j+1}, \ldots, N})\, d\{N-n-1\} \\ = \frac{1}{V^2}(n!b_n V) Z_{N-n},\end{aligned} \quad \text{(S5.6)}$$

where b_n is defined by equation (S3.25). The result (S5.6), follows because the two integrals are each taken over the coordinates of one less molecule than is included in the argument. Since that molecule can be regarded as the origin of coordinates in each case, integration over the coordinates of these two molecules simply results in the factor V for each term, which is balanced by the factor V^{-2}. Substituting (S5.4) and (S5.6) in (S5.1) with appropriate numerical factors, we obtain

$$\begin{aligned} g_N^{(2)}(1, 2) = V^2 \sum_{n=2}^{N} \binom{N-2}{n-2} (n-2)!\mathfrak{b}_n \frac{Z_{N-n}}{Z_N} \\ + \sum_{n=1}^{N} \binom{N-1}{n-1} n! b_n V \frac{Z_{N-n}}{Z_N} \\ - \sum_{n=2}^{N} \binom{N-2}{n-2} n! b_n V \frac{Z_{N-n}}{Z_N}. \end{aligned} \quad \text{(S5.7)}$$

The second term is, from (S3.30), just unity, so that

$$\begin{aligned} g_N^{(2)}(1, 2) - 1 = V^2 \sum_{n=2}^{N} \binom{N-2}{n-2} (n-2)!\mathfrak{b}_n \frac{Z_{N-n}}{Z_N} \\ - \sum_{n=2}^{N} \binom{N-2}{n-2} n! b_n V \frac{Z_{N-n}}{Z_N}. \end{aligned} \quad \text{(S5.8)}$$

Equation (S5.8) is exact, but awkward. However, it can be developed into a simpler form by employing the steepest descent approximation

(S4.67) in a way which does not affect the final accuracy. Equation (S4.67) may be written

$$\frac{Z_N z^N}{N!} = \frac{\Xi}{[2\pi\langle(\Delta N)^2\rangle]^{1/2}}. \tag{S5.9}$$

Since (S5.9) is derived from a consideration of the shape of the peak of $P_N(V, T)$, expressing the contribution from the peak in terms of the value at the peak, we assume that (S5.9) is true for a small number of different values $(N - n)$; $n \leq m$. By small is meant a number $m \ll N$. In fact, all that is required is that m, however small, is a monotonic increasing function of $\langle N \rangle$. Indeed, we have in mind a number of the order of the width of the peak $\langle(\Delta N)^2\rangle^{1/2} \sim N^{1/2}$. It is now possible to write

$$z^n = \frac{Z_{N-n} N!}{Z_N (N-n)!}, \tag{S5.10}$$

and, provided the series converges quickly enough, (S5.8) becomes

$$\begin{aligned} g_N^{(2)}(1, 2) - 1 &= \frac{V^2}{N(N-1)} \sum_{n=2}^{m(N)} b_n z^n \\ &\quad - \frac{V}{N(N-1)} \sum_{n=2}^{m(N)} n(n-1) b_n z^n. \end{aligned} \tag{S5.11}$$

Upon recalling the cluster expansion (eq. [S3.5])

$$\beta p = \sum_{n \geq 1} b_n(T) z^n,$$

we may write

$$\ln \Xi = V \sum_{n \geq 1} b_n z^n,$$

so that

$$N \simeq \langle N \rangle = V \sum_{n \geq 1} n b_n z^n,$$

and

$$\rho = \sum_{n \geq 1} n b_n z^n. \tag{S5.12}$$

It is, therefore, seen that

$$\sum_{n=2}^{m(N)} n(n-1) b_n z^n = \frac{\partial \rho}{\partial \ln z} - \rho, \tag{S5.13}$$

and since

$$\frac{\partial \rho}{\partial \ln z} = \frac{\partial \rho}{\partial p} \frac{\partial p}{\partial \ln z} = \kappa \rho^2 kT, \tag{S5.14}$$

equation (S5.11) becomes

$$g_N^{(2)}(1, 2) - 1 = \frac{1}{\rho^2}\sum_{n=2}^{m(N)} \mathfrak{b}_n z^n + \left(\frac{1}{N} - \frac{kT\kappa}{V}\right), \quad \text{(S5.15)}$$

where we have ignored the difference in the upper limits of the summations in equations (S5.11–12). It is easy to see that $g_N^{(2)}(1, 2)$ has the correct limiting properties. In the limit of infinite dilution, $z \to \rho \to 0$, so that

$$g_N^{(2)}(1, 2) - 1 \simeq \mathfrak{b}_2 = \exp[-\beta u(1, 2)] - 1 \text{ ,} \quad \text{(S5.16)}$$

and in the limit of large separation $R_{12} \to \infty$,

$$\lim_{R_{12}\to\infty} [\, g_N^{(2)}(1, 2) - 1] = \frac{1}{N} - \frac{kT\kappa}{V}, \quad \text{(S5.17)}$$

showing proper normalization in the Canonical Ensemble. If we were to work in the Grand Canonical Ensemble and normalize such that

$$\lim_{R_{12}\to\infty} g^{(2)}(1, 2) = 1 \quad \text{(G.C.E.), (S5.18)}$$

our equation would be

$$g^{(2)}(1, 2) - 1 = \frac{1}{\rho^2}\sum_{n=2}^{m(N)} \mathfrak{b}_n z^n, \quad \text{(S5.19)}$$

and on integration over space we recover the compressibility equation (S4.38). Equation (S5.19) may be converted to a series in powers of the density, by substitution of the relation $z = z(\rho)$, but the series is not of any particular interest, and we leave this as an exercise.

S5.2. The Cumulant Method [3]

We begin again with the definition of $g_N^{(2)}(1, 2)$, though in a slightly different form from (S5.1):

$$g_N^{(2)}(1, 2) = \frac{\langle \exp[-\beta U(\{N\})]\rangle^{(1,2)}}{\langle \exp[-\beta U(\{N\})]\rangle}, \quad \text{(S5.20)}$$

where

$$\langle \exp[-\beta U(\{N\})]\rangle^{(1,2)} = V^{2-N}\int\ldots\int \times \exp[-\beta U(\{N\})]\, d\{N-2\}, \quad \text{(S5.21)}$$

and, of course,

$$\langle \exp[-\beta U(\{N\})]\rangle = V^{-N} Z_N \text{ .} \quad \text{(S5.22)}$$

Now, (S5.21) may be rewritten as

$$\langle \exp[-\beta U(\{N\})] \rangle^{(1,2)} = \exp[-\beta u(1,2)] \times \langle \exp[-\beta U'(\{N\})] \rangle^{(1,2)}, \qquad (S5.23)$$

where $U'(\{N\})$ is now the potential energy of N molecules less that of the pair already singled out. From equations (S5.20), (S5.22–23), we obtain

$$\ln g_N^{(2)}(1,2) = -\beta u(1,2) + \ln \langle \exp(-\beta U') \rangle^{(1,2)} - \ln \langle \exp(-\beta U) \rangle. \qquad (S5.24)$$

Following the procedure developed in section S3.3, equation (S5.24) may be written

$$\ln g_N^{(2)}(1,2) = -\beta u(1,2) + \left\langle \exp_L \left({\sum_{i<j}}' f_{ij} \right) - 1 \right\rangle_c^{(1,2)} - \left\langle \exp_L \left(\sum_{i<j} f_{ij} \right) - 1 \right\rangle_c, \qquad (S5.25)$$

where Σ' does *not* include the term $i = 1, j = 2$. Consider the second term on the right-hand side of (S5.25); three types of contribution may arise:

a) Terms for n molecules $\langle \Pi^{(n)} f_{ij} \rangle_c^{(1,2)}$, none of which is 1 or 2. Integration over $d\{N-2\}$ then includes the coordinates of all molecules appearing in the term, so that

$$\sum_{(C_n)} \left\langle \prod^{(n)} f_{ij} \right\rangle_c^{(1,2)} = \frac{(n-1)!\beta_{n-1}}{V^{n-1}}, \qquad (S5.26)$$

where β_n is defined by (S3.17). The number of ways n molecules can be selected from $N-2$ is $\binom{N-2}{n}$, so that terms of this type contribute

$$\sum_{n=2}^{N-2} \binom{N-2}{n} \frac{(n-1)!\beta_{n-1}}{V^{n-1}} = \sum_{n=1}^{N-3} \binom{N-2}{n+1} \frac{n!\beta_n}{V^n}. \qquad (S5.27)$$

b) Terms in which either molecule 1 or molecule 2 is included, but not both. Then

$$\left\langle \prod^{(n-1|1)} f_{ij} \right\rangle_c^{(1,2)} = \frac{1}{V^{N-2}} \int \cdots \int \prod^{(n-1|1)} f_{ij} d\{N-2\}$$

$$= \frac{1}{V} \left(\frac{1}{V^{N-2}} \int \cdots \int \prod^{(n-1|1)} f_{ij} d\{N-2\} \right) d(1),$$

and

$$\sum_{(C_n)} \left\langle \prod^{(n-1|1)} f_{ij} \right\rangle_c^{(1,2)} = \frac{(n-1)!\beta_{n-1}}{V^{n-1}}. \qquad (S5.28)$$

Since there are two ways in which either molecule 1 or molecule 2 may appear in the cluster, the total contribution from terms of this type is

$$2\sum_{n=2}^{N-1} \binom{N-2}{n-1} \frac{(n-1)!\beta_{n-1}}{V^{n-1}} = 2\sum_{n=1}^{N-2} \binom{N-2}{n} \frac{n!\beta_n}{V^n}. \qquad (S5.29)$$

c) Terms in which both molecules 1 and 2 appear. Here we define a new irreducible cluster integral γ_n in analogy with (S5.5) by[1]

$$(n-2)!\gamma_n = \int \cdots \int \sum_{(C'_n)} \prod^{(n-2|1\ 2)} f_{ij} d\{n-2\}, \qquad (S5.30)$$

so that

$$\sum_{(C'_n)} \left\langle \prod^{(n-2|1\ 2)} f_{ij} \right\rangle_c^{(1,2)} = \frac{\gamma_n (n-2)!}{V^{n-2}}. \qquad (S5.31)$$

The total contribution from these terms is

$$\sum_{n=3}^{N} \binom{N-2}{n-2} \frac{(n-2)!\gamma_n}{V^{n-2}} \cong \sum_{n=3}^{N} \rho^{n-2}\gamma_n, \qquad (S5.32)$$

the term $n = 2$ having been already extracted in (S5.23). The last term in (S5.25) contributes (cf. eq. [S3.91])

$$-\left\langle \exp_L \left(\sum_{i<j} f_{ij} \right) - 1 \right\rangle_c = -\sum_{n=1}^{N-1} \binom{N}{n+1} \frac{n!\beta_n}{V^n}. \qquad (S5.33)$$

The contributions from equations (S5.27), (S5.29), and (S5.33) may be added to give

$$-\sum_{n=1} \frac{(N-2)!}{[N-2-(n+1)]![N-(n+1)][N-(n+2)]} \frac{n\beta_n}{V^n}, \qquad (S5.34)$$

apart from small terms arising from the fact that the upper limits of the series are for $(N-3)$, $(N-2)$, and $(N-1)$, respectively. If we let $N, V \to \infty$, $\rho = \text{const}$, these terms may be entirely neglected, and (S5.34) becomes

$$-\frac{1}{N} \sum_{n=1} n\beta_n \rho^n. \qquad (S5.35)$$

[1] C'_n denotes all connected diagrams of n labeled points, excluding the bond f_{12}.

From equation (S3.93) we have

$$p' = -kT\sum_{n=1} \frac{n}{n+1} \beta_n \rho^{n+1}, \tag{S5.36}$$

so that (S5.35) becomes

$$-\frac{1}{N}\sum_{n=1} n\beta_n \rho^n = \frac{\beta}{N}\left(\frac{\partial p'}{\partial \rho}\right)_{T,N} = \frac{\beta}{N\rho\kappa'}, \tag{S5.37}$$

where κ' is the potential energy contribution to the compressibility. We now obtain, for (S5.24), the final relation

$$\ln g_N^{(2)}(1, 2) = -\beta u(1, 2) + \sum_{n=3}^{\infty} \gamma_n \rho^{n-2} + \frac{\beta}{N\rho\kappa} - \frac{1}{N}, \tag{S5.38}$$

where we have used the fact that

$$\kappa^{-1} = \beta^{-1}\rho + \kappa'^{-1}. \tag{S5.39}$$

Let us compare (S5.39) with (S5.15). The main difference between them is due to the fact that the $\mathfrak{b}_n$ in (S5.15) are not irreducible cluster integrals, because the $\mathfrak{U}$-functions contain all connected diagrams, including those in which the coordinates of some molecules appear in only one bond f_{ij}. The γ_n are, of course, irreducible, by virtue of the properties of cumulants demonstrated in section S3.3. The fluctuation terms are similar, but not the same; in equation (S5.15) the term is

$$N^{-1}(1 - \rho kT\kappa),$$

while in (S5.38) it is

$$N^{-1}\left(\frac{1 - \rho kT\kappa}{\rho kT\kappa}\right).$$

This difference in an expression of the relation between the average value of a quantity and of its logarithm.

S6. EQUATIONS FOR THE PAIR CORRELATION FUNCTION

Exact equations for n-molecule correlation functions in terms of $(n + 1)$-molecule correlation functions may be obtained in several different ways. In order to calculate a correlation function of given order from these formalisms it is necessary to introduce some closure assumption to truncate the hierarchy of exact coupled equations. Without this closure, the calculation of the two-body correlation function cannot be divorced from the calculation of the three-body function, the three from the four, and so on. In this section we shall review the means by which various equations for the pair correlation function, in particular, are derived and the meaning of the assumptions used to truncate the hierarchy.

S6.1. The Yvon-Born-Green Equation [1, 8, 9, 10]

Consider the defining equation for the n-molecule distribution function, equation (S4.15). If we differentiate this equation with respect to the coordinates of one of the n molecules, say the molecule at $\boldsymbol{R}_1$, we obtain,

$$-kT\nabla_1\rho^{(n)} = \frac{1}{\Xi}\sum_{N\geq n}\frac{z^N}{(N-n)!}\int\exp(-\beta U)\nabla_1 U d\{N-n\}$$

$$= \sum_{i=2}^{n}\nabla_1 u(1,i)\rho^{(n)} + \frac{1}{\Xi}\int\nabla_1 u(1,n+1)\times \tag{S6.1}$$

$$\left[\int\sum_{N\geq n}\frac{(N-n)z^N}{(N-n)!}\exp(-\beta U)d\{N-n-1\}\right]d(n+1)$$

$$= \sum_{i=2}^{n}\nabla_1 u(1,i)\rho^{(n)} + \int\nabla_1 u(1,n+1)\rho^{(n+1)}d(n+1).$$

Thus, as forecast in the introduction, an exact equation for $\rho^{(n)}$ is obtained in terms of $\rho^{(n+1)}$. In order to truncate the hierarchy represented by equation (S6.1), we introduce the concept of the potential of the mean force, $W^{(n)}$, by

$$W^{(n)} = -kT\ln g^{(n)}, \tag{S6.2}$$

where, of course, $g^{(n)}$ is related to $\rho^{(n)}$ by (S4.22). That $W^{(n)}$ is indeed the potential of the mean-force field in which the n molecules are situated can be seen in the following way: equation (S6.2) is differentiated with respect to the coordinates of one molecule, giving

$$-\nabla_1 W^{(n)} = \frac{kT\nabla_1 g^{(n)}}{g^{(n)}}$$

$$= -\frac{\displaystyle\sum_{N\geq n}\frac{z^N}{(N-n)!}\int\exp(-\beta U)\nabla_1 U d\{N-n\}}{\displaystyle\sum_{N\geq n}\frac{z^N}{(N-n)!}\int\exp(-\beta U)d\{N-n\}}. \tag{S6.3}$$

In (S6.3) the factor $\rho^n \Xi^{-1}$ has canceled out (cf. eq. [S4.22] defining $g^{(n)}$ in terms of $\rho^{(n)}$). Equation (S6.3) clearly has the form of a properly normalized average of the force on the molecule at $\boldsymbol{R}_1$, when the n molecules are held fixed at the locations $\{n\}$. In order to obtain an equation for $g^{(2)}$ we must, therefore, consider ways in which $W^{(3)}$ may be expressed in terms of $W^{(2)}$. As a first approximation Kirkwood suggested that

$$W^{(3)}(1, 2, 3) = W^{(2)}(1, 2) + W^{(2)}(1, 3) + W^{(2)}(2, 3), \quad \text{(S6.4)}$$

or

$$g^{(2)}(1, 2, 3) = g^{(2)}(1, 2)\, g^{(2)}(1, 3)\, g^{(2)}(2, 3). \quad \text{(S6.5)}$$

The physical meaning of this assumption, called the superposition approximation, may be described qualitatively as follows: In evaluating $W^{(3)}$ we have neglected the effect of fixing a molecule at $\boldsymbol{R}_3$ on the distribution of the other $(N - 3)$ molecules around the molecules fixed at $\boldsymbol{R}_1$ and $\boldsymbol{R}_2$. In section S6.4 we shall consider briefly the quantitative significance of this assumption.

Substitution of (S6.5) in (S6.1) now leads to

$$\begin{aligned} -kT\nabla_1 \ln g^{(2)}(1, 2) &= \nabla_1 u(1, 2) \\ &\quad + \rho \int \nabla_1 u(1, 3)\, g^{(2)}(1, 3)\, g^{(2)}(2, 3)\, d(3). \end{aligned} \quad \text{(S6.6)}$$

This non-linear integral equation was first derived by Yvon, and later by Born and Green; it is to be solved subject to the boundary condition $g^{(2)}(1, 2) \to 1;\, R_{12} \to \infty$. We refer to it later as the YBG equation.

S6.2. The Kirkwood Integral Equation [1, 10]

A slightly different integral equation for $g^{(2)}$ was derived by Kirkwood. Let the coupling between a selected molecule, say 1, and the rest of the fluid be imagined to be variable from zero to unity. As the interaction is "switched on" the structure of the fluid around molecule 1 changes. If the fractional interaction is denoted by ξ, where $0 \leq \xi \leq 1$, then we obviously have

$$\Xi(\xi) = \sum_{N \geq 0} \frac{z^N}{N!} \int \exp[-\beta U(\xi)]\, d\{N\}, \quad \text{(S6.7)}$$

$$U(\xi) = \xi \sum_{i=2}^{N} u(1, i) + \sum_{2 \leq i < j \leq N} u(i, j), \quad \text{(S6.8)}$$

$$\rho^{(n)}(\{n\};\xi)=\frac{1}{\Xi(\xi)}\sum_{N\geq n}\frac{z^N}{(N-n)!}\times\int\exp[-\beta U(\xi)]\,d\{N-n\}. \tag{S6.9}$$

If we differentiate (S6.9) with respect to ξ and collect equivalent terms,

$$\begin{aligned}\Xi\left(\frac{\partial\rho^{(n)}}{\partial\xi}\right)_{z\,V\cdot T}&-\frac{\rho^{(n)}}{kT}\int u(1,2)\left\{\int\sum_{N\geq 2}\frac{z^N}{N!}(N-1)\right.\\&\left.\times\exp[-\beta U(\xi)]\,d\{N-2\}\right\}d(1)\,d(2)\\&=-\frac{1}{kT}\sum_{N\geq 0}\frac{z^N}{(N-n)!}\left[\!\left[\sum_{i=2}^{n}u(1,i)\int\exp[-\beta U(\xi)]\right.\right.\\&\times d\{N-n\}+(N-n)\int u(1,n+1)\\&\left.\left.\times\{\int\exp[-\beta U(\xi)]\,d\{N-n-1\}\}\,d(n+1)\right]\!\right].\end{aligned} \tag{S6.10}$$

Now, (S6.10) is divided by $-\rho^{(n)}\Xi(\xi)/kT$ to yield

$$\begin{aligned}-kT\left(\frac{\partial\ln\rho^{(n)}}{\partial\xi}\right)_{Z\,V\cdot T}&\\+\frac{1}{\langle N\rangle}\int u(1,2)\,\rho^{(2)*}(1,2;\xi)\,d\{2\}&=\sum_{i=2}^{n}u(1,i)\\&+\frac{1}{\rho^{(n)}}\int u(1,n+1)\,\rho^{(n+1)}d(n+1),\end{aligned} \tag{S6.11}$$

where $\rho^{(2)*}$ is defined by

$$\begin{aligned}\sum_{N\geq 2}\frac{z^N}{N!}(N-1)\int\exp[-\beta U(\xi)]\,d\{N-2\}&\\=\sum_{N\geq 2}\frac{1}{N}\frac{z^N}{(N-2)!}\int\exp[-\beta U(\xi)]\,d\{N-2\}&\\=\frac{1}{\langle N\rangle}\rho^{(2)*}(1,2;\xi)\Xi.&\end{aligned} \tag{S6.12}$$

If we allow $N, V\rightarrow\infty$, with $\rho=$ const, then $\rho^{(2)*}\rightarrow\rho^{(2)}$, since the maximum term approximation to Ξ is valid and the factor N^{-1} may be replaced in the first member of equation (S6.12) by $\langle N\rangle^{-1}$. For $n=2$, using the superposition approximation (S6.4), we finally obtain

$$\begin{aligned}-kT\ln g^{(2)}(1,2;\xi)&=\xi u(1,2)+\rho\int_0^{\xi}\int u(1,3)\\&\times g^{(2)}(1,3;\xi)[g^{(2)}(2,3)-1]\,d(3)\,d\xi,\end{aligned} \tag{S6.13}$$

where we have integrated over ξ. This equation was first obtained by Kirkwood.

Although (S6.11) is exactly equivalent to (S6.1), the superposition approximations are introduced in different ways, so that the final YBG and K equations are different. To see this, first write equation (S6.6) in terms of an arbitrary coupling parameter, ξ,

$$-kT\nabla_1 \ln g^{(2)}(1, 2; \xi) = \xi \nabla_1 u(1, 2) + \rho\xi \int \nabla_1 u(1, 3) g^{(2)}(1, 3; \xi) g^{(2)}(2, 3) d(3). \tag{S6.14}$$

Now differentiate (S6.13) with respect to $\boldsymbol{R}_1$, to obtain

$$-kT\nabla_1 \ln g^{(2)}(1, 2; \xi) = \xi \nabla_1 u(1, 2) + \rho \int_0^\xi \int \nabla_1 [u(1, 3) g^{(2)}(1, 3; \xi)] \times g^{(2)}(2, 3) d(3) d\xi, \tag{S6.15}$$

where we have used the fact that

$$\nabla_1 \int u(1, 3) g^{(2)}(1, 3; \xi) d(3) = 0. \tag{S6.16}$$

It is seen immediately that, apart from the different way ξ appears in the integral terms of the two equations, (S6.15) contains the extra term

$$\rho \int_0^\xi \int u(1, 3) \nabla_1 g^{(2)}(1, 3; \xi) g^{(2)}(2, 3) d(3) d\xi .$$

S6.3. The Equations of Cole and of Fisher [11, 12]

The superposition approximation (S6.4) and (S6.5) is, as we shall see in section S7, not entirely adequate to describe the thermodynamic properties of dense fluids. Consequently, a number of formal attempts have been made to improve upon it, and we review two of these here.

Suppose we form the tensor gradient of (S6.1) with respect to $\boldsymbol{R}_1$,

$$-kT\nabla_1\nabla_1 \rho^{(n)} = \sum_{i=2}^{n} [\nabla_1\nabla_1 u(1, i) + \nabla_1 u(1, i) \nabla_1 \rho^{(n)}] + \int \nabla_1\nabla_1 u(1, n+1) \rho^{(n+1)} d(n+1) + \int \nabla_1 u(1, n+1) \nabla_1 \rho^{(n+1)} d(n+1). \tag{S6.17}$$

In (S6.17) we now substitute for $\nabla_1 \rho^{(n+1)}$ from (S6.1), allowing $(n+1)$ to replace (n). The result is

$$
\begin{aligned}
-(kT)^2\nabla_1\nabla_1 g^{(n)} &= g^{(n)}\Big\{\Big[\sum_{i=2}^{n}\nabla_1 u(1,i)\Big]\Big[\sum_{i=2}^{n}\nabla_1 u(1,i)\Big] \\
&\quad + kT\sum_{i=1}^{n}\nabla_1\nabla_1 u(1,i)\Big\} \\
&\quad + 2kT\nabla_1 g^{(n)}\sum_{i=2}^{n}\nabla_1 u(1,i) \qquad \text{(S6.18)} \\
&\quad + \rho\int[kT\nabla_1\nabla_1 u(1,n+1) \\
&\quad - \nabla_1 u(1,n+1)\nabla_1 u(1,n+1)]\,g^{(n+1)}d(n+1) \\
&\quad - \rho^2\int\int\nabla_1 u(1,n+1)\nabla_1 u(1,n+2) \\
&\quad \times g^{(n+2)}d(n+1)\,d(n+2).
\end{aligned}
$$

The superposition approximation appropriate to a group of four molecules is obtained from the following recipe: select three molecules and express the correlation function as the product of that for the chosen three, and the pair correlation functions for the fourth molecule, and each of the chosen three separately. Thus,

$$g^{(4)}(\{4\}) = g^{(3)}(1,2,3)\,g^{(2)}(1,4)\,g^{(2)}(2,4)\,g^{(2)}(3,4). \qquad \text{(S6.19)}$$

This formulation obviously has the effect of singling out molecule 4. Using (S6.19), equation (S6.18) may now be expressed in terms of $g^{(2)}$ only,

$$
\begin{aligned}
-[(kT)^2/g^{(2)}]\nabla_1\nabla_1 \ln g^{(2)} &= [\nabla_1 u(1,2)\nabla_1 u(1,2) \\
&\quad + kT\nabla_1\nabla_1 u(1,2)] + 2kT\nabla_1 \ln g^{(2)}\nabla_1 u(1,2) \\
&\quad + \rho\int[kT\nabla_1\nabla_1 u(1,3) - \nabla_1 u(1,3)\nabla_1 u(1,3)] \\
&\quad \times g^{(2)}(1,3)\,g^{(2)}(2,3)\,d(3) - \rho^2\int\int\nabla_1 u(1,3) \qquad \text{(S6.20)} \\
&\quad \times \nabla_1 u(1,4)\,g^{(2)}(1,3)\,g^{(2)}(2,3)\,g^{(2)}(1,4) \\
&\quad \times g^{(2)}(2,4)\,g^{(2)}(3,4)\,d(3)\,d(4),
\end{aligned}
$$

an equation derived by Cole.

Alternatively, we may refine the superposition approximation more directly than in equation (S6.19) by applying the same *concept* as that expressed in equations (S6.4–5) to $g^{(4)}$:

$$
\begin{aligned}
g^{(4)}(\{4\}) &= g^{(3)}(1,2,3)\,g^{(3)}(1,2,4) \\
&\quad \times g^{(3)}(1,3,4)\,g^{(3)}(2,3,4). \qquad \text{(S6.21)}
\end{aligned}
$$

If we now introduce a triplet-indirect correlation function $h^{(3)}(1, 2, 3)$ by

$$g^{(3)}(\{3\}) = g^{(2)}(1, 2)\, g^{(2)}(1, 3)\, g^{(2)}(2, 3)\, h^{(3)}(\{3\}), \qquad \text{(S6.22)}$$

we may deduce two coupled vector equations by taking (S6.1), for $n = 2, 3$,

$$\begin{aligned} -kT\nabla_1 \ln g^{(2)}(1, 2) &= \nabla_1 u(1, 2) + \rho \int \nabla_1 u(1, 3) \\ &\quad \times g^{(2)}(1, 3)\, g^{(2)}(2, 3)\, h^{(3)}(\{3\})\, d(3), \end{aligned} \qquad \text{(S6.23)}$$

$$\begin{aligned} -kT\nabla_1 \ln h^{(3)}(1, 2, 3) &= \rho \int \nabla_1 u(1, 4)\, g^{(2)}(1, 4) \\ &\quad \times [g^{(2)}(2, 4)\, g^{(2)}(3, 4)\, h^{(3)}(1, 2, 4) \\ &\quad \times h^{(3)}(2, 3, 4)\, h^{(3)}(1, 3, 4) \\ &\quad - g^{(2)}(2, 4)\, h^{(3)}(1, 2, 4) \\ &\quad - g^{(2)}(3, 4)\, h^{(3)}(1, 3, 4)]\, d(4). \end{aligned} \qquad \text{(S6.24)}$$

These equations should be solved subject to the conditions

$$g^{(2)}(1, 2) \rightarrow 1, \qquad h^{(3)}(1, 2, 3) \rightarrow 1,$$

as any one of the molecules goes off to infinity, so that the proper normalization and physical significance of the correlation functions is preserved. Equations (S6.23) and (S6.24) were first derived by Fisher.

Equations (S6.20) and (S6.24) are much more difficult to solve than equations (S6.6) and (S6.13). No numerical solutions have, in fact, been obtained. Equation (S6.20) has been used by Cole to estimate first-order corrections to the superposition approximation, equation (S6.5), in a density expansion for dilute gases:

$$\begin{aligned} g^{(3)}(1, 2, 3) &= g^{(2)}(1, 2)\, g^{(2)}(1, 3)\, g^{(2)}(2, 3) \\ &\quad \times [1 + \alpha\rho k^{(3)}(1, 2, 3) + \ldots], \end{aligned} \qquad \text{(S6.25)}$$

where $k^{(3)}(1, 2, 3)$ is a known simple function of $\{3\}$ and α is the numerical factor which is determined by this procedure.

S6.4. The Meaning of the Superposition Approximation

It follows from the definitions of $\rho_N^{(n)}$, $\rho^{(n)}$, and $g^{(n)}$ in section S4.1, that, to terms of order N^{-1},

$$g^{(2)}(1, 2) = \frac{1}{V} \int g^{(3)}(1, 2, 3)\, d(3). \qquad \text{(S6.26)}$$

Use of the superposition approximation (S6.5) then results in

$$\int g^{(2)}(2, 3)\, g^{(2)}(1, 3)\, d(3) = V, \tag{S6.27}$$

which is clearly a contradictory result except in the limit of low density, since the left-hand side must depend upon $(\mathbf{R}_2 - \mathbf{R}_1)$. Thus, the superposition approximation has obvious shortcomings. However, this is not to say that it is not of use for calculating the thermodynamic functions of both gases and liquids. As we shall now show, the superposition approximation is a simple mathematical expression representing the sum of a class of diagrams (to all orders in the density) in a cluster expansion.

We recall the linked-cluster expansion derived in section S5.2 for $\ln g^{(2)}(1, 2)$: it is

$$\ln\, g^{(2)}(1, 2) = -\beta u(1, 2) + \sum_{n=1}^{\infty} \gamma_{n+2}\rho^n + O(N^{-1}), \tag{S6.28}$$

where the residual $O(N^{-1})$ is the fluctuation term previously given explicitly, although it is not now of interest. Let us consider a similar evaluation of $g^{(3)}(1, 2, 3)$. The starting point is

$$\begin{aligned} \ln\, g^{(3)}(1, 2, 3) &= \ln\langle \exp(-\beta U)\rangle^{(1, 2, 3)} - \ln\langle \exp(-\beta U)\rangle \\ &= -\beta\,[u(1, 2) + u(1, 3) + u(2, 3)] \\ &\quad + \Big\langle \exp_L\Big(\sum_{i<j}{}' f_{ij}\Big) - 1\Big\rangle_c^{(1, 2, 3)} - \ln\langle \exp(-\beta U)\rangle, \end{aligned} \tag{S6.29}$$

where the prime on Σ' denotes the fact that the intermolecular-potential terms for the specified group of molecules have been removed, and are displayed separately. Contributions to $\langle \exp_L(\Sigma'_{i<j} f_{ij}) - 1\rangle_c^{(1, 2, 3)}$ arise in four ways: terms for groups of n molecules, including none, any one, any two, or all three, of molecules 1, 2, and 3. The first two types of terms are just those which combine with the last term on the right-hand side of (S6.29) to give the fluctuation terms, and henceforth we ignore them. Consider all terms representing n molecules, including a particular pair, say 1, 2. We have

$$\sum_{(C'_n)} \Big\langle \prod^{(n-2|1, 2)}{}' f_{ij} \Big\rangle_c^{(1, 2, 3)} = \frac{1}{V^{N-3}} \int \sum_{(C'_n)} \prod^{(n-2|1, 2)} \times f_{ij}\, d\{N-3\}. \tag{S6.30}$$

The set $\{N - 3\}$ includes all of the $(n - 2)$ molecules, since this subgroup does not include molecule 3. Hence,

$$\sum_{(C'_n)} \left\langle \prod^{(n-2|1\ 2)} f_{ij} \right\rangle_c^{(1,2,3)} = \frac{1}{V^{n-2}} \int \sum_{(C'_n)} \prod^{(n-2|1\ 2)} \times f_{ij} d\{n-2\} \tag{S6.31}$$
$$= (n-2)!\gamma_n(1,2)V^{2-n},$$

where we have used the definition of γ_n in equation (S5.30). There are two other series of this type, involving, respectively, $\gamma_n(1, 3)$ and $\gamma_n(2, 3)$. A term of the third type for groups of n molecules is[2]

$$\sum_{(C''_n)} \left\langle \prod^{(n-3|1,\ 2\ 3)} f_{ij} \right\rangle_c^{(1,2,3)} = \frac{1}{V^{N-3}} \int \sum_{(C''_n)} \prod^{(n-3|1,\ 2\ 3)} \times f_{ij} d\{N-3\}$$
$$= \frac{1}{V^{n-3}} \int \sum_{(C''_n)} \prod^{(n-3|1,\ 2,\ 3)} \times f_{ij} d\{n-3\} \tag{S6.32}$$
$$= (n-3)!\delta_n(1,2,3)V^{3-n},$$

where the last member of (S6.32) defines the next higher order of irreducible cluster integral, $\delta_n(1, 2, 3)$, in which molecules 1, 2, and 3 are held fixed. The contribution of these terms is

$$\sum_{n=4}^{N} \binom{N-3}{n-3} \frac{(n-3)!\delta_n(1,2,3)}{V^{n-3}} = \sum_{n=4} \rho^{n-3}\delta_n(1,2,3), \tag{S6.33}$$

so that from (S6.31, S6.33), equation (S6.29) becomes

$$\ln g^{(3)}(1,2,3) = \ln g^{(2)}(1,2) + \ln g^{(2)}(1,3) + \ln g^{(2)}(2,3) + \sum_{n=1}^{\infty} \rho^n \delta_{n+3}(1,2,3). \tag{S6.34}$$

We see immediately from (S6.4–5) that the last term on the right-hand side of (S6.34) is the one which is neglected in the superposition approximation. Also, equation (S6.34) shows immediately that the superposition approximation sums a certain class of diagrams [viz., the $\gamma_n(i, j)$ class] to all orders in the density, and therefore is possibly

[2] C''_n denotes all connected diagrams of n labeled points, excluding the bonds $f_{12}, f_{13}. f_{23}$.

superior to an evaluation of individual virial coefficients for the description of a dense fluid because it represents an approximation to the asymptotic form of the *complete* virial series.

On the other hand, if the superposition approximation is used to calculate the virial coefficients for the equation of state of a dilute system, then it is easily shown that virial coefficients higher than the third are given incorrectly. To demonstrate this we include the correction term in equation (S6.6), thus rendering it exact:

$$-kT\nabla_1 \ln g^{(2)}(1,2) = \nabla_1 u(1,2) + \rho \int \nabla_1 u(1,3) \times g^{(2)}(2,3)\, g^{(2)}(1,3) \exp\left(\sum_{n=1}^{\infty} \rho^n \delta_{n+3}\right) d(3). \tag{S6.35}$$

We now expand each $g^{(2)}$ in a power series in the density as

$$g^{(2)}(i,j) = \exp[-\beta u(i,j)] \times \left\{1 + \rho\gamma_3(i,j) + \rho^2\left[\frac{\gamma_3^2(i,j)}{2!} + \gamma_4(i,j)\right] + \dots\right\}. \tag{S6.36}$$

After substituting (S6.36) in (S6.35) and equating coefficients of equal powers of the density, there is obtained a set of equations of which the first two are

$$\begin{aligned} -kT\nabla_1\gamma_3(1,2) &= \int \nabla_1 u(1,3) \times \exp\{-\beta[u(1,3) + u(2,3)]\}\, d(3) \\ -kT\nabla_1\gamma_4(1,2) &= \int \nabla_1 u(1,3) \times \exp\{-\beta[u(1,3) + u(2,3)]\} \\ &\quad \times [\gamma_3(1,3) + \gamma_3(2,3) + \delta_4(1,2,3)]\, d(3) \dots . \end{aligned} \tag{S6.37}$$

[The reader should note that this procedure is valid because the irreducible integrals are defined in such a way that they are volume independent in a system large enough that surface effects are negligible.] Since the first of the set of terms (the δ_n) neglected in the superposition approximation appears in the *second* equation of (S6.37), it follows that γ_3 is given correctly by the first equation, but that, when δ_4 is neglected, γ_4 is incorrect. Thus, $g^{(2)}$ is calculated correct only to terms of $O(\rho)$:

$$g^{(2)}(i,j) = \exp[-\beta u(i,j)][1 + \rho\gamma_3(i,j) + \dots]. \tag{S6.38}$$

Recalling now the pressure equation, (S4.49),

$$\frac{\beta p}{\rho} = 1 - \frac{2\pi}{3}\rho \int_0^\infty u'(R)\, g^{(2)}(R) R^3 dR, \tag{S6.39}$$

we see that $(\beta p/\rho)$ is given correctly to terms of $O(\rho^2)$ by (S6.38), i.e., up to the third virial coefficient.

It is informative to consider the reason that the neglect of a first-order term in the density for $g^{(3)}$ should lead to an incorrect evaluation of only the second-order density term in $g^{(2)}$. This stepping-down feature is easily traced to the factor ρ multiplying the integral term in equation (S6.35). This results in (S6.37) in γ_3 being expressed in terms of γ_2 [i.e., the "bare" potential $u(i, j)$], γ_4 being expressed in terms of γ_3, and so on. It follows that Fisher's use of the refined superposition approximation (S6.21), which has the two coupled equations (S6.23–24), results in two successive step-downs of the correction so that his theory predicts the fourth virial coefficient correctly, but not the fifth.

S6.5. The Hyper-netted Chain Equation [13–18]

In this section, so far, we have described the derivations of some integral equations for the pair correlation function in which an assumption (the superposition approximation) has been introduced *ad hoc* to truncate the hierarchy of coupled equations (S6.1). We *then* investigated the meaning of the assumption in terms of the classes of diagrams summed. The justification of this procedure is that one must find a tractable approximation in order to obtain numerical results, and having obtained the results one can then discuss the usefulness of the approximation. We now turn to the reverse procedure in which certain summable classes of diagrams are identified, other classes are ignored, and different corresponding integro-differential equations are obtained. The expansion of $g_N^{(2)}(1, 2)$ may be rewritten in the form

$$G_N(1, 2) \equiv g_N^{(2)}(1, 2) - 1$$

$$= f_{12} + (1 + f_{12}) \sum_{n=1}^{\infty} \frac{\rho^n}{n!} \sum \int \prod f_{ij} d\{N - 2\}, \tag{S6.40}$$

where the diagrams representing the integrals which are part of the coefficient of ρ^n will contain $n + 2$ points. Of these $n + 2$ points, the coordinates of n (field points) are variables of integration. In each case the two fixed points are taken to be 1 and 2. Note that no line connects points 1 and 2.

It is now necessary to make some definitions: (1) A point serving as the sole link between two subdiagrams, one of which does not contain either of the points 1 or 2, is called an articulation point. The $\gamma_n(1, 2)$ indeed contain such points, i.e., these clusters have a connectivity greater than unity. (2) A pair of points which constitute the entire link between two subdiagrams is called an articulation pair of points. (3) If the points 1 and 2 can themselves be an articulation pair of points, the diagram is called a general irreducible cluster mapping. For those diagrams where this is not possible, the terminology simple irreducible cluster diagram will be used.

The diagrams associated with the pair-correlation-function series are of the general irreducible type. Now, in the definition of any given cluster diagram, the field points are numbered. Clearly, an interchange of labels does not alter the value of the integral, so that there must be $n!$ equal terms arising from a diagram with n field points. The operation of generating $n!$ specific labeled diagrams from one generic diagram will overcount the total contribution to $g_N^{(2)}(1, 2)$ unless note is taken of the symmetry of the diagram. The symmetry enters because the integrand in any one of the cluster integrals is determined by the f_{ij} and nothing else. Thus, a diagram is determined entirely by its bonds, and two diagrams are equivalent if they contain the same bonds, even though they may differ by a permutation of labels. For example,

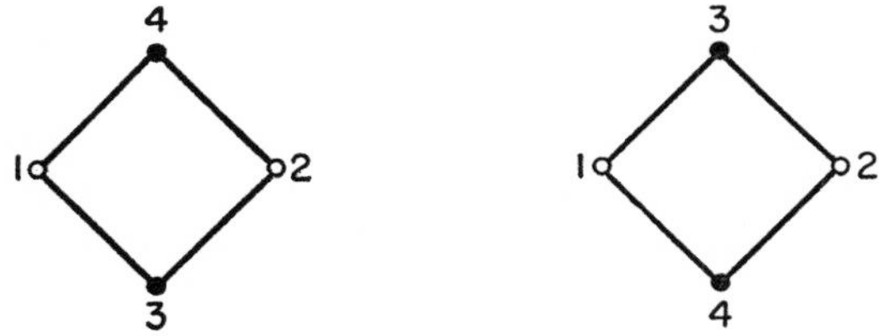

are identical since one need only rotate about an axis through 1 and 2, and they are superposable. In this operation no f_{ij} bonds need be broken. The series expansion for $g_N^{(2)}(1, 2)$ clearly contains only topologically distinct clusters. Therefore, some of the $n!$ diagrams generated by merely permuting labels on field points of a generic diagram will be redundant. To take account of this, we rewrite the series in the form

$$G_N(1, 2) = f_{12} + (1 + f_{12}) \times \sum_{n=1}^{\infty} \rho^n \sum{}^{*} \frac{1}{\mu(n, \gamma)} \int \prod f_{ij} d\{N-2\}, \tag{S6.41}$$

where $\mu(n, \gamma)$ is a symmetry number for a diagram of n field points and of type γ.

The diagrams included in the above sum are of three types: (a) parallel diagrams, which contain subdiagrams connected only at points 1 and 2 but having no other points in common, (*b*) series diagrams, which contain at least one point through which all paths between 1 and 2 must pass (nodal point), (*c*) bridge diagrams, which belong to neither (*a*) nor (*b*). We write, for (S6.41), therefore,

$$
\begin{aligned}
G_N(1, 2) = f_{12} + (1 + f_{12}) & \\
\times \Big[\sum_{n=1}^{\infty} \rho^n \Big(& \sum^{(S)} \frac{1}{\mu} \int \prod f_{ij} d\{N-2\} \\
& + \sum^{(P_1)} \frac{1}{\mu} \int \prod f_{ij} d\{N-2\} \\
& + \sum^{(B)} \frac{1}{\mu} \int \prod f_{ij} d\{N-2\} \Big) \Big],
\end{aligned}
\qquad \text{(S6.42)}
$$

where the superscripts on the sums indicate they are carried over series, parallel, and bridge diagrams, and only these, respectively. These separate sums will be denoted $S(1, 2)$, $P_1(1, 2)$, and $B(1, 2)$, respectively. In the new notation, (S6.42) may be written

$$G_N(1, 2) = f_{12} + (1 + f_{12})[S(1, 2) + B(1, 2) + P_1(1, 2)]. \qquad \text{(S6.43)}$$

We now consider some of the specific properties of the diagrams in this representation of the pair correlation function. Consider some general (1, 2) irreducible diagram. An arbitrary branch (i.e., parallel subdiagram joining points 1 and 2) can be any one of the series or bridge diagrams, but cannot be one of the parallel diagrams. Consider a typical parallel diagram having r branches of which p are of the series type and q of the bridge type. Nowhere in the integrand corresponding to such a diagram does there appear a factor f_{ij} with i in one branch and j in the other branch. Thus, the integral, whose integrand is mapped into a diagram of this type, factors into a product of integrals, each of which is over the coordinates of the field points of one branch. The symmetry number also factors into a product of two terms, one of which removes diagrams that differ only by permutation of identical entire branches, and the other of which removes redundancies within the branches (again a product of symmetry numbers for each branch). We write the contribution of the jth branch as

$$\frac{1}{\mu_j} \alpha_j(1, 2) \rho^{n_j},$$

where $\alpha_j(1, 2)$ represents the particular series or bridge graph which is that branch, μ_j its symmetry number, and n_j the number of field points in the branch.

To proceed further we single out a particular series branch in the typical parallel diagram and designate it the variable branch; the remaining $r - 1$ branches are designated fixed branches. Now consider the subset of all diagrams which contribute to Σ^* which have r branches, $r - 1$ of which are identical with the $r - 1$ branches of the selected typical diagram, while the rth branch is any member of the set of series diagrams. Let $\Gamma_1(1, 2)$ denote the sum of the contributions of the members of this subset and $\Gamma_2(1, 2)$ that of all remaining diagrams. Then

$$G_N(1, 2) = f_{12} + (1 + f_{12})[\Gamma_1(1, 2) + \Gamma_2(1, 2)]. \qquad (S6.44)$$

But

$$\Gamma_1(1, 2) = \tau(1, 2) \sum_{n_j} \frac{a_j(1, 2)}{\mu_j(n_j, \gamma)} \rho^{n_j}, \qquad (S6.45)$$

where $\tau(1, 2)$ is the contribution arising from the $r - 1$ fixed branches. Since the sum runs over all series diagrams, it is equivalent to $\Sigma^{(S)}$, whereupon

$$\Gamma_1(1, 2) = \tau(1, 2) S(1, 2).$$

Of course, a similar result is obtained from consideration of each branch separately. One obtains, thereby, for the total contribution from diagrams having r branches, p of which are of the series kind,

$$\frac{\tau(1, 2)[S(1, 2)]^p}{p!},$$

where $p!$ removes the redundant diagrams introduced in the process of allowing each branch to vary independently ($p!$ is the symmetry factor for the interchange of p entire branches).

A similar argument can be applied to the summation of the bridge-graph branches, so that one obtains a total contribution of

$$\frac{[S(1, 2)]^p [B(1, 2)]^q}{p!q!} \qquad (S6.46)$$

from all diagrams having r branches, p of which are of the series type and q of which are of the bridge type. Now p and q may range in magnitude from 0 to ∞, and $r = p + q \geq 1$, so that the total contribution from all diagrams $[\Gamma_1(1, 2) + \Gamma_2(1, 2)]$ is, from (S6.45–46),

$$\sum_{\substack{p,\, q=0 \\ (p+q\geq 1)}}^{\infty} \frac{[S(1, 2)]^p}{p!} \frac{[B(1, 2)]^q}{q!} = \sum_{r=1}^{\infty} \frac{[S(1, 2) + B(1, 2)]^r}{r!}$$

$$= \exp[S(1, 2) + B(1, 2)] - 1,$$

whereupon

$$\begin{aligned} G_N(1, 2) &= f_{12} + (1 + f_{12})\{\exp[S(1, 2) + B(1, 2)] - 1\} \\ &= \exp[-\beta u(1, 2) + S(1, 2) + B(1, 2)] - 1 \,. \end{aligned} \tag{S6.47}$$

It is sometimes convenient to include the factor f_{12} directly in the diagrammatic mapping. Let $\Sigma^{(Q)}$ represent any of the operations $\Sigma^{(S)}$, $\Sigma^{(P_1)}$, $\Sigma^{(B)}$. The sums $(1 + f_{12})\Sigma^{(Q)}$ can be described by the terms originally in $\Sigma^{(Q)}$ (all of which come from the term unity) plus a set of parallel diagrams obtained by taking each diagram of $\Sigma^{(Q)}$ and adding a bond from 1 to 2 (from the factor f_{12}). The set of diagrams defined by $(1 + f_{12})\Sigma^{(Q)}$ is denoted the augmented set of parallel diagrams. If we define a function $P(1, 2)$ by the relation

$$P(1, 2) = f_{12}[S(1, 2) + B(1, 2) + P_1(1, 2)] + P_1(1, 2), \tag{S6.48}$$

then

$$G_N(1, 2) = f_{12} + S(1, 2) + P(1, 2) + B(1, 2), \tag{S6.49}$$

which equation represents $G_N(1, 2)$ as the sum of the single line, series, bridge, and augmented parallel diagrams. If $T(1, 2)$ represents the sum of all non-series diagrams,

$$G_N(1, 2) = T(1, 2) + S(1, 2), \tag{S6.50}$$

$$T(1, 2) = f_{12} + P(1, 2) + B(1, 2). \tag{S6.51}$$

Then

$$\begin{aligned} T(1, 2) = \exp[&-\beta u(1, 2) + S(1, 2) \\ &+ B(1, 2)] - S(1, 2) - 1 \,. \end{aligned} \tag{S6.52}$$

Consider now a typical series diagram. These diagrams have at least one nodal point other than 1 or 2. The part of such a diagram contained between two nodal points, at least one of which is neither 1 nor 2, can be any member of the augmented parallel or bridge classes. Let the nodal point nearest 1 be labeled 3, and designate the diagram between 3 and 2 the fixed diagram, and that between 3 and 1, the variable diagram. Consider in $\Sigma^{(S)}$ the sum of all diagrams having the same fixed diagram between 3 and 2, but having any allowed diagram between 1 and 3. The sum will contain a common factor $[\alpha(3, 2)]$ for the fixed portion of the total diagram. The variable portion, being a sum over all augmented parallel and bridge graphs and the line f_{12}, gives just $T(1, 3)$. A factor ρ is needed for the point 3, since it is a field point for the entire diagram which has been fixed for these subdiagrams. There also remains an integration over (3). From these considerations we find

$$S(1, 2) = \rho \int T(1, 3)\, \alpha(3, 2)\, d(3). \qquad \text{(S6.53)}$$

But the diagrams connecting 3 with 2 can be any one of the G_N diagrams since they have not been specified (i.e., single line, series, augmented parallel, or bridge types), so that the sum over all diagrams of $\Sigma^{(S)}$ yields

$$S(1, 2) = \rho \int T(1, 3) G_N(3, 2)\, d(3) \qquad \text{(S6.54)}$$

$$\begin{aligned} G_N(1, 2) &= T(1, 2) + \rho \int T(1, 3) G_N(3, 2)\, d(3) \\ &= T(1, 2) + \rho \int G_N(y) T(|\boldsymbol{R} - \boldsymbol{y}|)\, d\boldsymbol{y}\,, \end{aligned} \qquad \text{(S6.55)}$$

where $\boldsymbol{R} = \boldsymbol{R}_2 - \boldsymbol{R}_1$, and $\boldsymbol{y} = \boldsymbol{R}_2 - \boldsymbol{R}_3$, and the dependence is only upon magnitudes in a fluid. Equation (S6.55) is the Ornstein-Zernicke equation relating the direct correlation function, $T(R)$, to the radial distribution function, $g_N^{(2)}(R)$. Since no diagrams have been omitted from the accounting, the equation can be seen to be exact.

We can perform the summation a different way. Let $S_m(1, 2)$ be a series diagram with m nodes (apart from the points 1 and 2). If we treat each node as a fixed point and vary the diagrams connecting each node, a repetition of the previous argument shows that

$$\begin{aligned} S_m(1, 2) = \rho^m \int T(1, 3) T(3, 4) \ldots \\ \times T(m+2, 2)\, d(3) \ldots d(m+2). \end{aligned} \qquad \text{(S6.56)}$$

But this diagram may be remapped onto a diagram in which each $T(i, j)$ is replaced by a line joining the nodes labeled i, j. Thus, the integrand maps into a chain diagram, and if we denote the Fourier transform of $T(R)$ by $\tilde{T}(\boldsymbol{k})$, then, by the convolution theorem,

$$\tilde{S}_m(\boldsymbol{k}) = \rho^m \tilde{T}^{m+1}(\boldsymbol{k}), \qquad \text{(S6.57)}$$

since there are $(m + 1)$ links $T(R)$. Since

$$\sum_{m=1}^{\infty} S_m(R) = S(R), \qquad \text{(S6.58)}$$

$$\tilde{S}(\boldsymbol{k}) = \frac{\rho \tilde{T}^2(\boldsymbol{k})}{1 - \rho \tilde{T}(\boldsymbol{k})}, \qquad \text{(S6.59)}$$

which can be derived from equations (S6.54–55) if it is assumed that $\rho \tilde{T}(\boldsymbol{k}) < 1$, so that the series converges.

Finally, we turn to an examination of the properties of bridge diagrams. It will be recalled that bridge diagrams are defined as those which have no nodal points other than 1 and 2, and for which 1 and 2 are not an articulation pair of points. Consider a typical bridge diagram. This will, in general, contain articulation pairs of points. Replace the (complex) diagrams between each such pairs of points by single-line bonds. The resulting diagram is still a bridge diagram but has no articulation pairs of points. In general, replacing any line in a bridge diagram by some more complicated diagram does not remove that diagram from the class of bridge diagrams. Since the original diagram had no nodal point, there were at least two paths connecting 1 and 2. Replacing a line by a more complex graph does not connect these separate paths. Further, the original diagram cannot have two paths connecting 1 and 2 which are not themselves connected at some other point. Replacing a line by some other diagram cannot disconnect these paths. In view of these remarks we see that the replacement of complex diagrams between articulation pairs of points by lines between each pair of points removes the articulation pairs of points by denying the possibility of any pair of points being the sole connection between two subdiagrams. Bridge diagrams which do not have articulation pairs of points are denoted fundamental diagrams: any bridge diagram can be reduced to a fundamental diagram and, conversely, one can build up a unique set of bridge diagrams from a fundamental diagram. Thus, the set of all bridge diagrams can be generated from the set of all fundamental diagrams.

Consider some particular fundamental diagram which represents a mapping of the term

$$\rho^n \int \prod f_{ij} d(3) \ldots d(n+2).$$

Suppose there is a bond between 1 and 3, representing the factor f_{13} in the integrand. If f_{13} is replaced by any diagram of $G_N(1, 2)$, then some member of the set of all bridge diagrams is produced. The sum of all such diagrams will include all the f_{ij} other than f_{13} of the original diagram, but between 1 and 3 there will be a sum over all allowed diagrams of $G_N(1, 2)$. The net effect is, then, that $G_N(1, 3)$ replaces f_{13}. If the same procedure is followed for each f_{ij} there is obtained

$$\rho^n \sum_m \rho^{m+1} \int \prod G_N(i, j)\, d\{n\},$$

where the summation is over all fundamental diagrams of n field points, and m is the number of f_{ij} bonds in the diagram. The factor ρ^{m+1} appears because $m + 1$ field points are held fixed while generating the successive subdiagrams. It is clear that the expression obtained by the preceding arguments can also be mapped into a bridge diagram, but one in which the line bonds represent the functions $G_N(i, j)$. Such diagrams do not have articulation pairs of points. The entire set of bridge diagrams may now be generated by summing the new set of mappings over n from $n = 2$ to $n = \infty$. Finally,

$$B(1, 2) = \sum_{n=2}^{\infty} \sum_{m} \rho^{n+m+1} \int \prod G_N(i, j)\, d\{n\}, \quad (S6.60)$$

and the summations are over fundamental graphs only.

The original exact cluster expansion for $G_N(1, 2)$ has now been replaced by a set of exact equations, each the result of a different summation procedure. To find $G_N(1, 2)$ we must now solve simultaneously the set of equations:

$$T(R) = \exp[-\beta u(R)] \exp[S(R) + B(R)] - S(R) - 1, \quad (S6.61)$$

$$\tilde{S}(k) = \frac{\rho \tilde{T}^2(k)}{1 - \rho \tilde{T}(k)}, \quad (S6.62)$$

$$B(R) = \sum_{n=2}^{\infty} \sum_{m} \rho^{n+m+1} \int \prod G_N(i, j)\, d\{n\}, \quad (S6.63)$$

where we have again written $R = |R_2 - R_1|$.

The approximation to $G_N(R)$ obtained if the set of equations (S6.61–63) is solved with $B(R) = 0$, is called the hyper-netted chain (HNC) equation. We have

$$G_N(R) = \exp[-\beta u(R) + S(R)] - 1, \quad (S6.64)$$

so that the potential of the mean force $W^{(2)}(R)$ is given by

$$W^{(2)}(R) = u(R) - kTS(R). \quad (S6.65)$$

From (S.6.52) we, therefore, obtain

$$\begin{aligned} T(R) &= g_N^{(2)}(R) - S(R) - 1 \\ &= g_N^{(2)}(R) - 1 - \ln g_N^{(2)}(R) - \beta u(R), \end{aligned} \quad (S6.66)$$

which is the desired result. It is thus clear that the HNC approximation consists in retaining the contributions from all series and parallel diagrams and neglecting the contributions from all bridge diagrams. Any improvement of the HNC approximation requires the enumeration of the set of fundamental bridge diagrams for n field points. Partial enumeration of these sets has been made by Rushbrooke.

S6.6. The Percus-Yevick Equation [19, 20]

Another integral equation for the radial distribution function is that derived by Percus and Yevick. It yields a description of dense fluids of comparable accuracy to the other equations previously derived. The original derivation of this equation is long and difficult but, knowing the result in advance, it is possible to give a much simpler derivation. We give here the derivation due to Stell.

It should be clear to the reader, from a consideration of the previous section, that many rearrangements of the cluster expansion are possible. Therefore, by the use of different topological arguments many approximate integral equations can be generated. We define new cluster sums[3] $M(R)$, $Y(R)$, and $D(R)$ by

$$G_N = S + T \qquad \text{(cf. eq. [S6.50])}, \tag{S6.67}$$

$$T = f(1+S) + M \tag{S6.68}$$

$$\begin{aligned} g_N^{(2)} &= \exp(-\beta u)(1+S) + M \\ &= \exp(-\beta u)\, Y \end{aligned} \tag{S6.69}$$

$$\begin{aligned} Y &= 1 + S + \exp(\beta u) M \\ &= 1 + S + D, \end{aligned} \tag{S6.70}$$

$$T = fY + D, \tag{S6.71}$$

where G_N, T are related by (S6.55). If, for brevity, we introduce the notation

$$A(x) * B(x) = \rho \int A(x-y) B(y)\, dy, \tag{S6.72}$$

then it is seen that

$$S = T * G_N = T * (T+S), \tag{S6.73}$$

and

$$Y = 1 + D + T * G_N. \tag{S6.74}$$

In the approximation $M = 0$, which is the same as $D = 0$ for non-singular potentials, we find

$$Y = 1 + S, \tag{S6.75}$$

$$T = fY, \tag{S6.76}$$

and

$$Y = 1 + (fY) * G_N. \tag{S6.77}$$

[3] Hereafter, in this section, the arguments R of all quantities, and the subscripts of f_{12} are omitted, without ambiguity.

Equation (S6.77) is the Percus-Yevick equation. We can now construct an iterative solution of (S6.77). Because of the Fourier transform property of convoluted integrals (cf. eq. [S6.57]), (S.6.73) may be written

$$\tilde{S} = \rho\tilde{T}(\tilde{T}+\tilde{S}) = \frac{\rho\tilde{T}^2}{1-\rho\tilde{T}}\,, \tag{S6.78}$$

where $\tilde{S}$ is the Fourier transform of S, etc. Equation (S6.78) may be expanded in a series in powers of $\rho\tilde{T}$. We assume that $\rho\tilde{T} < 1$, so that

$$\tilde{S} = \rho\tilde{T}^2 \sum_{m=0}^{\infty} (\rho\tilde{T})^m\,. \tag{S6.79}$$

By retransforming (S6.79), S is obtained as the sum of convolutions of T with itself; this is the reverse of the process leading from (S6.56) to (S6.59). The basic equations of the iterative scheme are (S6.67) and (S6.73) with (S6.75):

$$S = T * T + T * S\,,$$

$$T = f + fS\,,$$

$$G_N = T + S\,,$$

so that, diagrammatically,

a) 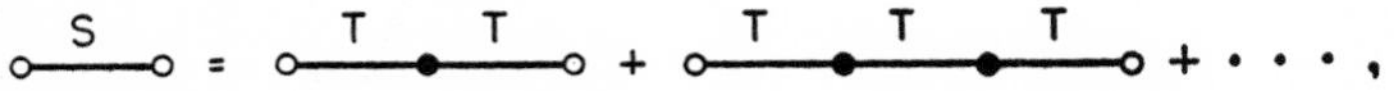

b) 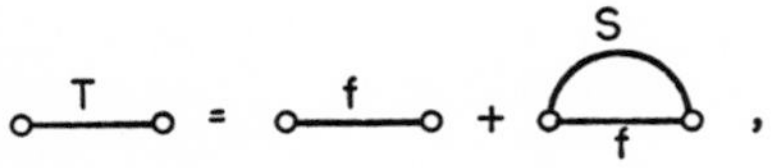

(S6.80)

c) 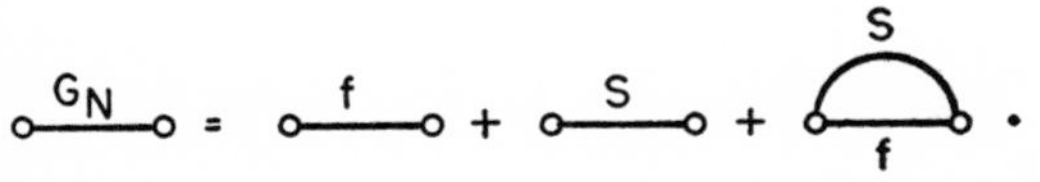

The product fS in the expression for T in (S6.80b) is represented by

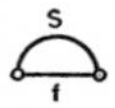

because, as we saw in section S6.5, the product of f with any diagram (i.e., cluster integral) with two fixed points turns that diagram into one of the parallel type. Thus, any diagram consisting of f-bonds in the set giving G_N is either (*a*) the single *f*-bond, (*b*) a member of the set S, or (*c*) a member of the set formed by the union (product) of an *f*-bond and set S. Thus, equation (S6.80c), for G_N, is called the series-union expansion.

Suppose the iteration for G_N begins with $S_0 = 0$, so that $T_0 = f$ and $G_{N,0} = f$. We find

a)
b)
c)
d)

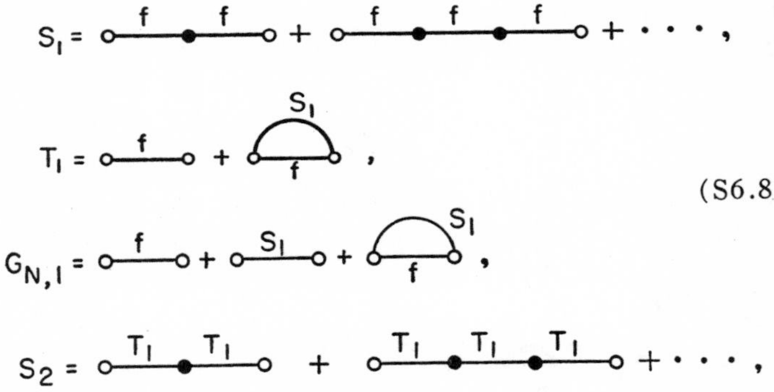

(S6.81)

and so on. S_n may be expressed in terms of *f*-bonds only. For example, (S6.81b), for T_1, may be written in terms of *f*-bonds only as

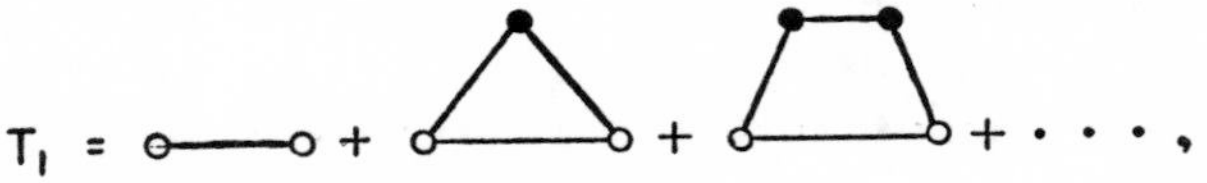

(S6.82)

so that (S6.81d) becomes

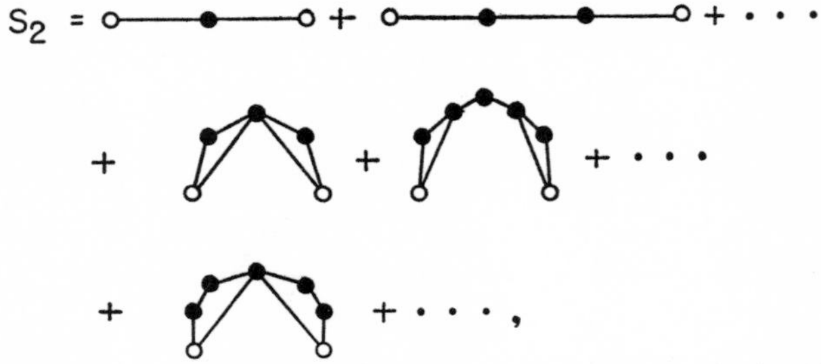

(S6.83)

where the terms in the nth line come from (S6.81d) and the nth term of (S6.82). If $\lim_{n\to\infty} S_n = S$ exists, then diagrams appearing in the sum for S may be generated by the following prescription: For any convex polygon, label two adjacent vertices as the fixed points and delete the line joining them, and then add any number of non-intersecting straight lines (including zero) between the vertices in such a way that the final diagram may be divided into two topological mirror-images by a line passing between the two fixed points. The polygons are, of course, constrained to a plane during this construction. A prescription for the diagrams appearing in the sum for $G_N = \lim_{n\to\infty} G_{N,n}$ (if this exists) follows by a simple modification of the foregoing description, according to (S6.80c).

We see from (S6.67–68) and (S6.74) that the exact equation for the radial distribution function is

$$g_N^{(2)} - 1 = G_N = f(1+S) + S + M\,, \qquad \text{(S6.84)}$$

or

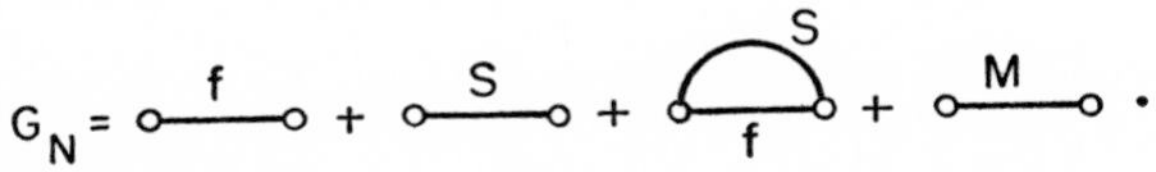

. (S6.85)

The Percus-Yevick approximation obtains when we set $M = 0$, for all R. By comparison of equations (S6.48), (S6.51), and (S6.68) we see that

$$M = (B + P_1)(1 + f)\,, \qquad \text{(S6.86)}$$

so that the Percus-Yevick approximation entails the neglect of all bridge and parallel diagrams without 1–2 bonds, and the parallel diagrams formed by inserting the 1–2 bonds in these diagrams; this is a much larger class than the class (bridge diagrams) neglected in the HNC approximation.

The HNC equation can be discussed in terms of an iterative scheme similar to that just described for the Percus-Yevick equation. If we introduce the approximation

$$M = \exp(-\beta u)(e^S - 1 - S)\,, \qquad \text{(S6.87)}$$

equations (S6.67–68) give

$$S = \beta u + \ln g_N^{(2)}\,, \qquad \text{(S6.88)}$$

so that, since

$$\begin{aligned} T &= G_N - S \\ &= g_N^{(2)} - 1 - \beta u - \ln g_N^{(2)}\,, \\ S &= T * G_N \\ &= \{g_N^{(2)} - 1 - \beta u - \ln g_N^{(2)}\} * \{g_N^{(2)} - 1\}. \end{aligned} \qquad \text{(S6.89)}$$

Substitution of (S6.89) in (S6.88) gives the HNC equation in the form

$$\ln g_N^{(2)} = -\beta u + \{g_N^{(2)} - 1 - \beta u - \ln g_N^{(2)}\} * \{g_N^{(2)} - 1\}. \qquad \text{(S6.90)}$$

The equations linking S, T, and G in this approximation may be written

$$S = T * T + T * S \qquad \text{(S6.90a)}$$

$$T = f\,e^S + e^S - 1 - S\,, \tag{S6.90b}$$

$$G_N = S + T\,. \tag{S6.90c}$$

Equation (S6.90a) may be expressed as a chain sum as in equation (S6.80a). Equation (S6.90b) may also be expressed as a chain sum when the exponentials are expanded. Thus, we have

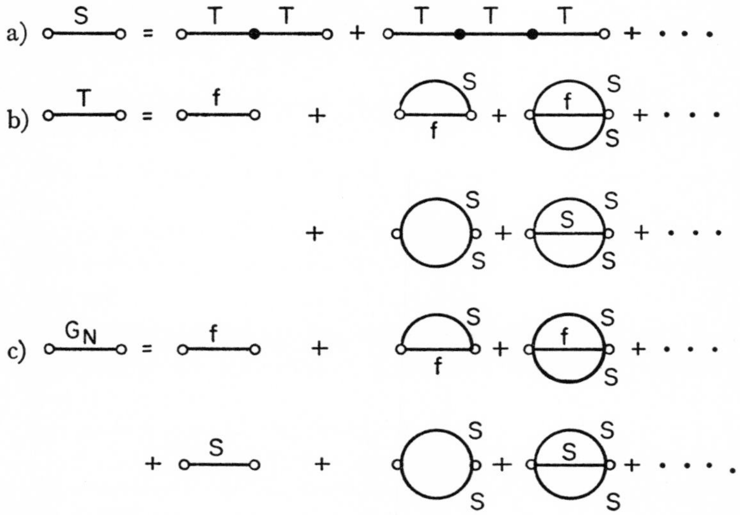
a) S = T T + T T T + . . .
b) T = f + S f + S f S + . . .
+ S S + S S S + . . .
c) GN = f + S f + S f S + . . .
+ S + S S + S S S + ...

(S6.9

The solution may be obtained by iteration in the following way. The initial choice of S is $S_0 = 0$. Then $T_0 = f$ and $G_{N,\,0} = f$, so that

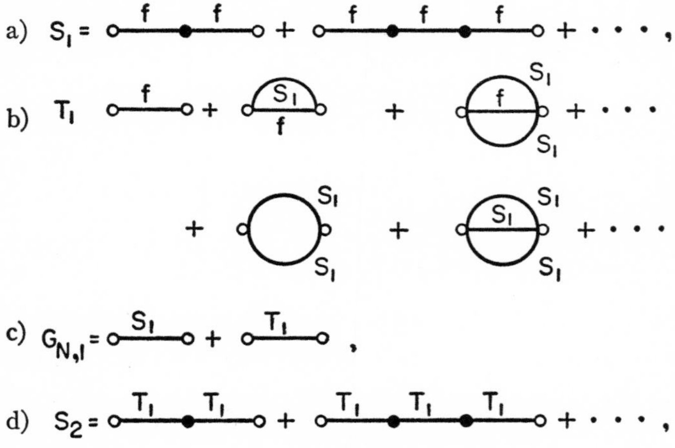
a) S1 = f f + f f f + . . . ,
b) T1 f + S1 f + S1 f S1 + . . .
+ S1 S1 + S1 S1 S1 + . . . ,
c) GN,1 = S1 + T1 ,
d) S2 = T1 T1 + T1 T1 T1 + . . . ,

(S6.92)

and so on. The limit $G_N = \lim_{n\to\infty} G_{N,n}$, if it exists, can be seen from the form of (S6.92a, b, c) to comprise a series and parallel summation of f-bonds.

It is interesting to note that the assumption that the direct correlation function is identically zero for $R > R_0$, if the potential is zero for $R > R_0$, leads, in the case of rigid spheres, to just the Percus-Yevick equation. For any potential that vanishes for $R > R_0$, the assumption that $M \equiv 0$ still implies that $T(R) = 0$, but it does not completely specify $T(R)$. Thus, the approximation $M \equiv 0$ is an extreme statement on the short-range nature of the direct correlation function. In these terms, the HNC approximation is not so extreme since it assumes that $T(R)$ falls off as $g_N^{(2)}(R) - 1 - \ln g_N^{(2)}(R)$.

At this point it is pertinent to mention that interest in the equilibrium theory, from the point of view of transport theory, centers entirely on the pair correlation function. Because of this we shall not treat in any detail the interesting scaled particle theory of Reiss, Frisch, Lebowitz, and Helfand. In that theory the pair correlation function is not computed and other means are utilized to calculate the thermodynamic properties of the liquid.

S6.7. The Method of Functional Differentiation [21, 22]

The method of functional differentiation described in section S4.3 can be used to derive the integral equations for the radial distribution function discussed in this section in a very compact way. The basis of this method lies in the representation of an n-molecule distribution function, $\rho^{(n)}$, as the distribution function for one molecule in a suitable external potential.

The defining equation for $\rho^{(n)}$ in the Grand Canonical Ensemble is equation (S4.15):

$$\rho^{(n)} = \frac{1}{\Xi}\sum_{N\geq n}\frac{z^N}{(N-n)!}\int\cdots\int \exp[-\beta U(\{N\})]\,d\{N-n\}. \quad (S6.93)$$

From this definition we obtain

$$\frac{\rho^{(n+1)}}{\rho^{(n)}} = \frac{\displaystyle\sum_{N\geq n+1}\frac{z^N}{(N-n-1)!}\int \exp[-\beta U(\{N\})]\,d\{N-n-1\}}{\displaystyle\sum_{N\geq n}\frac{z^N}{(N-n)!}\int \exp[-\beta U(\{N\})]\,d\{N-n\}}. \quad (S6.94)$$

Now, it is always possible to represent the total potential energy of the system as the sum of the potential energies of two groups of n and $N - n$ molecules, and their respective interaction. In an obvious notation,

$$U(\{N\}) = U(\{n\}) + U(\{N-n\}) + U(\{n; N-n\}). \quad (S6.95)$$

Upon changing the summation variable N to $N = M + n$, we obtain

$$\frac{\rho^{(n+1)}}{\rho^{(n)}} = \frac{\displaystyle\sum_{M\geq 1} \frac{z^M}{(M-1)!} \int \exp\{-\beta[U(\{M\})+U(\{n; M\})]\} d\{M-1\}}{\displaystyle\sum_{M\geq 0} \frac{z^M}{M!} \int \exp\{-\beta[U(\{M\})+U(\{n; M\})]\} d\{M\}}. \quad (S6.96)$$

Equation (S6.96) defines a 1-molecule distribution function when the system is subjected to an external potential (due to the n fixed molecules). It is clear that the denominator of the right-hand side represents a generalization of the Grand Partition Function to this circumstance. The 1-molecule distribution function defined by (S6.96) is a functional of the imposed potential, so that

$$\frac{\rho^{(n+1)}(1, \ldots, n, n+1)}{\rho^{(n)}(1, \ldots, n)} = \rho^{(1)}[n+1 \mid U(\{n\})], \quad (S6.97)$$

where the functional dependence upon the potential of the n-molecule group is represented by the symbol $U(\{n\})$ set off by a vertical bar. Consider the case when $n = 1$. Then

$$U(\{1; M\}) = \sum_{i=2}^{M+1} u(1, i), \quad (S6.98)$$

where the M molecules of the system are labeled $2, \ldots, M + 1$, and

$$U(1) = u(1, 2). \quad (S6.99)$$

Suppose that the strength of the interaction $u(1, i)$ between molecule 1 and M molecules of the system is varied in some way from u to u':

$$u'(1, i) = u(1, i) + \delta u(1, i). \quad (S6.100)$$

After examining (S6.100) it is pertinent to ask: What is the effect of this variation upon $\rho^{(1)}[2 \mid U(1)]$? This effect can be calculated by taking the functional derivative of equation (S6.96) with respect to $u(1, i)$. First, we rewrite (S6.96) in a slightly different form as

$$\rho^{(1)}[2 \mid U(1)] = \frac{1}{\Xi[U(1)]} \sum_{M \geq 1} \frac{z^M}{(M-1)!} \int \cdots \int \times \exp\left\{-\beta\left[U(\{M\}) + \sum_{i=2}^{M+1} u(1, i)\right]\right\} d\{M-1\}. \tag{S6.101}$$

Upon varying $u(1, i)$, there is obtained the relation

$$-\delta\rho^{(1)}[2 \mid U(1)] = \frac{\delta\beta u(1, 2)}{\Xi[U(1)]} \sum_{M \geq 1} \frac{z^M}{(M-1)!} \int \cdots \int \times \exp\left\{-\beta\left[U(\{M\}) + \sum_{i=2}^{M+1} u(1, i)\right]\right\} d\{M-1\}$$
$$+ \frac{1}{\Xi[U(1)]} \sum_{M \geq 1} \frac{z^M}{(M-1)!} \int \cdots \int \tag{S6.102}$$
$$\times \exp\left\{-\beta\left[U(\{M\}) + \sum_{i=2}^{M+1} u(1, i)\right]\right\}$$
$$\times \sum_{i=3}^{M+1} \delta u(1, i)\, d\{M-1\} + \rho^{(1)}[2 \mid U(1)] \frac{\delta\Xi}{\Xi}.$$

The second term on the right-hand side of equation (S6.102) contains $(M-1)$ identical contributions, so that the equation may be written

$$-\delta\rho^{(1)}[2 \mid U(1)] = \rho^{(1)}[2 \mid U(1)]\, \delta\beta u(1, 2) + \int \rho^{(2)}[2, 3 \mid U(1)]\, \delta\beta u(1, 3)\, d(3) + \rho^{(1)}[2 \mid U(1)] \frac{\delta\Xi}{\Xi}. \tag{S6.103}$$

The term $(\delta\Xi/\Xi)$ is determined by integrating (S6.103) over (2). We have

$$\int \rho^{(1)}[2 \mid U(1)]\, d(2) = \langle N \rangle$$
$$\int \rho^{(2)}[2, 3 \mid U(1)]\, d(2) = \langle N - 1 \rangle \rho^{(1)}[3 \mid U(1)]$$
$$\int \delta\rho^{(1)}[2 \mid U(1)]\, d(2) = 0\,,$$

so that

$$-\frac{\delta\Xi}{\Xi} = \int \rho^{(1)}[3 \mid U(1)]\, \delta\beta u(1, 3)\, d(3)\,. \tag{S6.104}$$

Equation (S6.103) now becomes

$$-\delta\rho^{(1)}[2\,|\,U(1)] = \int \rho^{(1)}[2\,|\,U(1)]\,\delta(\boldsymbol{R}_3-\boldsymbol{R}_2)\,\delta\beta u(1,3)\,d(3) + \int \rho^{(2)}[2,3\,|\,U(1)]\,\delta\beta u(1,3)\,d(3) - \rho^{(1)}[2\,|\,U(1)]\int \rho^{(1)}[3\,|\,U(1)] \times \delta\beta u(1,3)\,d(3), \qquad (S6.105)$$

and the functional derivative of $\rho^{(1)}[2|U(1)]$ with respect to $\beta u(1, 3)$ is therefore

$$-\frac{\delta\rho^{(1)}[2\,|\,U(1)]}{\delta\beta u(1,3)} = \rho^{(1)}[2\,|\,U(1)]\,\delta(\boldsymbol{R}_3-\boldsymbol{R}_2) + \rho^{(2)}[2,3\,|\,U(1)] - \rho^{(1)}[2\,|\,U(1)]\,\rho^{(1)}[3\,|\,U(1)]. \qquad (S6.106)$$

We are interested in the form taken by equation (S6.106) when molecule 1 is far removed from molecules 2 and 3, i.e., in the limit $U(1) \to 0$. Equation (S6.106) becomes

$$-\left[\frac{\delta\rho^{(1)}[2\,|\,U(1)]}{\delta\beta u(1,3)}\right]_{U(1)=0} = \rho^{(1)}(2)\,\delta(\boldsymbol{R}_3-\boldsymbol{R}_2) + \rho^{(2)}(2,3) - \rho^{(1)}(2)\,\rho^{(1)}(3). \qquad (S6.107)$$

The functional inverse $A^{-1}(1, 2)$ of a quantity $A(1, 2)$ is defined by

$$\int A^{-1}(1,2)\,A(2,3)\,d(2) = \delta(\boldsymbol{R}_1-\boldsymbol{R}_3), \qquad (S6.108)$$

so that if we *define* a quantity $T(2, 3)$ by

$$-\left[\frac{\delta\beta u(1,2)}{\delta\rho^{(1)}[3\,|\,U(1)]}\right]_{U(1)=0} = \frac{\delta(\boldsymbol{R}_2-\boldsymbol{R}_3)}{\rho^{(1)}(2)} - T(2,3), \qquad (S6.109)$$

then, by (S6.108), it follows that $T(2, 3)$ is the direct correlation function given by (cf. eq. [S6.55])

$$g^{(2)}(1,3) - 1 = T(1,3) + \rho^{(1)}(1)\int [g^{(2)}(1,2) - 1]\,T(2,3)\,d(2). \qquad (S6.110)$$

Any function $A[2|U(1)]$ may be regarded as a functional of a function $B[3|U(1)]$ and may be expanded in a functional Taylor expansion as

$$A[2\,|\,U(1)] = A(2) + \int \{B[3\,|\,U(1)] - B(3)\} \times \left[\frac{\delta A[2\,|\,U(1)]}{\delta B[3\,|\,U(1)]}\right]_{U(1)=0} d(3) + \frac{1}{2!}\int\int \{B[3\,|\,U(1)] - B(3)\}\{B[4\,|\,U(1)] - B(4)\} \times \left[\frac{\delta^2 A[2\,|\,U(1)]}{\delta B[3\,|\,U(1)]\,\delta B[4\,|\,U(1)]}\right]_{U(1)=0} d(3)\,d(4) + \cdots, \qquad (S6.111)$$

where

$$A(2) = A[2 \mid U(1) = 0], \qquad \text{(S6.112)}$$

etc. Now, it is evident from the derivation of equation (S6.107) that the second derivative of $\rho^{(1)}[2 \mid U(1)]$ will introduce the 3-molecule distribution function $\rho^{(3)}(2, 3, 4)$, and so on for higher derivatives. Since the integral equations previously discussed in this section involve 2-molecule distribution functions only, it follows that they correspond to truncating the expansion (S6.111) after the first derivative. Alternatively, these equations are derived by choosing some functions $A[2 \mid U(1)]$, $B[3 \mid U(1)]$ and approximating A as a linear functional of B everywhere in the domain in which they are defined. Obviously great physical insight is needed to make a good choice of A and B. If we choose $A = \rho^{(1)}[2 \mid U(1)] \exp[\beta u(1, 2)]$ and $B = \rho^{(1)}[3 \mid U(1)]$, then, by (S6.109),

$$\begin{aligned}
&\frac{\delta\{\rho^{(1)}[2 \mid U(1)]\exp[\beta u(1, 2)]\}}{\delta\{\rho^{(1)}[3 \mid U(1)]\}} \\
&\quad = \left[\exp[\beta u(1, 2)]\frac{\delta\rho^{(1)}[2 \mid U(1)]}{\delta\rho^{(1)}[3 \mid U(1)]}\right]_{U(1)=0} \\
&\qquad + \Big[\exp[\beta u(1, 2)]\,\rho^{(1)}[2 \mid U(1)] \qquad \text{(S6.113)} \\
&\qquad\qquad \times \frac{\delta\beta u(1, 2)}{\delta\rho^{(1)}[3 \mid U(1)]}\Big]_{U(1)=0} \\
&\quad = \delta(\mathbf{R}_2 - \mathbf{R}_3) + \rho^{(1)}(2)\left[T(2, 3) - \frac{\delta(\mathbf{R}_2 - \mathbf{R}_3)}{\rho^{(1)}(2)}\right],
\end{aligned}$$

where the Dirac δ-function arises because

$$\delta\rho^{(1)}[2 \mid U(1)] = \int \delta(\mathbf{R}_2 - \mathbf{R}_3)\,\delta\rho^{(1)}[3 \mid U(1)]\,d(3). \qquad \text{(S6.114)}$$

Substitution of the given forms of A, B, and (S6.113), in equation (S6.111) yields the Percus-Yevick equation (S6.77) in the form

$$\begin{aligned}
&\rho^{(2)}(1, 2)\{\exp[\beta u(1, 2)] - 1\} \\
&\qquad = -\rho^{(1)}(1)\rho^{(1)}(2)T(1, 2).
\end{aligned} \qquad \text{(S6.115)}$$

Similarly, expansion of $\ln\{\rho^{(1)}[2 \mid U(1)] \exp[\beta u(1, 2)]\}$ as a linear functional of $\rho^{(1)}[2 \mid U(1)]$ yields the HNC equation, while the expansion of $\rho^{(1)}[2 \mid U(1)]\nabla\beta u(1, 2)$ as a linear functional of

$$\ln\{\rho^{(1)}[2 \mid U(1)] \exp[\beta u(1, 2)]\}$$

yields the Yvon-Born-Green equation.

It will be shown in section S7 that the Percus-Yevick equation is superior to the others for hard-sphere fluids. This is because the required relation between $\rho^{(1)} \exp(\beta u)$ and $\rho^{(1)}$ is strictly obeyed, even at the boundary of a hard sphere. Even for a more realistic model in which molecules interact with soft potentials of finite range the linear relationship is satisfied outside the range of the potential, and, in addition, continues its boundary value and slope for some distance inside the range. However, for separations of interest in calculating the pressure from equation (S4.49), considerable deviations from linearity are bound to occur.

S7. NUMERICAL SOLUTIONS OF THE INTEGRAL EQUATIONS

The four approximate equations relating $g^{(2)}$ to u, which we have derived in the previous section, are the only ones with which sufficient work has been done to permit a comparison to be made between theory and experiment. As might be expected from their complexity, analytic solutions of the integral equations are not generally possible at present, and numerical integration must be employed. However, an analytic solution to the Percus-Yevick equation has been found for the special case of hard spheres.

S7.1. Low Density Solutions [23, 24]

It has already been pointed out that if $g^{(2)}$ were known exactly the various forms of the equation of state, e.g., (S4.38) and (S4.49), would yield identical results. However, when approximations are introduced, consistency is destroyed, as was shown in section S6.4, particularly equations (S6.26–27). Consider now the low-density limit in which the virial expansion of the equation of state is valid. If we write the equation of state in the form

$$\frac{\beta p}{\rho} = 1 + B\rho + C\rho^2 + D\rho^3 + \dots, \tag{S7.1}$$

we can evaluate the coefficients $B, C, \dots$ from either (S4.38) or (S4.49) and the various $g^{(2)}$ functions determined by equations (S6.6, S6.13, S6.66, or S6.115). In practice, the exact values of $B, C, \dots$ are known only for the special case of rigid spheres, so that our comparison is necessarily restricted to this example. The actual computation of the virial coefficients is tedious and we shall not consider the methods used herein. Using the superscripts p to refer to (S4.49) and c to refer to (S4.38) one finds the results displayed in Table 1.

The first and most important observation to be made is that none of the approximate theories is consistent past the third virial coefficient. It is possible to develop procedures which insure consistency of all of the equations up to the fourth virial coefficient, but the fifth virial coefficient remains both inconsistent and incorrect. For example, when the coefficient D is made exact by extending the PY and HNC equations through the inclusion of extra terms neglected in equations (S6.115) and (S6.66), the fifth virial coefficient becomes $E^p_{\mathrm{PY}} = 0.493\ b^4$ and $E^p_{\mathrm{HNC}} = 0.398\ b^4$. These values are even poorer than those obtained from the lower order PY and HNC equations. The values of the fifth virial coefficient from the extended Yvon-Born-Green or Kirkwood equations are not available, but there is no reason to believe they will be improved over the values obtained from the simple theory.

TABLE 1

Virial Coefficients for the Rigid-Sphere Fluid from the Several Approximate Theories*

	$B^p(b)$	$B^c(b)$	$C^p(b^2)$	$C^c(b^2)$	$D^p(b^3)$	$D^c(b^3)$	$E^p(b^4)$	$E^c(b^4)$
Exact.....	1	1	5/8	5/8	0.2869	0.2869	0.1103	0.1103
YBG.....	1	1	5/8	5/8	.2252	.3424	.0475	.1335
K........	1	1	5/8	5/8	....	....	....	....
HNC.....	1	1	5/8	5/8	.4453	.2092	.1447	.0493
PY.......	1	1	5/8	5/8	0.2500	0.2969	0.0859	0.121

* The unit $b = \frac{1}{3}(2\pi\sigma^3)$, where σ is the hard-core diameter.

It is important to emphasize that the failure of the theories to reproduce the virial coefficients does not necessarily imply that the theories are useless in the liquid region. In each case, contributions from all orders of the density are included in the integral-equation representation. We may, therefore, expect the equation of state to be superior to a four- or five-term virial expansion. Indeed, if the contributions of each order of the density are those most important in the liquid range (highly connected diagrams), the approximate theories might be quite good at high densities even if the virial coefficients are not exact. It is, therefore, important to examine other predictions of the various theories before deciding on their relative merits.

S7.2. High Density Solutions [25–37]

The numerical solution of the various equations for the pair correlation function is a calculation of considerable magnitude. Nevertheless, we shall not concern ourselves with the details of the technique and will only examine the results of the calculations.

First, consider the properties of a hypothetical rigid-sphere fluid. For this case

$$\begin{aligned} u(R) &= 0\,, & R &\geq \sigma\,, \\ u(R) &= \infty\,, & R &< \sigma\,, \end{aligned} \tag{S7.2}$$

and all the properties of the liquid are determined by the statistical geometry of the packing of N spheres in a volume V. Since there is no real system which can be used as an experimental standard with which to compare theory, the approximate theories of the correlation function must be examined with different criteria.

Using high-speed digital computers it is now possible to solve, simultaneously, the equations of motion for a limited number of molecules. In three dimensions this number is of order 10^3, whereas in two dimensions it is larger. Alternatively, Monte Carlo methods can be used. The Monte Carlo method as used in statistical mechanics consists of the generation of a Markov chain of successive states of the system being studied. The successive states in the chain are generated in such a manner that a given state will occur with a frequency proportional to its probability in a given ensemble as the chain length is increased indefinitely. Thus, the method is just a means of directly averaging the properties of interest over the configuration space of the system, with each state receiving its correct weight according to a particular ensemble.

Calculations for the case of the hard-sphere fluid have been made by both the method of molecular dynamics and by the Monte Carlo technique. The results are in agreement and will be considered herein to represent the "experimental" equation of state of the dense rigid-sphere fluid.

For a rigid-sphere fluid, the potential (S7.2) when inserted into (S4.49) leads to a simple equation of state

$$\frac{\beta p}{\rho} = 1 + \frac{2\pi\sigma^3}{3}\,\rho\, g^{(2)}(\sigma)\,, \tag{S7.3}$$

with $g^{(2)}(\sigma)$ the value of the pair correlation function when $R = \sigma$. Of course, $g^{(2)}(\sigma)$ is a function of the density, ρ, but because of the singular nature of the hard-core potential, $g^{(2)}(\sigma)$ is not a function of the temperature (at constant density).

The results of calculations based on the various approximate theories of $g^{(2)}(\sigma)$ are displayed in Figures 1 and 2. For the case of the PY equation an analytic solution can be found. This solution leads to the two equations of state,

$$\left(\frac{\beta p}{\rho}\right)_{\mathrm{PY}}^{p} = \frac{1 + 2\left(\frac{\pi\rho\sigma^3}{6}\right) + 3\left(\frac{\pi\rho\sigma^3}{6}\right)^2}{\left[1 - \left(\frac{\pi\rho\sigma^3}{6}\right)\right]^2}, \tag{S7.4}$$

$$\left(\frac{\beta p}{\rho}\right)_{\mathrm{PY}}^{c} = \frac{1 + \left(\frac{\pi\rho\sigma^3}{6}\right) + \left(\frac{\pi\rho\sigma^3}{6}\right)^2}{\left[1 - \left(\frac{\pi\rho\sigma^3}{6}\right)\right]^3}. \tag{S7.5}$$

It is even more remarkable that equation (S7.5) is identical with an analysis of the dense rigid-sphere fluid given by Reiss, Frisch, and Lebowitz. The essential idea in the RFL theory of the rigid-sphere fluid is that there are discontinuities in the number of molecules than can

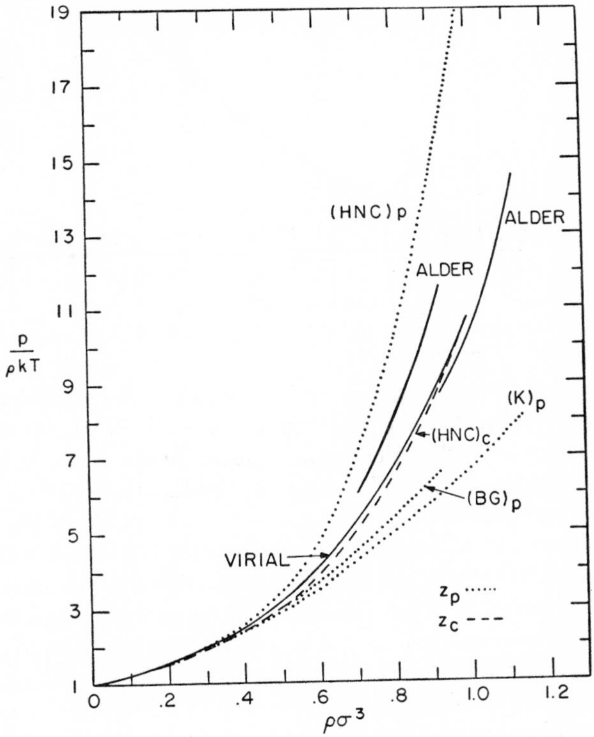

FIG. 1.—The equation of state for a rigid-sphere fluid as a function of density

occupy a void in a liquid as a function of the void volume, i.e., the volume when small can hold only one molecule and this discontinuously jumps to two molecules when the volume of the void exceeds a critical volume, etc. The discussion proceeds in terms of the nearest-neighbor distribution function, rather than in terms of the pair correlation function. (Of course, these two distribution functions may be related to one another.) By exploiting the discontinuous relationship between particle occupation number and void volume, RFL are able to obtain

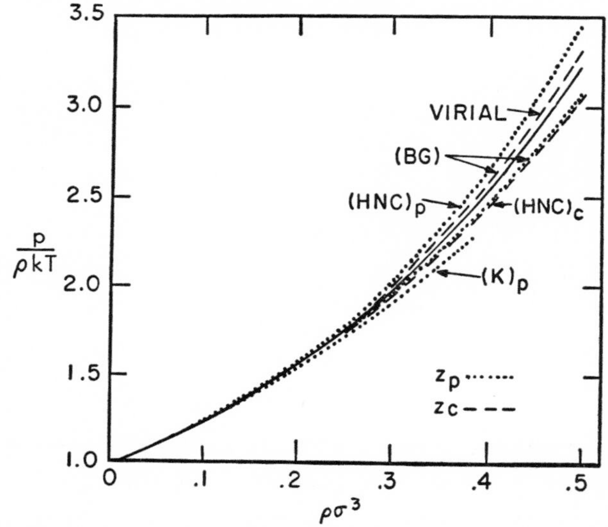

FIG. 2.—The equation of state for a rigid-sphere fluid as a function of density in the low density region.

an exact representation over a limited region of the conditional probability, $G^{(RFL)}(R)$, that the center of a molecule will be found within a spherical shell at R when the region enclosed by the shell is known to be free of molecular centers. When $R = \sigma$, the function $G^{(RFL)}(\sigma)$ is equal to $g^{(2)}(\sigma)$, from which the equation of state is determined. By use of an analytic polynomial approximation to $G^{(RFL)}(R)$ for R outside the range in which $G^{(RFL)}$ is known exactly, equation (S7.5) is obtained. Although the theory has been generalized to the case of real potentials, no calculations have as yet been made, and we therefore pursue this topic no further. The RFL analysis does appear to offer an alternative approach to those considered and is worthy of further intensive study.

An examination of Figure 1 shows that: (*a*) the "experimental" equation of state displays a discontinuity corresponding to a phase transition; (*b*) the various theories all reproduce the qualitative trend

TABLE 2

EQUATION OF STATE FOR THE DENSE RIGID-SPHERE FLUID

$\rho\sigma^3$	Virial Series			YBG		K	HNC		PY		"Expt"*
	z_3	z_4	z_5	z_p	z_c	z_c	z_p	z_c	z_p	z_c	z_p
0.1	1.237	1.239	1.240	1.239	1.240	…	1.242	1.232	1.240	1.240	…
0.2	1.528	1.549	1.553	1.546	1.557	…	1.562	1.546	1.549	1.555	…
0.3	1.874	1.946	1.963	1.937	1.980	1.938	2.000	1.946	1.954	1.974	…
0.4	2.276	2.444	2.499	2.431	2.542	2.423	2.604	2.455	2.480	2.536	…
0.5	2.731	3.060	3.194	3.047	3.284	3.013	3.463	3.124	3.173	3.307	…
0.6	3.244	3.813	4.090	…	…	3.725	4.650	3.990	4.093	4.381	…
0.7	3.809	4.713	5.226	…	…	4.541	6.874	5.052	5.323	5.905	5.85
0.8	4.430	5.780	6.654	…	…	5.396	9.711	6.481	7.000	8.124	7.95
0.9	5.106	7.027	8.428	…	…	6.285	13.767	8.332	9.328	11.447	10.50
1.0	5.836	8.472	10.607	…	…	…	19.145	10.767	12.773	16.883	…

$z_c = (p/\rho kT)^c$, $\quad z_p = (p/\rho kT)^p$, $\quad z_3 = 1 + B\rho + C\rho^2$, $\quad z_4 = 1 + B\rho + C\rho^2 + D\rho^3$,

$z_5 = 1 + B\rho + C\rho^2 + D\rho^3 + E\rho^4$.

* The entries labeled "experiment" are from the calculations by the molecular dynamics method. The figures listed have been obtained by graphical interpolation of the published results.

of the "data" but are not in quantitative agreement with the "data"; (*c*) there is a tendency for the two equations of state to bracket the correct isotherm. A more quantitative comparison of the agreement can be made by examination of Table 2.

The existence of a phase transition in a fluid of hard spheres is of great interest. It was first suggested by Kirkwood and Monroe in 1942 and later by the numerical solution of the YBG and K equations: it is found that no solutions exist for which $R^2[g^{(2)}(R) - 1]$ is integrable if ρ exceeds a critical value. In the case of the YBG equation the critical density is $(\rho_0/\rho) = 1.48$, while for the K equation one finds $(\rho_0/\rho) = 1.24$, where $\rho_0\sigma^3 = \sqrt{2}$ corresponds to the closest packing density. It was suggested at that time that the lack of solutions probably represented the limit of stability of a fluid phase of rigid spheres. For greater densities a crystalline phase is presumably the stable phase. This interpretation has been strikingly confirmed by the numerical calculations of Alder and Wainwright.

It is also of interest to note that although the PY equation gives a superior representation of the equation of state to that derived from the YBG or K equations, it predicts that there is no phase change. Thus alerted by this discrepancy, the reader should not be misled into believing that an approximate theory is equally good in predicting all phenomena. Although the YBG and K theories give poorer thermodynamic functions in the fluid phase than does the PY theory or the HNC theory, they are qualitatively correct (where the PY theory is qualitatively incorrect) in predicting a phase change.

The reader should also note that the radial distribution functions of a rigid-sphere fluid show the characteristic features of the distribution of matter in a real liquid. In Figure 3 are plotted some distribution functions for varying density. As $\rho\sigma^3$ increases toward $\sqrt{2}$, the ordering in the fluid extends to longer and longer distances from the origin (see Fig. 3). To the extent that the statistical geometry determined by the packing of rigid spheres is characteristic of real fluids, the excess entropy of the rigid sphere liquid should approximate that of a real liquid.[4] The excess entropy calculated from the YBG and K equations

[4] The excess entropy S_E is defined as the entropy difference between the fluid and an ideal gas:

$$S_E = S_f - S_{ig} \,.$$

From equations (S4.41) it follows that

$$S_E = \frac{2\pi}{3} \frac{\langle N \rangle \rho}{T} \int_0^\infty (Ru' + 3u)\, g^{(2)}(R) R^2 dR + \langle N \rangle (\mu_f - \mu_{ig}) \,.$$

The chemical potential μ_f of the fluid may be calculated by remembering that it is the free-energy change upon adding one molecule. We can do this conceptually by

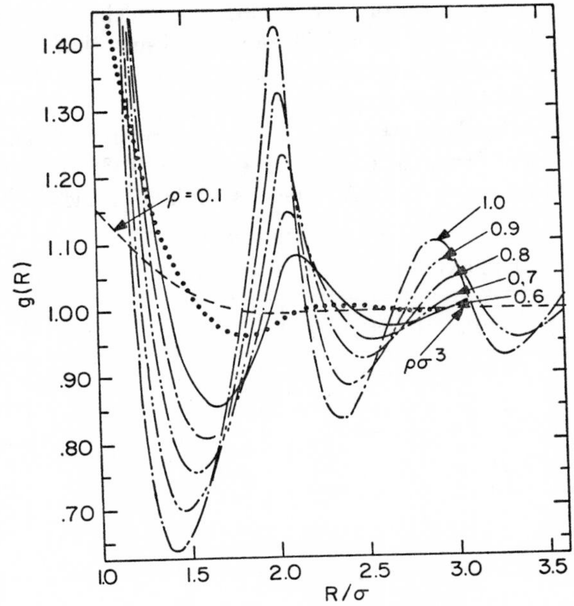

FIG. 3.—The radial distribution function of a rigid-sphere fluid as a function of intermolecular separation.

is displayed in Table 3. These numbers are of interest in the analysis of the ordering in the liquid phase, and clearly show the inadequacy of the overordered cell models.

We now turn to an examination of the agreement between theory and experiment for the case of a realistic pair-interaction potential. Almost all numerical calculations made have been for a potential of the form

$$u(R) = 4\epsilon\left[\left(\frac{\sigma}{R}\right)^{12} - \left(\frac{\sigma}{R}\right)^{6}\right], \qquad (S7.6)$$

---

varying the coupling ξ between the molecule and the rest of the system (cf. sec. S6.2). We then find

$$\frac{z}{\rho} = \frac{\Xi(\xi = 0)}{\Xi(\xi = 1)},$$

where the relation of z to μ_f is given in section S7.3.1. It may then be shown that

$$\mu_f - \mu_{ig} = 4\pi\rho\int_0^1\int_0^\infty u\, g^{(2)}(R, \xi)R^2 dR d\xi,$$

where

$$\mu_{ig} = kT \ln\left(\frac{\langle N\rangle}{Q_1}\right).$$

or for a modified form of this potential in which equation (S7.6) is maintained for $R \geq \sigma$ and a rigid core is used such that $u(R) = \infty$, for $R < \sigma$. The available experimental data do not permit the determination of the pair-interaction potential with great accuracy. For example, the data of Michels on Ar permit the extreme parameter pairs for a potential of the form (S7.6) to be $(\epsilon/k) = 119.8°$, $\sigma = 3.401$ A and $(\epsilon/k) = 115.4°$, $\sigma = 3.508$ A. The first pair of values fits the high-

TABLE 3

THE EXCESS ENTROPY OF A RIGID-SPHERE FLUID

$\rho\sigma^3$	$(S^E/k)_K$	$(S^E/k)_{YBG}$	$\rho\sigma^3$	$(S^E/k)_K$	$(S^E/k)_{YBG}$
0.169.....	−0.03	−0.03	0.794.....	−1.14	−1.23
.299.....	− .12	−0.11	0.862.....	−1.37	−1.49
.407.....	− .24	−0.23	0.924.....	−1.60	−1.77
.500.....	− .39	−0.37	0.982.....	−1.80	....
.585.....	− .55	−0.56	1.032.....	−2.07	....
.658.....	− .73	−0.76	1.089.....	−2.32	....
0.729.....	−0.92	−1.00	1.141.....	−2.60	....

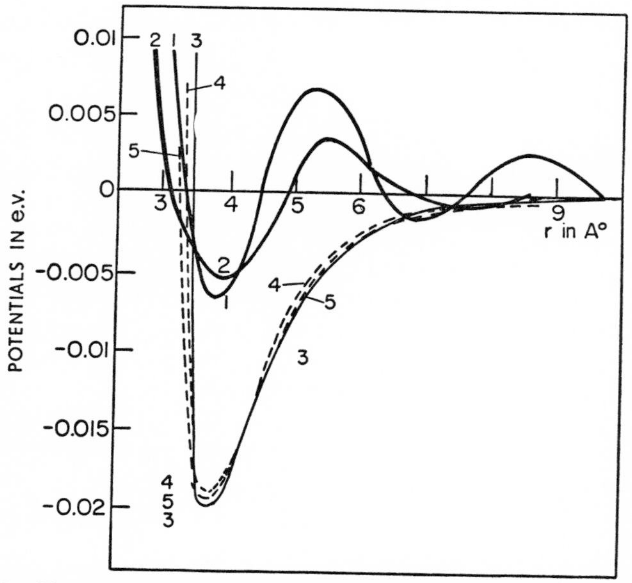

FIG. 4.—The intermolecular pair potential deduced from gas-phase measurements and from inversion of the Yvon-Born-Green equation and the experimental radial distribution function. Curve 1, $W^{(2)}(R)$ at 84° K; curve 2, $W^{(2)}(R)$ at 149° K; curve 3, $u(R)$ as given by Dobbs and Jones; curve 4, $u(R)$ derived from $W^{(2)}(R)$ of curve 1; curve 5, $u(R)$ derived from $W^{(2)}(R)$ of curve 2.

temperature second virial coefficient best, while the second pair is a better fit to B at low temperatures. Moreover, the effective two-body potential is likely to be a function of the density, because of the interactions between induced moments in a dense system. Calculations by Kestner and Sinanoglu suggest that this effect may reduce the attractive portion of the effective potential between two Ar atoms by approximately 5 per cent. Although these may seem to be small effects, they are of enormous importance when interactions in a dense system

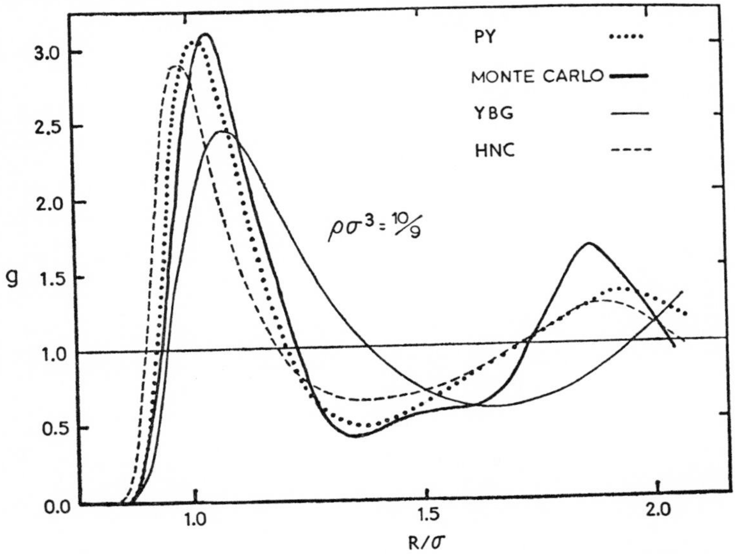

FIG. 5.—The radial distribution function for a Lennard-Jones fluid as computed from the several theories discussed.

are studied. To demonstrate this sensitivity of $g^{(2)}(R)$ to $u(R)$, March compared two potential energy curves in Figure 4. If one assumes the YBG equation to be exact, and inverts the equation to determine $u(R)$ from the experimentally known $g^{(2)}(R)$, the derived potential is surprisingly close to that derived from other data. Nevertheless, the small differences displayed in Figure 4 are responsible for the deviation of the $g^{(2)}(R)$ calculated from the YBG equation and that observed for liquid Ar.

Consider now the consistency of the various $g^{(2)}(R)$ determined by the several approximate integral equations. In Figure 5 is displayed $g^{(2)}(R)$ for $\rho\sigma^3 = 1.111$ and $kT/\epsilon = 2.74$. Although all curves have the same qualitative features, the quantitative discrepancies are large. As in the case of the rigid-sphere fluid, we temporarily take as reference Monte Carlo calculations performed for a fluid of molecules interacting with a potential of the form (S7.6).

The differences in $g^{(2)}(R)$ will, naturally, lead to differences in the predicted thermodynamic functions. A comparison of these predictions is made in Table 4.

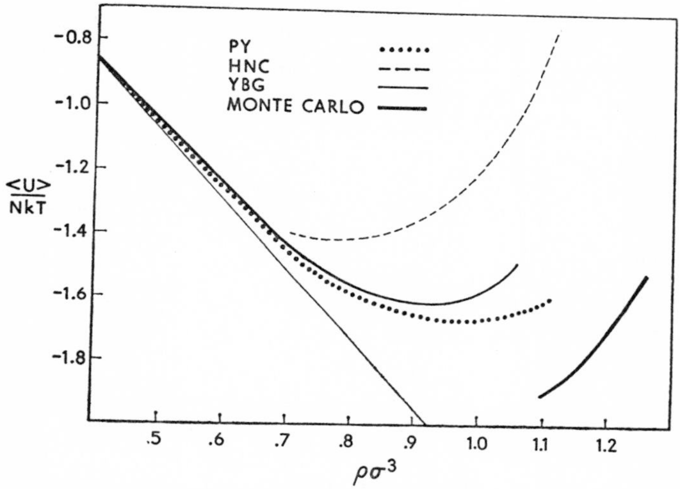

FIG. 6.—The internal energy of a Lennard-Jones fluid as computed from the several theories discussed.

TABLE 4

COMPARISON OF THERMODYNAMIC FUNCTIONS FROM THE YBG, HNC, PY, AND MC CALCULATIONS

$\rho\sigma^3$	MC	PY	HNC	YBG
		$(p/\rho kT)^p$		
0.400......	1.2–1.5	1.24	1.28	1.26
0.833......	4.01	4.01	5.11	2.3
1.000......	7.0	6.8	9.1	3.1
1.111......	7.8	9.2	13.2	3.8
		$\langle U\rangle/NkT$		
0.400......	−0.86	−0.865	− 0.859	−0.85
0.833......	−1.58	−1.61	− 1.40	−1.8
1.000......	−1.60	−1.67	− 1.19	−2.2
1.111......	−1.90	−1.59	− 0.78	−2.6

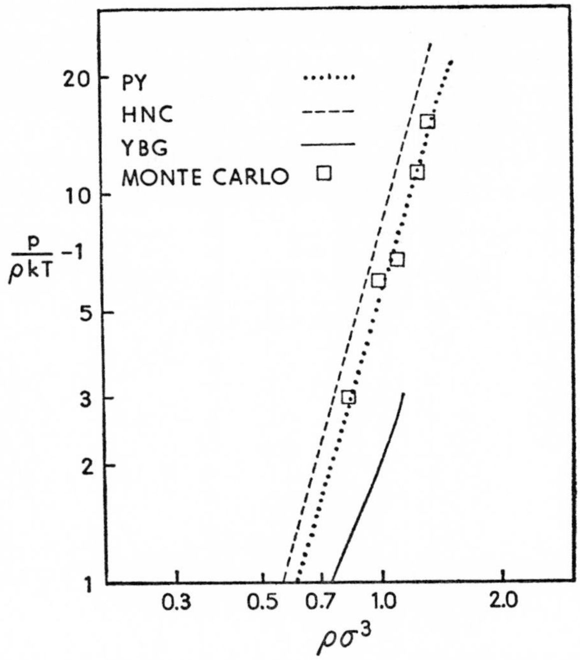

FIG. 7.—The equation of state of a Lennard-Jones fluid as computed from the several theories discussed.

TABLE 5

COMPARISON BETWEEN THEORETICAL AND EXPERIMENTAL INTERNAL ENERGIES AND ENTROPIES OF FLUID AR

T °K	ρ_m gm cm^{-3}	$\langle U\rangle_K$	$\langle U\rangle_{HNC}$	$\langle U\rangle_{expt}$	S^E_{HNC}	S^E_{expt}
		cal/mole			cal/mole °K	
273.	1.12	−1155	−916	−911	−3.02	−3.38
273.	0.609	− 588	−536	−516	−1.61	−1.53
153.	0.522	. . . .	−554	−555	−1.82	−1.86
153.	0.696	. . . .	−693	−688	−2.31	−2.30
143.	1.044	. . . .	−996	−978	−3.90	−3.70

Clearly, the agreement in calculation of the internal energy is better than that in the calculation of the pressure. Indeed, the pressure is so sensitive a function of the relative positions of the first maximum of $g^{(2)}(R)$ and the minimum of $u(R)$ that large discrepancies arise from minor errors in $g^{(2)}(R)$ and $u(R)$. In Figures 6 and 7 are plotted the internal energy and pressure as a function of $\rho\sigma^3$. For $\rho\sigma^3 < 0.7$, the theories are in good agreement with each other and with the Monte Carlo calculations. For $\rho\sigma^3 > 0.7$, there are large discrepancies, al-

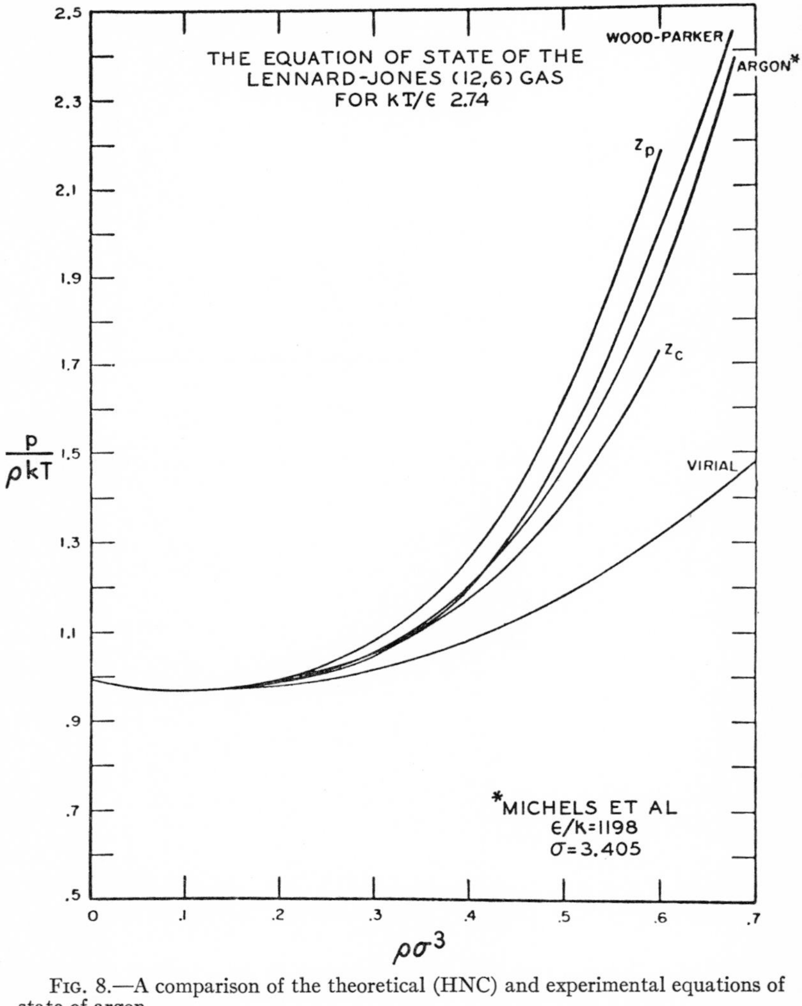

FIG. 8.—A comparison of the theoretical (HNC) and experimental equations of state of argon.

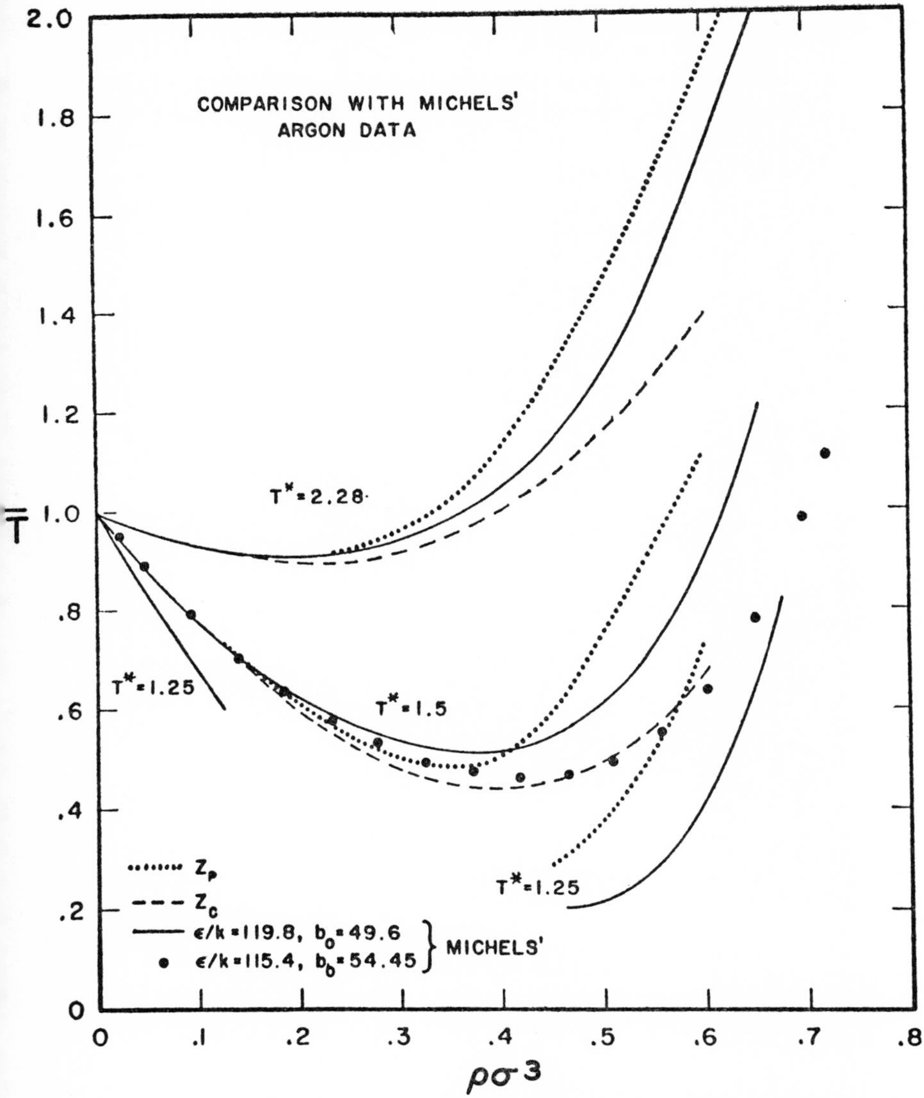

[F]IG. 9.—The effect of changes in the intermolecular potential on the HNC equation of state of argon

though the computed pressures show almost parallel slopes as a function of $\rho\sigma^3$, indicating some consistency in the predicted values of the compressibility.

We now turn to a more detailed analysis of the fit between theory and experiment. In particular we examine the agreement between the predicted and observed properties of Ar. The reader should recall that even for this simple system, the pair potential is not known accurately.

It has already been noted that calculations of the pressure are much more sensitive to errors in $g^{(2)}(R)$ than are calculations of the internal energy. We therefore examine first the agreement between theory and

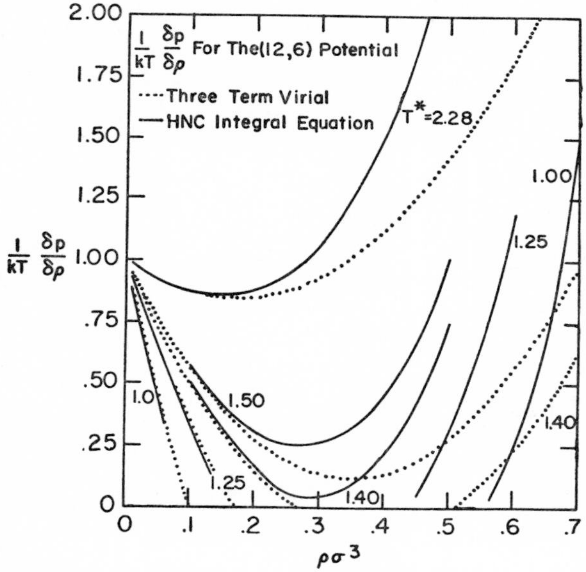

FIG. 10.—A comparison of the theoretical and experimental compressibilities of argon.

TABLE 6

BOUNDARY OF THE TWO-PHASE REGION

T °K	p(HNC)	p(Expt)	$\rho_{m,l}$(HNC)	$\rho_{m,g}$(HNC)	$\rho_{m,l}$(Expt)	$\rho_{m,g}$(Expt)
	atm		gm cm^{-3}			
148...	45.4	43.2	0.617	0.392	0.775	0.31
143...	37	35.3	0.696	.235	0.89	.21
138...	29	28.8	0.757	.156	0.96	.15
84...	1.2	0.8	1.24	0.007	1.40	0.0049

experiment for the internal energy and entropy. The results are displayed in Table 5, the potential parameters being: $(\epsilon/k) = 119.8°$ K, $\sigma = 3.405$ A.

We again note the superiority of the HNC approximation to the YBGK approximation. For the cases cited in Table 5, the agreement is all that could be desired in view of the uncertainty in the pair potential.

When we consider the agreement between predicted and observed equations of state, the situation is less satisfactory, as shown in Figure 8. The effect of varying the pair potential between the limits defined by the second virial coefficient is shown in Figure 9, and the agreement between calculated and observed compressibilities in Figure 10. Again, the agreement between theory and experiment is qualitatively good, but only semiquantitative in detail.

Finally, we consider the coexistence curve between liquid and vapor. A comparison between theory and experiment is presented in Table 6. The agreement is seen to be very satisfactory.

REFERENCES

[1] T. L. Hill, *Statistical Mechanics* (New York: McGraw-Hill Book Co., 1956).
[2] J. E. Mayer and M. G. Mayer, *Statistical Mechanics* (New York: John Wiley and Sons, 1940).
[3] R. Kubo, *J. Phys. Soc. Japan*, **17** (1962), 1100.
[4] M. S. Green, *J. Math. Phys.*, **1** (1960), 391.
[5] A. Taylor, *Functional Analysis* (New York: John Wiley and Sons, 1960).
[6] J. E. Mayer and E. W. Montroll, *J. Chem. Phys.*, **9** (1941), 2.
[7] J. de Boer, "Contribution to the study of compressed gases," thesis, University of Amsterdam, 1940.
[8] J. Yvon, *Actualités Scientifiques et Industriel* (Paris: Hermann et cie, 1935).
[9] M. Born and H. S. Green, *Proc. Roy. Soc. London, Ser. A*, **188** (1946), 10.
———, *A General Kinetic Theory of Liquids* (Cambridge, England: Cambridge University Press, 1949).
H. S. Green, *Molecular Theory of Fluids* (Amsterdam: North Holland Publishing Co., 1952).
[10] J. G. Kirkwood, *J. Chem. Phys.*, **3** (1935), 300.
J. G. Kirkwood and E. Monroe, *ibid.*, **9** (1941), 514.
J. G. Kirkwood and E. M. Boggs, *ibid.*, **10** (1942), 394.
[11] G. H. A. Cole, *Adv. Phys.*, **8** (1959), 225.
[12] I. Z. Fisher, *Soviet Phys.—Uspekhi*, **5** (1962), 239 [=*Uspekhi Fiz. Nauk*, **76** (1962), 499].

[13] J. M. van Leeuwen, J. Groenweld, and J. de Boer, *Physica*, **25** (1959), 792.
[14] M. S. Green, Hughes Aircraft Report, September, 1959.
[15] E. Meeron, *J. Math. Phys.*, **1** (1960), 192.
[16] T. Morita and K. Hiroike, *Progr. Theor. Phys.*, **23** (1960), 1003.
[17] G. S. Rushbrooke, *Physica*, **26** (1960), 259.
[18] L. Verlet, *Nuovo Cimento*, **18** (1960), 77.
[19] J. K. Percus and G. J. Yevick, *Phys. Rev.*, **110** (1958), 1.
[20] G. Stell, *Physica*, **29** (1963), 517.
[21] J. Yvon, *Nuovo Cimento*, **9** (1958), 144.
[22] J. K. Percus, *Phys. Rev., Letters*, **8** (1962), 462.
[23] R. W. Hart, R. Wallis, and L. Pode, *J. Chem. Phys.*, **19** (1951), 139.
[24] B. R. A. Nijboer and L. van Hove, *Phys. Rev.*, **85** (1952), 777.
[25] A. A. Broyles, *J. Chem. Phys.*, **33** (1960), 456; **34** (1961), 359 and 1068.
A. A. Broyles, S. V. Chung, and H. L. Sahlin, *J. Chem. Phys.*, **37** (1962), 2462.
[26] J. G. Kirkwood, E. K. Maun, and B. J. Alder, *J. Chem. Phys.*, **18** (1950), 1040.
[27] J. G. Kirkwood, V. A. Lewinson, and B. J. Alder, *J. Chem. Phys.*, **19** (1951), 139.
[28] E. Thiele, *J. Chem. Phys.*, **39** (1963), 474.
M. S. Wertheim, *Phys. Rev., Letters*, **8** (1963), 321.
———, *J. Math. Phys.*, **5** (1964), 643.
[29] L. Verlet and D. Levesque, *Physica*, **28** (1962), 1124.
[30] H. Reiss, H. L. Frisch, and J. L. Lebowitz, *J. Chem. Phys.*, **31** (1959), 369.
[31] M. N. Rosenbluth and A. W. Rosenbluth, *J. Chem. Phys.*, **22** (1954), 881.
B. J. Alder and T. Wainwright, *J. Chem. Phys.*, **27** (1957), 1209; **31** (1959), 459.
W. W. Wood and J. D. Jacobson, *ibid.*, **27** (1957), 1207.
W. W. Wood and R. F. Parker, *ibid.*, p. 720.
T. Wainwright and B. J. Alder, *Nuovo Cimento, Suppl.*, **9** (1958), 116.
[32] M. Klein and M. S. Green, *J. Chem. Phys.*, **39** (1963), 1367.
[33] M. Klein, "An evaluation of the HNC approximation for the pair correlation function of a fluid," Ph.D. thesis, University of Maryland, 1962.
[34] A. Michels, H. Wijker, and H. K. Wijker, *Physica*, **15** (1949), 629.
A. Michels, J. M. Levelt, and W. de Graaff, *ibid.*, **24** (1958), 659.
A. Michels, J. M. Levelt, and G. J. Wolkers, *ibid.*, p. 769.
A. Michels, J. C. Abels, C. A. Ten Seldam, and W. de Graaff, *ibid.*, **26** (1960), 381.
A. Michels, W. de Graaff, and T. A. Ten Seldam, *ibid.*, p. 393.
[35] M. D. Johnson and N. H. March, *Phys. Letters*, **3** (1963), 313.
[36] N. Kestner and O. Sinanoglu, *J. Chem. Phys.*, **38** (1963), 1730.
[37] E. R. Dobbs and G. O. Jones, *Rept. on Progress in Phys.*, **20** (1957), 516.

INDEX

Absolute activity, definition of, 241
Adiabatic approximation, 94
Adiabatic modulus of compression, 60
Argon: compressibilities, theoretical and experimental, (Fig. 10), 328; equation of state, (Fig. 18), 221, 326; HNC equation of state, effect of changes in intermolecular potential, 327; liquid, fluctuations of coordination numbers in, (Table 6), 88; liquid, isotherms of, at 0° C., 150; liquid, isotherms in gaseous, liquid, and transition regions, 150; liquid, radial distribution functions for, (Fig. 8), 149, (Fig. 17), 221; liquid, volume of, along melting curve, (Table 10), 201; values of $F_1(O)$ for, (Table 9), 165
Articulation points, 262–68, 296
Average values, calculation of, 44–46

Bogolyubov equation: boundary condition for, 143; general examination of, 137–40; radial distribution function, 131–34, 140–43; stability and instability of solutions of, 183–86
Boltzman factor for N molecules, 247
Bridge diagrams, 301–3

Canonical ensemble, 239, 268–69
Cell, uncertainty principle for, 240
Chemical potential: equation for, 61–63; of a system, 15
Cluster cumulant function, equation for, 255–57
Cluster integrals, 242; "irreducible," 243
Clusters, topological properties of, 261–69

Coefficient of structural diffusion, 83
Cole and Fisher, equations of, 290–92
"Collective" interactions, 121
Composition, according to G.C.E., expression for, 239
Compressibilities of argon, theoretical and experimental, (Fig. 10), 328
Compressibility: isothermal, coefficient of, 57; of a system of particles, 53
Configuration integral, 14, 19; calculation of, 17, 23–27
Configurational free energy, interaction contribution to, 260
Configurational partition function, 242
Constants ϵ and a for noble gases, (Table 1), 20
Coordination numbers: fluctuations of, in liquid argon, (Table 6), 88; in simple liquids, 84–90
Correlation function $g^{(n)}$ defined, 271–72
Correlation functions, 40–68, 269–72; asymptotic, for a system of charged particles, 110; asymptotic, of a two-phase system, equations for, 162; case of a uniform gas or liquid, 42; conditional, 43; corresponding to an n-molecule generic distribution function, 269–70; equations for, 97–130; general properties, 40–44; lower-order, 152; partial cluster expansion-integral for, 152; of a two-phase system, 156–66; singlet, describing microstructure of transition layer, 163
Critical point, 202–5; reduced parameters for noble gases, (Table 2), 20
Crystallization, kinetics of, 3
Crystals; *see* Structures of

Cumulant expansion, rearrangement into a cluster expansion, 254–55
Cumulants: definition of, 242; Kubo's method of, 250–57; properties of, 250–54
Cylindrical coordinates, simplification by use of, 142

De Boer parameter, 23
Debye: radius, 111; waves, 8
Deformations, compression expansion and transverse-elastic types, 7
Densities of gas and liquid, experimental values for argon, krypton, and zenon, (Fig. 2), 21
Density, generic-probability, 269
Dipole interaction, 118–22
Dipole lattice, 122–26
Disorder parameter, 91–92
Distribution functions, 268–79

Elastic-relaxational phenomena, 7
Electron scattering, 69
Energy: configurational free, interaction contribution to, 260; equation for, 118; internal, computation of, 273; internal, of a Lennard-Jones fluid, (Fig. 6), 324; internal, or a system of N particles, 46; mean, according to G.C.E., expression for, 239; of a system, 15, and equation for, 19; potential, equation for, 46; total potential, of interaction, 243; *see also* Free energy
Ensembles, definition and properties of, 236–39
Equation, Gibbs-Helmholtz, 171
Equation of state: of argon, (Fig. 8), 326; HNC, of argon, effect of changes in intermolecular potential, (Fig. 9), 327; for a rigid-sphere fluid, (Fig. 1), 317, (Fig. 2), 318, (Table 2), 319; of imperfect gas, equation for, 245; of a Lennard-Jones fluid, (Fig. 7), 325; of a uniform system, 48
Equations: Bogolyubov, 99; integro-differential, 97
Equilibrium configuration, definition of, 237
Entropy: according to G.C.E., expression for, 239; contributions to, from groups of particles, 55; for an ensemble, 237; equation for, 16; excess, of a rigid-sphere fluid, (Table 3), 322; of a system, 15

Fluctuation, quadratic, of the number of particles in a given volume, 52
Fluctuations in the number of particles and their correlations, equation for, 54
Fluid, thermodynamic properties of, 272–75
Fluidity of liquids, 6
Flux of particles, 100
Force: average, acting on all particles of a given volume, 49; total, acting on a particle at a given point, 101
Free energy: calculation of, 14; equations for, 22, 30, 32, 35; Helmholtz, 277; of an ideal gas, 27; of any system, 16; *see also* Pair distribution function
Free volume per particle of the liquid, 30
Free-volume theory, 27–31
Fugacity, definition of, 241
Function, one-dimensional $g(x)$ for a system of hard spheres, (Fig. 6), 76
Functional differentiation, method of, 309–14
Functions, thermodynamic, comparison of, (Table 4), 324

Gas, solution of equations for correlation functions, 101–6
Gases, imperfect, theory of, 241–68
Gibbs distribution, 13
Gibbs-Helmholtz equation, 171
Grand Canonical Ensemble, definition of, 263; 270–71
Grand Partition Function, 238, 272

Hamiltonian function of a system of monoatomic particles, 12–13
Hard spheres: equation of state for a system of, (Fig. 19), 224; one-dimensional function $g(x)$ for a system of, (Fig. 6), 76; problem of a system of, 144–47; system of, dynamical calculations in, 226–31; system of, results of calculations for, 222–26
Helmholtz free energy, 277
Hole theory of liquids, 28, 30
Hooke's law, 57
Hyper-netted chain equation, 296–303

Ideal wall, molecular system at, 106–9
Impenetrability of particles, 70
Integral, surface, 50
Integro-differential equations for correlation functions in phase-space, 127–30

Interatomic distances, frequency of appearance of various, (Fig. 5), 72
Intermolecular forces and the law of corresponding states, 17–21
Intermolecular pair potential, (Fig. 4), 322
Intermolecular potential, schematic trend of, (Fig. 1), 18, 19
Irreducible cluster, definition of, 244
Irreducible integral, 25–27
Isotherms for argon in gaseous, liquid, and transitional regions, (Fig. 10), 150
Isotherms of liquid argon at 0° C., (Fig. 9), 150

Kirkwood equation for the radial distribution function, 136
Kirkwood integral equation, 288–90
Kirkwood's method and the chemical potential, 61–63

Laplace transform of the function $f(x)$, 33–34
Lattice model theories, 27–28
Leontovich theorem for the correlation function, 185
Lifetime of an atom, 5
Light, scattering of by liquids, 64–67
Limiting line of stability of a system, 187
Limiting points of stability, classification of, 188–89
Limiting volume, comparison of theoretical and experimental data for, 201
Liouville equation, 128
Liquid: monoatomic, radial distribution function of particles in, (Fig. 4), 70; structural-diffusional model of a, 81–84
Liquid dielectrics, 95
Liquid metals, 10
Liquid state, peculiarities of, 1–5
Liquids: elastic properties of, 57–61; kinetic properties of, 94; simple, instantaneous and average order in, 90–93; simple, structure of, 69–96; simple and non-simple, 8–11; structure of, in relation to physical properties, 93–96; surface phenomena in, 156–79; theories of, 28–31; theory of, present status, 1–11; theory of, in the superposition approximation, 131–55; *see also* Structures of

Markov chains, convergence of, (Fig. 20), 225
Mayer cluster theory, 257–261
Mean-force field, potential of, 287
Melting curve: approximate theory of, 198–202; reduced experimental, for argon, krypton, and xenon, (Fig. 3), 21
Metals: liquid, 10; values of r_{M1} and r_1 for, in vicinity of melting point, (Table 4), 79
Microcanonical ensemble, definition of, 239
Microdensity $F_1(z)$: in liquid vapor transition layer, (Fig. 11), 164; in one-dimensional model near ideal wall, (Fig. 13), 170; near critical point, (Fig. 12), 169
Momentum, rate of change of, in a system, 48
Monoatomic liquid, radial distribution function of particles in, (Fig. 4), 70
Monoatomic substances, values of n_1 and z_1 for, near melting point, (Table 5), 80
Monte Carlo method: implementation of, 212–17; in statistical physics, 208–12
Morse potential, 19

Neutron scattering, 69
Noble gases: constants ϵ and a for, (Table 1), 20; critical point, (Table 2), 20; densities of gas and liquid, (Fig. 2), 21; reduced experimental melting curve, (Fig. 3), 21; triple point, (Table 2), 20; values of λ for, (Table 3), 23
Non-central forces, calculations with, 118–22
Normalization, of correlation functions, 41
Normalization conditions for correlation functions of a two-phase system, 157–58
Notation, 235
Numerical methods in the theory of liquids, 206–31

Order, short-range and long-range, in liquids, 71

Packing coefficient, 83
Pair correlation function, equations for, 286–314
Pair distribution function, relationship to free energy, 276–94

Particles: electrically charged, a more precise solution, 113–18; in a liquid, fluctuations in the number of, 51–54; projection of motion of, (Fig. 21), 229; system of electrically charged, equations for correlation functions, 109–13; system of interacting, numerical integration of Bogolyubov equation for, 147–52
Percus-Yevick equation, 304–09
Phase-space, correlation functions in, equations for, 126–30
Phase-space description of a system, 239
Phase transformations, stability of, 180–83
Phases: of a simple substance, (Fig. 15), 181; stability of, 180–83
Poisson integral, 34
Potential: chemical, and Kirkwood's method, 61–63; full thermodynamic, equation for, 35; intermolecular, of a real liquid, 199; self-consistent, determination of, 30
Pressure: expression for, 274; limiting, equation for, 200; in a liquid or gas, calculation of, 46; of a system, 15, 19
Properties, physical, of liquids in relation to structure, 93–96

Quantum corrections to the statistical integral and the Law of Corresponding States, 22–23
Quasi-crystallinity of liquids, 81

Radial distribution function, 4, 44; accuracy of Bogolyubov equation for, 140–43; Bogolyubov equation for, 131–34; definition of, 281; equation for determination of asymptotic form of, 139; Kirkwood equation for, 136; for a Lennard-Jones fluid, (Fig. 5), 323; of liquid argon, (Fig. 8), 149; for liquid argon, experimental and theoretical, (Fig. 17), 221; of a one-dimensional model of a liquid, 72–77; of particles in a monoatomic liquid, (Fig. 4), 70; of real liquids, 69–72; of a rigid-sphere fluid, (Fig. 3), 321; in a system of rigid spheres, (Fig. 7), 148; theoretical, calculated by three methods, (Fig. 16), 220; when distances between particles are large, 140
Radius of correlation in a liquid, 83
Rayleigh scattering of electromagnetic waves by a liquid, 64
Real system, model of, results of calculations for, 217–22
Rigid spheres, theoretical radial distribution functions in a system of, (Fig. 7), 148

Self-diffusion coefficient, temperature dependence of, 5–6
Semiconductors, 95
Semi-invariants of Thiele; *see* Cumulants
Shear modulus of a liquid, 50; expression for, 58
Short-range order in simple liquids, 3, 90
Solutions: high density, numerical solutions of integral equations for, 315–29; low density, numeral solutions of integral equations for, 314–15
Spectrum of light scattered by a liquid, 7
Stability: boundaries of, of liquid and gases, 180–205; of the first type, limiting points of, 190–93; limit of, of a one-dimensional phase, 186–90; limit of, of a system with exponential repulsion between pairs of particles, 196–98; limit of, of a system of hard non-interacting spheres, 194; of phases and phase transformations, 180–83; of the second type, limiting points of, 193–96
Star trees and rooted star trees, 262–68, *passim*
Stars, 262–68, *passim*
Statistical integral: classical, 12–39; of a one-dimensional model of a liquid, 31–35
Stress tensor, 46–51; in a deformed liquid, 58; expressed by correlation functions, 173; "kinetic" part, 49; "potential" part, 50
Structures of liquids and crystals, comparison of, 77–81
Superposition approximation, 153–55; in the Kirkwood method, 134–37; meaning of, 292–96; refinement of, 152–55; theory of liquids in the, 131–55
Surface phenomena in liquids, 156–79; application of Gibbs distribution function to, 156; equation for, 176–77

Surface tension: approximate theories of, 175–79; diagram for deriving an equation for, (Fig. 14), 172; Fowler's approximate theory of, 178; of a liquid in terms of correlation functions, 171–75
System with constant electric dipole or quadrupole moments, 120–21
System of non-spherical molecules, solution of equations for, 120

Thermal motion of molecules in liquids, 5–8
Thermodynamic functions, expressions for, 27
Thermodynamic properties of solid crystalline bodies and liquids, 2
Thermodynamics: of a one-dimensional system, 35–38; statistical, principles of, 12–16
Topological arguments, 261–68
Transition layer between liquid and vapor, 156–69, *passim;* structure of, 166–71; thermodynamic theory of, 167–69
Transport processes in liquids, theory of, 3
Triple point, reduced parameters for noble gases, (Table 2), 20
Two-phase region: boundary of, (Table 6), 328; correlation functions of, 159–66

Ursell cluster functions, definition of, 246
Ursell development, 246

Values of λ^* and $u(1)$ corresponding to some values of the density, (Table 8), 146
Van der Waals theory, 4
Virial coefficients for the rigid-sphere fluid, (Table 1), 315
Virial series: for all thermodynamic functions of a gas, 106; for the radial distribution function, 105

X-ray structural studies of liquids, 2
X-rays, scattering by liquids, 64–67

Yvon-Born-Green equation, 286–88